To my dear wife, Diane, who has supported my endeavours for more than sixty years.

THE EDGE OF THE LAND

Memories of one person's enchantment with the coast

JOHN WHITTOW

Riverside Publishing Solutions

ISBN (Paperback): 978-1-913012-01-4
ISBN (Hardback): 978-1-913012-02-1
ISBN (ePub): 978-1-913012-03-8

A full CIP record for this book is available from the British Library.

Published by Riverside Publishing Solutions, Salisbury, UK
www.riversidepublishingsolutions.com

Printed and bound in the UK.

CONTENTS

LIST OF ILLUSTRATIONS

7. WESTERN SCOTLAND

8. CORNWALL

9. EAST ANGLIA

ACKNOWLEDGEMENTS

Foremost amongst those people who have supported and counselled me in the conception of this book I must thank several members of the National Trust: Phil Dyke, for his constant guidance and assistance over many years; Fiona Reynolds DBE and Gill Raikes for their friendship and their unending support of Enterprise Neptune; Peter Nixon, for his belief in the Second Neptune Survey; Huw Davies for his expertise in producing its final report and data analysis; Richard Neale, whose friendship and kindness made our visits to North Wales such a delight; Susan Foster who, when she took over from Gill Raikes to administer the Trust's fund-raising, expressed her deep love of coastlines; Victoria Egan who has managed some of the East Anglian shores, especially those around Blakeney, where she welcomed us ashore from "The Whittow" and, finally Megan Evans, who assisted with approving the copyright issues of some of the book's illustrations. I am particularly grateful to Adrian Woodhall who gave me constant advice and support during the 'Neptune years'.

Amongst my academic colleagues I have to thank Ian Fenwick, without whose assistance the 1965 Northern Ireland Neptune Survey would never have been completed; Sheila Dance, who worked tirelessly in the cartographic office in order to produce such wonderful copies; Bob Parry, the map curator, also in the University's Geography department, who not only helped with the safe delivery of the finished archive but also resolved the problem of the 'lost' maps of South Devon. I must give particular thanks to David Pinder, who, from the start in 1965, has given up an inordinate amount of his time to provide assistance with the entire Neptune concept. In addition to being a very close friend, David Starkie, a former academic, has given me the confidence and encouragement to press on with this publication. He has also provided me with a publisher, Duncan Potter, who has carefully guided the book through his own publishing house and who has been very patient with my constant changes and new ideas. It was he who kept calm when the completed proofs circled Hampshire and Wiltshire in a Parcel Force van for an entire week.

My thanks must also be expressed to two of my new neighbours, Martin Graystone and Martin Dronfield. The first of these friends metaphorically 'saved my life' after I had wiped more than half of the manuscript from my computer when I inadvertently hit the wrong key. After a painstaking effort he managed to retrieve the original script. Martin Graystone also provided me with a dramatic record of old Lowestoft. Martin Dronfield, by contrast, furnished me with major data on modern North Sea wind-farms. To each of these gentlemen I give my warmest thanks.

The majority of the illustrations are my own, and I apologise for any inadequacies, but I am happy to acknowledge the National Trust's permission for me to reproduce fourteen of their own copyright pictures. Duncan Potter supplied the magnificent photograph which adorns the front cover and I am very grateful that the 'Hebridean Island Cruises' company gave me permission to use one of their photographs.

Last, but by no means least, I must thank my family for their constant help throughout this lengthy exercise: My dear wife, Diane, who travelled with me on the majority of those coastal journeys, often driving, always route-finding, regularly mapping and being extremely patient in coping with my never-ending demands. Moreover, she has had to tolerate long hours of my absence in the study during which I have managed to write more than a dozen books over the decades. I believe that both the National Trust and the Forestry Commission should also be indebted to her fortitude. Our daughter Fiona, her husband, Andrew, and our granddaughter, Charlotte, have, on numerous occasions, helped out with the many computer 'glitches' along the way. Thank you all.

PREFACE

I started writing this book in a 17th century converted farmhouse in Midland England, looking across to the wooded and sandy hill country of Cannock Chase, England's smallest AONB. God willing, I am hoping that I will have time to complete it from a different venue because at Christmas 2017 we moved to a modern house on the edge of the Norfolk Broads, the largest wetland area in Britain. This was an enforced change to be nearer to our daughter, Fiona, but it had the added advantage of being closer to a stretch of coastline with which I have a great affinity. Because of my advanced age I was encouraged to set down my thoughts and memories by some of my academic colleagues and also by certain of my friends at the National Trust. I make no apologies for expressing my views on coastal management or for trying to explain the reasons why it sometimes became tedious when spending years mapping parts of the coastline for a variety of scientific reasons. My visits to the shore were not always hedonistic delights so I have included somewhat over-lengthy descriptions of those working perambulations in order to demonstrate the vicissitudes of my coastal experiences. In general, however, my memories remain full of nostalgia for all the cliffs, beaches, coves, salt-marshes, shingle spits and muddy creeks that I have visited over a lifetime. Moreover, such thoughts of those journeys to that ever-shifting boundary, where the land meets the sea, have been constantly revived by the numerous chances to take generations of university undergraduates to study coastlines and share with them the delights of our shores. From one viewpoint these types of visits can be viewed as a series of 'pilgrimages' that have given me endless pleasure and a feeling of fulfillment. Almost seventy years ago I myself was an undergraduate and was encouraged to read a textbook written by my own tutor, Professor Austin Miller. It was entitled "Land, Air & Ocean" and inspired me to think that where these three elements truly conflate can be regarded as "The Edge of the Land". I make no apologies for using miles and feet instead of kilometres and metres in my descriptions because my mind-set has stayed in those halcyon days before the metric system was imposed upon us. I do apologise, however, for any mistakes that may occur despite hours of proof reading. At the age of 89 I find that my arthritic fingers sometimes hit the wrong keys!

Bergh Apton, Norfolk, 2019

FOREWORD

It gives me enormous pleasure to write this Foreword. One of my favourite stories when I worked for the National Trust was of the brave and hard-working troupe of students, led by John Whittow, who surveyed the entire coast of England, Wales and Northern Ireland at a cost (effectively) of twopence halfpenny, because they slept in tents, ate home-made sandwiches and put in far more hours than the Trust could reasonably have hoped for. John himself surveyed large parts of the Welsh coast, and this work led to arguably the National Trust's greatest achievement, Enterprise Neptune. As a result, our coastline is better protected than almost anywhere else in the world. How I loved that story, and I told it often.

So I was delighted to hear that John planned to write a book about it and here, indeed, it is. The real story, told by the man who did it. And my goodness what a story it is – every bit as exciting as I guessed. But what is even more exciting is the place that story occupied within this remarkable man's lifelong fascination for the coast. His Neptune ventures, important though they were, are but one part of the enormous contribution he's made to our understanding of the complex geology and ever changing processes that define the place where the land meets the sea.

John describes how he became a geologist, and how his discoveries, including the limits of the North Wales ice sheets and explanations for many extraordinary coastal features, have shaped our understanding of the coast. I only now realise that much of what I was taught as a geography student in the late 1970s had only just been explained by John and his colleagues. He achieved this through a really intimate understanding of the coast, whether surveying, using the coastline as a classroom, chasing his remarkable family history in Pembrokeshire, discovering the joys of the Ulster coastline just as the Troubles intensified, and purchasing – madly yet joyfully – a run-down cottage on the remote island of Fladda in the Hebrides.

He's more than a geologist though, and wherever his travels took him he was fascinated by the culture of the sea, the history of places and the art they inspired, and ways of life as they fast disappeared, often to be replaced by tourism and ugly modern development.

He describes in particular, in loving and enthusiastic detail, the west coast of England, Scotland and Wales (plus much of the Irish coast) before suddenly (and surprisingly, it seems) finding himself in the east, where he confesses he is 'forced to write in a more muted style' to engage with a newly horizontal environment. Even here he finds coasts to love, though he yearns for the rocky west.

And then, just as we think he's seen and enjoyed everything, he only goes and sails around the coast! But try as he might to have an 'ordinary' holiday, the geomorphologist in him could never be suppressed. I salute his wife Diane who appears never to have complained as he dragged her up and down cliffs, and on and off boats, perpetually in search of new insights.

This is a lovely book, whose final chapter affirms the enduring impact of the National Trust's Neptune with, of the 900 miles he recommended for acquisition, 775 acquired. He concludes by reflecting on today's challenges, including the dreaded scourge of plastic, and in a reflective passage describes himself in words beginning with 'I'. To that I can only add 'indefatigable': thank goodness for John Whittow and people like him who have made our world a better place.

Fiona Reynolds
Master of Emmanuel College, Cambridge
former Director-General of the National Trust

INTRODUCTION

"The greatest thing a human soul ever does in this world is to see something, and tell what it saw in a plain way"
(Modern Painters. John Ruskin, 1843)

There have been numerous books written about the coastline, so why on earth write yet another? In the libretto of his opera "Pagliacci", Leoncavallo maintained (albeit in Italian) that "A man's memories are a window to his soul". Thus, after lengthy pondering I decided to expose my own soul.

Having visited and/or researched many of the World's coastlines at various stages of my life I believe that some of these memories are worthy of recording, because most of the episodes to which they refer have proved never to have been replicated by others. It would be impossible to reflect on all of those memories and impressions of the far-distant shores that I have visited in many parts of Europe, Africa, Australia and America so I decided to concentrate on my lifetime's experiences along the great variety of shorelines that border the British Isles.

An academic Physical Geographer is trained to explain the complex relationships that exist between people and their environment. There are many who say that they would welcome such information in order to understand why some people develop a feeling of 'belonging' to a certain location, usually where they were born. What is it about a place that generates homesickness? It is true that others are born to be wanderers and may never develop a 'Sense of Place' or 'genius loci'. So why is it that someone like myself, born almost ninety years ago in The Potteries of North Staffordshire, has retained a longing to visit shorelines? This remains somewhat paradoxical for my birthplace is about as far from the sea as it is possible to live, although no one in our islands is more than 75 miles from the ocean. It is, perhaps, a matter of interest that at Meaford Hall, a few miles from Stoke on Trent, there once dwelt one of Britain's most renowned maritime heroes, no less than Sir John Jervis, later to become Earl St Vincent, Head of the Admiralty during Nelson's famous sea battles. Moreover, at my former home in Staffordshire, I was able to look out of my bedroom window across the National Trust's Shugborough estate, the mansion of which was built by the descendants of another famous admiral, George Anson, who, in the 18th century, plundered Spanish treasure ships and brought home a fortune sufficient to found the abode of the well-known family of Lord Lichfield. Even more notorious was a Captain, who was born very close to my own birthplace but although he was Commodore of the Naval Reserve he was also Captain of the Titanic! Like myself, these seafarers from Staffordshire must also have had a desire to flee to maritime waters. Nevertheless, our present home is not far from the coast in Norfolk, a lowland shore with which I now have a close relationship (See chapter 9).

In the very earliest centuries of the British Islands' history it was simpler for people to settle and trade around the coastal periphery by means of sailing or rowing. As overland communications slowly improved, however, a rudimentary transport system began to evolve along a network of trackways and roads. Such linkages led to the growth of a matrix of inland villages and towns, some of which grew into cities. A largely rural population drifted to these urban settlements over the centuries, especially after the Industrial Revolution which led to a vast number of English and Welsh people moving to the coalfields where 'new' industries offered employment. However, in this respect Scotland and Ireland, were somewhat different from England and Wales because in the 18th and 19th centuries a significant proportion of the rural population was 'forced' to vacate their inland dwellings and move to the poorer soils of the rockbound Atlantic coast where they eked out little more than a subsistence lifestyle prior to emigrating overseas.

It is ironic that today the very shores that they left behind make up some of our most treasured coastlines. In general, therefore, until the 19th century, the coast remained largely the realm of the navy, the overseas traders, the seafarers and the fisherfolk, to say nothing of the peripheral farming community, some of whom were my ancestors. This is not to say that, after the Industrial Revolution, some of our coastal villages, towns and harbours became derelict backwaters until they were re-discovered by the 'Tourist Revolution'. Far from it, because as island countries some of the ports of both Britain and Ireland were already growing into major cities, illustrating their role in global trading nations. Nevertheless, a substantial proportion of the population of both countries has continued to live inland, quite divorced from their coastal environments. Thus, the mass seasonal exodus to the seaside has become a modern phenomenon, bringing with it a host of related problems for the fragile 'edge of the land'. These can be summed up by the term 'environmental impact'. Most of my academic life has been spent in research and in teaching undergraduate courses in an attempt to explain the genesis of such impact and to attempt to examine a number of methods to lessen or resolve the effects of human pressure on our marine environment. This has necessitated following a path already trodden by major conservation bodies who, having already perceived the future dangers to our coastal environment, have sprung into action, especially after the end of World War II. It will be seen how I willingly became involved in some of their enterprises. Perhaps this gives the impression that it is only humankind that threatens the well-being of our shores but nothing could be further from the truth. In the last few decades most people have accepted that the world is witnessing an accelerating degree of climate change, exemplified by major oscillations in our weather patterns. There are two aspects of these climatic shifts that offer the greatest physical threats to our coastlines: rising sea-levels and increased storminess. In later chapters I will attempt to examine the ways in which we are, or are not, attempting to cope with such hazards.

In order to understand whether my forbears had any maritime connections I spent some years researching our family tree and in doing so made some remarkable discoveries. After listening to a few of the family's old wives' tales, after which I learned that the early Whittows were not Vikings, as I had believed because of my father's second name of Noot (? Cnut), but that my ancestors came from Flanders, from the island of Nord Beveland in The Netherlands. This low-lying dune-fringed island at the mouth of the River Scheldt had been subject to tidal and storm surge flooding from time immemorial and it appears that it was one devastating inundation that finally drove the Whittow family (then known as Wizo) to seek refuge in Britain. It will be seen in the next chapter how there seems to be something atavistic that links this almost primeval family history and my presence on a scientific excursion to one of the Danish Friesian Islands in the 1960's to learn how to cope with such shoreline catastrophes, long before I became aware of the family 'homeland' in Flanders.

There are numerous stories of catastrophic inundations in coastal Flanders during earlier centuries but the most significant from my own viewpoint is that recorded in a 13th century Welsh text "Brut y Tywysogyon" from which we learn how Flemish coastal dwellers lost their lands to a major storm surge and, as a result, requested King Henry I of England to allow them to settle in Britain. Thus, in 1110, my ancestors were given land in Pembrokeshire as part of the Norman conquest of Wales and were created Lords of Daucleddau. The history of this Flemish settlement will be described later, when I re-visited Pembrokeshire to trace my family history. It seems that my family connections with the seashore stretch back for over one thousand years and may explain my enchantment with the coast. My love of the coast extended to an innate appreciation of rural scenery in general. This in turn guided me into my most rewarding hobby, that of collecting pictures which illustrate views of the countryside. Because of my wife's training in the History of Art, Diane has accompanied me on virtually all of the many visits to galleries, exhibitions, art fairs and antique shops as we built up a collection over the decades. The majority of our pictures are watercolours from the so-called 'Golden Age of British Art' (Early 19th century) but there are also oil paintings, acrylics, etchings, aquatints, silk-screen prints, engravings, lithographs and giclee prints, to say nothing of the framed maps. It goes without saying that many of these pictures depict coastal scenes and wherever pertinent I will endeavor to refer to the ways in which a variety of artists have attempted to depict their own distinctive interpretation of coastal landscapes. Moreover, our shores have inspired generations of writers, poets and musicians, to say nothing of scientists, so, wherever possible, I will introduce some of their own personal attitudes to and representations of this unique environment.

During my 6th-form years in the 1940's I was sufficiently motivated to attend the school art classes, often on a voluntary basis, in order to gain an insight into the aesthetics of landscape, a feeling that has never deserted me. Henceforward, I was often to view scenery in terms of a painting. But herein lay a dichotomy because my chosen career was that of a Geomorphologist (a type of Physical Geographer) in which I attempted to decipher the physical form of landscape and how it evolved over millions of years. However, the question has been posed: Were the two fields mutually exclusive?

Could geomorpholgy and landscape aesthetics ever be integrated in one person? To seek an answer to what at first appeared to be a conundrum I sought the guidance of Jay Appleton, the British expert on landscape perception and I feel that I must quote his explanation in full because it expresses my own heartfelt beliefs throughout my academic career: "If the idea that the principles of the earth sciences have anything to do with the principles of aesthetics seems somewhat far-fetched, recollect that the concept of beauty as a manifestation of some underlying principle which can only find expression when reflected in physical matter is central to the Platonic aesthetic condition. The main difference between geomorphology and Platonic aesthetics is that the former seeks to interpret shapes in terms of physical rather than metaphysical principles, but this does not lead us so far from finding a common conceptual framework as to justify abandoning the search. If you think it a waste of time to look for an explanation of beauty in the mathematical terms in which geomorphologists describe the slopes of valley-sides or the amplitude of river meanders, recollect that artists and architects have for centuries been persuaded that there is aesthetic significance in the no less mathematical concept of the Golden Mean or the Golden Section", (The Experience of Landscape. Jay Appleton, 1976). Such a philosophy underpinned my own feelings when, in the future, I stood on the Danish coastal dunes of the North Sea or attempted to decipher the landforms on the rockbound coast of North Wales, with one eye always straying to admire the beauties of the shoreline.

My longstanding interest with all things coastal can be divided into four categories: first, my childhood memories of seaside holidays (discussed in Chapter 1); secondly, my scientific research on British and Irish shorelines (discussed mainly in Chapters 3 and 6);

thirdly, my use of the seaboard as a means of teaching both coastal processes and environmental impact studies (all chapters); finally, my perception of the coast as a hedonistic delight and as a means of tracing the extent to which, as mentioned above, it has inspired naturalists, artists, poets, writers and composers over many years (all chapters). Several years ago, I read Nick Crane's well-known book "Coast" and discovered someone with an affection for the British and Irish coasts to match that of my own. Whilst being well aware that his extremely well-researched thematic approach was intended to accompany the much-vaunted BBC television series, I have no intention of trying to replicate the masses of fascinating information that he included in his book. But, significantly, we seem to have travelled along very similar shores and found particular inspiration on identical coastal stretches. As I read through his graphic descriptions I have experienced a remarkable sense of déjà vu. Is it little wonder that these are largely the same tracts of our sea coasts that have been singled out by such large-scale bodies as the National Trust and the Countryside Commission, plus scores of other conservation bodies, as worthy of special protection? I will attempt to describe how such heartfelt inspiration led me to assist some of these institutions in their respective conservation undertakings, largely in the national interest.

PROLOGUE

Neptune Rises from the Ocean

Under a sullen sky a stiff westerly wind drove the North Sea breakers far up the beach and sent billows of sand scything into the lofty dunes beyond. It was there that a group of scientists huddled together for shelter and to hear a lecture that was almost drowned by the roar of the gale. They had gathered in order to learn the benefits of marram-grass planting as a means of 'fixing' the unstable sand hills in an attempt to counter coastal erosion. For this was the island of Rømø, off the western shores of Denmark, adjacent to the grey waters where the renowned naval battle of Jutland was fought during World War I. I was one of those scientists, participating in a symposium in the early 1960's, hoping to learn more about coastal management in order to enhance my lectures on Environmental Planning to final year Reading University students in the School of Earth Sciences, of which I was ultimately to become Chairman. It was on this excursion, as part of an International Geographical Union's Seminar, that I first met Professor J. A. Steers, the celebrated Head of Geography at Cambridge University and the author of many standard texts on the British coastline. A decade previously I had asked for a copy of his acclaimed book "The Coastline of England & Wales" (1947) as part of the so-called Mackinder Prize awarded for the leading dissertation in the graduate year of 1952. Thus I felt able to introduce myself and seek his advice on coastal geomorphology. Little was I to know that this fortuitous meeting was to lead to my involvement in one of the most significant undertakings in my life, no less than the founding of the National Trust's campaign to purchase great swathes of the coastline of England, Wales and Northern Ireland in order to conserve it for the nation and protect it from unplanned development. This campaign was to be known as Enterprise Neptune and no less than a former Director General of the National

Trust has claimed that it was arguably the Trust's most proactive and influential ever. (The Fight for Beauty, Fiona Reynolds, 2016). Not only was I privileged to be part of the founding committee of this momentous undertaking but, after continuing to contribute to the cause for half a century, I was fortunate to be at its 50th anniversary celebrations as the only surviving member of the five who planned the scheme. The history of this venture will be described in later chapters but it would be interesting to consider how the nation both perceives and values its wonderful heritage – the coastline.

Some people may regard the shores of our realm as little more than a barrier, a full stop at the end of the land. At times in our island's history this has indeed been the case when it proved to be a bulwark against invasion and marauders. To others it offers an alternative challenge, a means of escape to settle in foreign parts or to sail away on quests of discovery. How else would the British Empire have been cobbled together over the centuries? Today, we probably take the shoreline for granted and feel some sense of reassurance that the coastline will always be there to enjoy. In this respect I must agree with the hedonistic sentiments of Philip Larkin who, after his childhood's visit to Southwold in Suffolk, was inspired to write about the unforgettable pleasures of the seaside on a sunny and windless afternoon, whilst looking out across the wide expanse of the North Sea. (High Windows. Philip Larkin, 1974).

Such poetry encapsulates the way in which the seaside has been perceived by millions of people as a symbol of their pleasurable childhood memories. Indeed, it has been pointed out by Christina Hardyment, in her book "Writing Britain" (2012), that the psychologists, Jung and Freud, identified their childhood experiences of the sea as having had a profound influence on their psychological development. Another writer, Vaughan Cornish, in his discerning book "The Beauties of Scenery" (1943) writes perceptively about our coastline by pointing out that the edge of the land gives a cross-section of the rocks which contribute to the very foundations of our scenery. This particular coastal phenomenon, where the sea-cliffs are constantly freshened by the waves, was something with which I was to become deeply involved for most of my lifetime, because it was the very core of my teaching and writing.

In essence, the coastline of the British Isles is a resource, something capable of being utilised, but it all depends, once more, on how one values this resource. I believe that our seaside perception is likely to vary during one's lifetime. In childhood the holiday vision is little more than a simplistic enjoyment of the rewarding pleasures of sea, sand and sunshine. It would appear that as one grows older the vision slowly changes as the coast is viewed from a more mature perspective. It will continue to remain a source of pleasurable activities, be they strenuous, such as boating, swimming, surfing, snorkeling, water-skiing or sea angling, or less active, such as beachcombing, foraging in the rock pools or simply relaxing on the beach and watching the children at play. To some, however, the linear but complex meeting of the land and the sea offers a unique scenic experience of long-distance walking, which can only be enjoyed by traversing and encountering as many of the coastal idiosyncrasies as possible in order to gain stimulating new vistas and experiences. George Borrow in his classic book "Wild Wales" spoke vehemently about such a pastime: "I am fond of the beauties of nature; now it is impossible to see much of the beauties of nature unless you walk". Hence the growth of long-distance trails and especially our celebrated coastal footpaths which continue to be commissioned by the Governments of both Britain and Ireland. Such a plethora of opportunities has encouraged hosts of urban dwellers to visit the coast where they may decide to paint or photograph its remarkable scenery in order to carry home a memento of their holiday. Professional artists, writers, TV film producers and composers have long realised of the potential appeal of this coastal environment. England's most famous artist, Turner, loved the challenge of the ever-changing maritime weather to produce some of his finest canvases; the spectacular Dorset coast appears to have played no small part in literature, spanning the decades from Thomas Hardy to John Fowles; and where would the TV cameraman discover a better shore on which to film the popular Poldark series than that of the rugged Cornish cliffs backed by their romantic sunsets? Several classical music composers have also found inspiration on our shores. Who can forget the swirling crescendo of Mendelssohn's "Hebrides Overture" or fail to be moved by Delius's "Sunset" in which his orchestral colours perfectly illustrate the sun slowly descending to the ocean's horizon? In the following chapters I will attempt to decipher the motives of some of these masters and explain how their mannerisms relate to our coastlines. Nicholas Crane, in his celebrated book "Coast", coined two very befitting sentences to describe such feelings: "The flowering of art, music and literature around our shores would not have happened if the coast hadn't been a reservation of the soul; a place where tranquility and inspiration are brought in with the tide. That creativity, practiced on the edge, was a form of endorsement which has given certain places an additional aura". I can only concur wholeheartedly for these words encapsulate all of my own convictions.

There is, however, yet another response to our shoreline, a more purposeful one, and therein lies a dichotomy. Firstly, is the coast there to be exploited largely in a commercial fashion? This is a viewpoint that must be exhibited by virtually all coastal dwellers:

it is the world of tourism, fishing, farming, trading, shipbuilding and all types of industrial development, be it civil or military. Moreover, one must not forget that thousands of people choose to live on the coast because they like both the view and the maritime climate. We shall see in the "Neptune" chapter that such an ever-increasing 'rash of bricks and mortar' was one of the reasons which provoked the National Trust into entering the realms of conservation and of coastal management. 'God forbid that there should be another Peacehaven on the pristine grasslands of the chalk cliffs of Sussex and Kent', seemed to be their mantra. Or is this attitude merely patronising especially when it extends to the location of caravan sites and holiday camps on certain of our shores? It has been argued very forcefully that our urban population is entitled to enjoy the appeal of the seaside, so that I, for one, have long been appraised of the conflict that exists between conservation and development in both Britain and Ireland. Secondly, there are multitudes of people who view the coast as a vast laboratory, a place to gather natural material in order to map it, catalogue it, experiment with it and simply describe it, largely in the cause of conservation and/or environmental planning and management. This attitude encompasses the fields of Geography, Geology, Botany, Zoology, Oceanography and Ornithology. It is a world of Earth and Biological Sciences in which I have spent almost all of my working life, spanning years of coastal research, university teaching and Higher Degree supervision right through to my voluntary work for the National Trust and the Forestry Commission. One of the products of my research has been the publication of several books explaining both the genesis and the diversity of the geology and the scenery of both British and Irish landscapes, all of which include large sections that describe their respective coastlines. Such undertakings have allowed me to travel widely along our shores, and in my leisure moments to ponder the multitude of threats to this treasured resource. It was during a university field trip to the Thames Estuary, a decade after the catastrophic North Sea storm surge which devastated both the lives and the shoreline of South East England, that I was driven to write my book on Environmental Disasters (Disasters: The Anatomy of Environmental Hazards, 1980). It was only then, after having visited the devastation at Canvey Island and viewed the newly opened Thames Barrier, that I really became aware of the magnitude of the growing threat to the British coastline from rising sea-levels. So, it might be said that, in many respects, the seaboard has become an obsession, an idée fixe in my entire persona.

1. CHILDHOOD

"The childhood shows the man, as morning shows the day"
(Paradise Regained. By John Milton, 1608–1674)

Llandudno Bay from the Great Orme looking eastwards to the Little Orme – *See plate section for colour version*

Blackpool Sands, Start Bay, Devon, where my father was almost drowned

When writing my autobiography almost twenty years ago I often pondered, as I trawled through the hazy kaleidoscope of childhood memories, what it was that made certain of them to stand out in my mind. There is no question that the list included a major surgical operation; being bitten by a dog; my first day at school; witnessing a serious road accident; being rescued from a quarry face that I had climbed as a challenge. All of these instances still rate highly in my vivid recollections and all of them were negative. There were, however, many positive ones and of these my excursions to the seaside must rank first and foremost. One can never forget the excitement of packing; the seemingly endless days of anticipation engendered by my parents; the tedium of the car journey (there were no motorways in the 1930's). "Are we there yet?" or "A penny for the first one to glimpse the sea". And the subsequent arguments with my older sister as to who saw it first. These are the treasured mental visions that must have been retained by millions of children long after they had experienced those glorious summer holidays of their early years. Some must have travelled by train, some by car and some by charabanc, but all were heading for that ultimate prize – the seacoast. No one has described these memorable events of one's formative years better than our former Poet Laureate, John Betjeman, who wrote with feelings akin to those of Larkin, about the joys and the setbacks of childhood visits to the beach at Trebetherick in Cornwall. (John Betjeman. Collected Poems. 1955)

And no one has illustrated the nostalgia of children playing on the Cornish shores better than Henry Scott Tuke or Dame Laura Knight. Is it a figment of my imagination or were those halcyon pre-war summers of the 1930's always bathed in endless sunshine? I fear not, for in retrospect I have come to accept that it must have been a cruel mirage, a misconception based on rose-tinted expectations. Look more closely and sieve through your memories and you will discover some occasions when the last of the three images of 'sea, sand and sunshine' was disappointingly absent. As we have all grown older we have begun to accept that British summers never have been all that we had hoped for, because, after all, we live on "a cloudy little island". In my own case, I cannot recall any sunshine on my very first visit to the seaside, nor even catching a glimpse of the open ocean.

My own recollections all began at the age of five when my father insisted on re-visiting his birthplace on the coast of Pembrokeshire. It was cold, it was Easter in 1935 and the weather was as capricious as ever, so it turned out not to be a 'bucket and spade holiday'. On arrival in Milford Haven (hence the name of our house) there were no shining sands or glittering seas to be seen but merely the clamour and clutter of a dockside, for this was a prosperous fishing port, located far up a deep-water estuary. Thoughts must have passed through my head relating to the futility of packing my swimsuit, rubber-ring, bucket and spade. Instead I can only recollect rain-swept quays, noisy shunting engines, rattling dockside-cranes as they unloaded endless fish-catches on to slippery cobbles slick with rain. (I especially remember this aspect because of the number of times that I lost my balance in my rubber-soled sandals). It seemed to be a world of raucous toil amongst the loose ice-blocks that slithered across the quay, itself wreathed in the miasma of the nearby smoke-houses. It certainly left me with awesome feelings, for this must have been how my forebears earned their living once they had abandoned generations of farming. But was this the sort of coastal experience that I had been given to expect? Hardly an auspicious introduction! This holiday proved to be an exception, however, for in succeeding summers our family trouped off to what I regarded as 'proper' seaside resorts. Although we lived so far from the sea our Midland location allowed us to strike off in all directions. Rarely did we bother with inland venues such as the Lake District, the Cotswolds or Snowdonia, whilst Scotland was quite beyond the question. No, it had to be the coast and almost always the west or south coast. It is true that we enjoyed 'days out' to The Wirral, where my little legs were pushed to the limits when we all trekked across to Hilbre Island at low tide. I felt that this was more like it, my first island and a frisson of traversing some distance off-shore. Blackpool was very different. True, it is a seaside resort and it has miles of golden sand but its seawater never appeared to be blue and the 'bracing' sea breeze merely blew my hat across the beach or sand into my eyes. The ice creams were fine and so were the donkey rides and the trams, but I only remember Blackpool's famous Illuminations on a day-outing with fellow students many years later. I soon began to judge that this type of resort was not really 'my scene'. Nor was Skegness, on our only excursion to England's east coast and I cannot recall one single thing about the resort itself. The highlight was a lengthy drive on winding roads around The Wash to visit Sandringham, that allowed us a fleeting glimpse of Queen Mary and King George V as they swept by in their limousine. I was later told how lucky I had been to have this royal experience because a few months later our king had died. Nonetheless, in my young mind it didn't really count as a memorable coastal visit. Little was I to know, at that tender age, that this book would be written in our final abode, a house on the fringes of the Norfolk Broads, a mere handful of miles from the North Sea coast.

My seemingly never-ending pessimism concerning the coastal experiences of my early years may well have been engendered by the widespread gloom and apprehension of the impending wartime years, when there was a constant danger of my father being called up for military service. But also, I seem to have been a sickly child, apparently missing school on frequent occasions; I often heard my parents discussing that "I needed to be taken to the fresh air of the sea coast in order to improve my health". This was really no surprise because our family had all suffered bronchial complaints, having been born amidst the smoking miasma of The Potteries, one of England's most polluted cities. The angst of those formative years must have started to dissipate because I certainly remember a succession of seaside holidays spent on what I then regarded as more conventional beaches. Moreover, I may have become less introspective as I grew older, accepting whatever life threw at me and becoming less worried as my father was eventually deemed to be in a 'reserved occupation' which contributed to the war effort without being 'called to the colours'. How lucky we were that such a privileged but onerous position gave us sufficient petrol rations to enable us to visit the coastline rather more frequently than some of my friends. Such constraints meant, of course, that our journeys had to be relatively short ones, so North Wales was to be our chosen means of 'escape to the shore'.

I have an affection for Rhyl, a modest resort on the Welsh coast but whose pastel-painted hotels face across its yellow sands. Furthermore, the eastern end of the promenade once terminated in a line of dunes. Like all children I loved dunes: they give shelter even on the windiest of days but best of all they provide countless opportunities to scamper up their slopes prior to slithering back down again. Even at that age I noticed that sandhills were mobile and their ever-changing shapes and 'blowouts' sent sand grains skittering across the promenade. Sadly, it was partly for this reason that the authorities cleared away this natural coast and with it a sort of paradise for young children. I suppose that this was my first lesson in coastal management. But I was lucky to have witnessed a scene that must barely have changed since the time of David Cox, one of Britain's most famous artists, and one who was skilled in being able to capture the effects of weather on the British landscape. (Scott Wilcox [Ed.], 2008). Cox painted pictures of "Rhyl Sands" in 1854, showing Victorian visitors leaning against a blustery wind as they strolled along its beach. There were no signs of beach games, swimmers or wind-shields in those days! Needless to say, in the 1930's I'd never heard of David Cox but came to make a collection of his pictures somewhat later in my life. I was to return to Rhyl a few years later, but this time not with my parents but with an aunt and uncle merely to be a companion for their young son. I recall that this proved to be one of the bleaker of my coastal visits because the weather was dreadful, we never once ventured onto the beach and spent much of our time listening to records of George Formby and Gracie Fields or in the town cinema. This 'challenging' wartime experience was highlighted by my first visit to Snowdon's summit, in which the mountain train reached a cloud-shrouded summit but at least it was something worthwhile.

A slightly more impressive holiday in North Wales was when, for some unknown reason, my parents decided to spend Christmas on the coast. On this occasion they had chosen to move further west from Rhyl to stay at a recommended mansion which took 'paying guests'. Situated on a wooded hill overlooking the resort of Colwyn Bay, this somewhat disconcerting venue still retained images of faded grandeur, with its antique furniture, valuable ornaments and heavy red damask 'blackout' curtains. It was commonplace to hear cries of "Don't touch" or "Don't sit on that chair", although the Yuletide fare was quite reasonable in view of the rationing restrictions. But one has to remember that it was the early years of World War II and my most striking memories were of deserted beaches and promenades beneath lowering clouds. Moreover, to add to the melancholia, a genteel widow was amongst the guests, having travelled all the way from South Devon to say goodbye to her only son who was on embarkation leave from his local army camp. We later learned that he was soon to be captured in Singapore before spending the duration of the war in a Japanese prison camp. What made this memory even more tragic was that this young soldier had fallen hopelessly in love with my teenage sister and for us later to discover that on his return to England he had become both a mental and physical wreck fit only for permanent care. Yet another somewhat joyless holiday on the coast for all concerned.

Finally, the war came to an end and it was about this time that I discovered Llandudno. I remember thinking that this was something like a resort, a place that lived up to the guide books' propaganda. It certainly has style for it had been strictly planned by Lord Mostyn in Victorian times and he had been able to take full advantage of its wonderful setting. Who can ever forget the parabolic sweep of its two-mile long beach backed by an immaculate promenade set between two prominent limestone headlands? Such a disposition of coastal landscape features, in which a perfectly curvilinear bay also bears a sense of closure, will always produce aesthetic pleasure, somewhat reminiscent of a miniature Bay of

Naples without the sun. Llandudno also has other attributes for it proudly possesses two shores, the better known pebbly East Shore and the lesser visited West Shore with its widespread shining sands. This is because the town has been built on the neck of a peninsula which links the Great Orme limestone headland to what was formerly the Welsh mainland. This means, of course, that the Great Orme was formerly an island and that the narrow strip of linking sand dunes is, geologically speaking, very recent indeed. Such a feature is technically known as a 'tombolo'. By this time, I had reached my teenage years, thereby developing a keener sense of perception in which I became much more observant of both people and their environment. As I slowly began to appraise and understand the make-up of our sea coast I began to understand why it has played such an important role in the British psyche. Such remarkable scenery, as that exemplified by Llandudno, was certain to have acted as a 'magnet' to holiday makers and will continue to do so for many years to come. One Victorian visitor was the Rev Charles Dodgson (Lewis Carroll), who is said to have been inspired to write "Alice in Wonderland" after meeting little Alice Liddell at Llandudno and is commemorated by a statue of the White Rabbit on the West Shore. The East Shore too has its literary claim to fame because it is reputed that Carroll based the character of the Bellman in "The Hunting of the Snark" on an old sailor who announced the arrival of the Liverpool steamer by ringing a bell on the promenade. Although many holidaymakers came to enjoy a typical beach-orientated holiday, visit the traditional concert parties at the end of the pier, or take steamer trips to Liverpool or the Isle of Man (sadly no longer available), I quickly concluded that in my own case I had moved on from such youthful pleasures and was now seeing the shoreline in an entirely different light. Henceforth it was to become my 'laboratory'. It was here that I first perceived that the edge of the land was not merely a line but a zone because in an environment such as Britain the tidal range is so large that in some flatlands the tide can retreat for as much as one mile, exposing swathes of sandbanks or, in the case of estuaries, a wilderness of mudbanks and saltmarshes. It is only on steep cliffs that high and low water can be discerned simply by a 'wave-cut notch' or, more likely, a change in the colouration on the cliff-face marked by the termination of marine shells and seaweed, sometimes termed the 'fucus zone'.

It was on one of my earliest visits, at a time when I had chosen Geology as one of my sixth-form subjects, that I started to take a closer look at Llandudno's beach pebbles and wonder why the strip of shingle grew wider and steeper towards the Little Orme's Head, leading me eventually into the complex realms of 'longshore drift', 'tidal currents' and 'wave dynamics', but such studies were for rather later in life as described below. Sufficient to say that, during this particular childhood holiday, I found it more significant when I noticed that amidst the multi-coloured shingle mixture it was very easy to pick out those pebbles that had been derived locally from the grey limestone cliffs of both the Great and Little Ormes, for they were the most preponderant. But the question remained: what were those black, red, brown and white pebbles and where had they come from? This early enquiry undoubtedly led me into a hobby of pebble and rock-sample collecting which, many years later, brought an invitation to re-write a Penguin Book Nature Guide that had been translated from the Danish. (Rocks & Pebbles of Britain and Northern Europe. 1980. Penguin Books). During my years in the sixth form, studying for my Higher School Certificate,

I finally began to peruse books on shoreline processes in order to discover how waves and tidal currents had fashioned not only Llandudno's shingle phenomenon but such spectacular shingle shorelines as Chesil Beach in Dorset. Such enquiry led me further into the realms of geological literature and to finally discover that the red, brown and white pebbles were derived from afar and that they had been washed out of deposits laid down by former ice sheets. These glacial deposits were termed 'boulder clay' from which the 'foreign' pebbles, or 'erratics' had been removed by coastal erosion. Closer research was to reveal that the rocks from which the pebbles had originally been quarried by glacial action were located to the North in far distant regions of Scotland and the Lake District. It is difficult to convey how exciting this discovery was to my receptive mind and how much it would influence my future career. In later chapters I will describe how a considerable amount of my academic research would be focused on mapping and deciphering glacial deposits and the landforms which they created. By far the greater part of this research would be carried out on the coastline of North Wales. Therefore, I owe an enormous debt to those early holidays in Llandudno whose beaches inspired me to replace my bucket and spade with a geological hammer.

Before leaving the world of childhood and its distant memories it is important to return to those pre-war days when my parents chose to visit coastlines in other parts of Britain, in between our regular holidays in Wales. Three resorts on the South Coast have lingered longest in my recollections: in chronological order these were in Cornwall, Sussex and Devon.

My parents told me that, in the summer of 1936, we took our holiday in the north Cornish resort of Newquay. I have seen a black-and-white box-camera photograph of myself dressed in an old-fashioned bathing costume sitting on one of the cliff-foot foreshore rocks. I was actually smiling, so it must have been sunny! Since those days of simple seaside pleasures, Newquay has witnessed something of a 'sea change' in which its sea cliffs now overlook sands thronged not only with bathers but also with international surfers. As a child I certainly remember the sea cliffs and sands but have no recollections of surfboards. When one looks back on the history of Newquay it is not surprising to find that, like many of Cornwall's fishing villages, it flourished in the 19th century owing to the glut of pilchards in the surrounding waters. The toils of the flourishing fishing industry of this coast have been captured by a Cornish artist, Charles Napier Henry, in his lively canvas "Pilchards" (1897) in which the art of 'seine-netting' is graphically illustrated. Moreover, such writers as Wilkie Collins described this arduous undertaking in his "Rambles beyond Railways" (1851). Life must have been tough, although some sort of living could be eked out whilst the fish stocks remained plentiful. However, thirty years before my visit the pilchards had disappeared and many of the Cornish fishing ports had been forced to diversify. Fortunately, the age of the motor car coincided with this decline and we now think of Cornwall largely in terms of tourism. Thus, Newquay's tiny harbour, enfolded by its granite quays, dries out at low tide to provide a safe haven for tiny tots to dig in its white sand. This is where I must have played on the sand or dabbled in the sheltered paddling pool beneath the so-called "Island" whose shrubby summit is linked to the mainland by a suspension bridge. Just round the headland one can now discover a different kind of Newquay, for its most famous showpiece is Fistral Beach where bronzed surfers now cavort on their 'Malibu boards', riding the gigantic Atlantic waves which catapult them up the shoreline. The sport is one more commonly seen in California or on Australia's Bondi Beach, both of which I have witnessed, but never could I have imagined in those far-off pre-war years that Newquay's ambience would change so dramatically.

Throughout those early years of my childhood, I was never really aware of the surrounding vegetation of trees, shrubs and plants; the few flower beds in our urban garden merely left an impression of colour, whilst the local trees were there simply to climb. I have often wondered why from the earliest age boys seemed destined to clamber up most things that pose a vertical challenge. In this respect I proved to be no different, as will be seen in subsequent chapters. But one certainly didn't attempt to climb the trees at the next watering place where we spent the summer holidays in 1937. Torquay, nestling in a corner of the sweeping extent of Torbay, was different from any seaside resort that I had ever experienced in my short life, for its promenade was lined with palm trees. Renowned for its mildness, its vegetation was more like that of France's Mediterranean coast; indeed, Torbay has often been termed the "English Riviera". Although it has its own small harbour, Torquay has never really competed with its nearby fishing port of Brixham, just across the bay.

Torquay's architecture is the epitome of Georgian and Victorian elegance for its history can be traced back to the time when the British fleet found a safe anchorage during the Napoleonic Wars. Beneath the yellow sands of Torbay there lies a seabed of sticky clay which held ships' anchors firmly whatever the force of the Channel gales. Naval officers installed their wives in houses around the harbour and once the clemency of the local climate, enhanced by the waters of the Gulf Stream, had been discovered, Torquay's attractive villas and hotels began to flourish along its hilly and crenulated shoreline. Guide books inform us that "Torquay is a sheltered town built on a rock-girt headland surrounded by clear waters. The upper slopes of the headland are studded with fine houses set in large gardens; tree-lined drives lead motorists to attractive parks and clifftop footpaths". This is the resort that I recall where, apart from enjoying the normal beach activity, one of the tree-lined drives took us high on to the headland known as Daddy Hole Plain. Not only did this provide us with widespread views across Torbay but also gave us an opportunity to examine an old World War I tank that, for some unknown reason, had been installed on the plateau turf. Needless to say, I had to climb on to its rusty top for a photograph and, believe it or not, that was one of the most memorable features that remained in my mind from that particular holiday. It will be described below, however, that there followed another episode that was less pleasurable and it occurred on one of the many trips that we made from the resort.

Much of this particular holiday seems to have been spent in the car during which we had all revelled in the spectacular cliff scenery of nearby Anstey's Cove and Babbacombe village and had even ventured into the depths of Kent's Cavern. Their striking coastal cliffs and bays had long proved attractive to artists, drawn there partly as a result "...of the publicity of such locations by the natural history handbooks, partly an aspect of the search for 'real' nature, unspoiled by tourism" (Where the Sea Meets the Land. Christiana Payne, 2007). The author recounts how, during the mid-19th century, in an attempt to depict the rugged cliff scenery carved from the local red sandstone, J. W. Inchbold painted "Anstey's Cove" (1854) which was then almost devoid of visitors. It was such images that drew the discerning Victorians to the coast of South Devon. But it was during a similar visit, some eighty years later, when we drove to view the remarkable shingle bar of so-called Slapton Sands in nearby Start Bay, that my father came close to losing his life. A guide book describes how, at the northern end of Slapton Sands, there is the tiny beach of Blackpool Sands where a stretch of clean coarse-grained white sand lies between high rocky points, backed by a picturesque stand of pine trees. We learn that bathing is safe in fine weather but that the beach shelves steeply and the surf is sometimes hazardous. In later years I was to learn all about tidal currents and submerged beach 'berms' and their intervening deep troughs but at the time such dangers never entered our heads. In a successful attempt to rescue a swimmer caught in an undertow my father was almost drowned, leaving the whole family in shock. This was the first occasion when I became aware of the perils inherent in the marine environment. Such elements will be examined further in a later chapter. Sufficient to say that it was a salutary lesson that I will never forget.

Elizabeth Barrett (Browning) must have had similar feelings, when she came to Torquay a century before, in the hope that the mild climate would improve her health, but any efficacious results were ruined when her favourite brother was drowned in Babbacombe Bay, an experience from which she never recovered. Many other writers and poets also came this way, including Oscar Wilde. Previously, in 1838, Tennyson described Torquay as "The loveliest sea-village in England" and it was the inspiration for his poem "Audley Court". Charles Kingsley brought his wife here in 1853, also to restore her health, and enjoyed the scientific society he met in Torquay, after which he wrote that it was "...a place that must be as much endeared to the naturalist as to the patriot and the artist". Such thoughts were almost certainly induced after weeks of rambling along the rocky foreshore, examining the flora, fauna and the geology because he writes of the "...happy evenings spent over the microscope...examining the wonders and labours of the day". As I too was much later to discover, he probably found that the shoreline was a sort of laboratory. It is no surprise, therefore, to discover that UNESCO designated Torbay as the only "Geopark" in the whole of England in recognition of its singular geology. Even now I can recall that my very first amateurish oil painting, at the tender age of eight, was of a red coastal headland on the coast of Torbay.

I have revisited Torquay on subsequent occasions, notably on the very day that the end of World War II in the Far East (VJ Day) was announced. I have vivid memories of the floodlit celebrations and, because an American warship was anchored in Torbay, scores of American sailors were scaling the balconied facade of the Grand Hotel. Compulsive climbing yet again! The latest visit, some fifty years after that childhood holiday I now regard as an anticlimax. I was to discover that Torquay had lost something of its pristine gentility and had descended into little more than a sprawling urban spectacle. It still sported its deck chairs, band stand, coloured lights and boat trips but its streets had become notorious for their ubiquitous traffic jams whilst its aquarium had been overwhelmed by a multi-storey car park. The quaint fishing port of Brixham, with its narrow streets is, if anything, even more choked with traffic and exhaust fumes. One began to wonder if the flight from our inland cities to find peace, contentment and the clean fresh air of our coastline is still worth all the effort of driving hundreds of miles on overburdened roads. We shall see in the next chapter why the National Trust rapidly became aware of the escalating problems facing our coastline and began to take positive action.

The pre-war years, however, had not reached the overwhelming pressures described above, so that our annual holiday in 1938 was to the breezy shores of 'Sussex by the Sea'. Eastbourne proved to be another Channel holiday resort with genteel pretensions, but I loved its location at the foot of dazzling chalk cliffs. Indeed, the elegant dove-grey and off-white facades of the sea-front hotels were almost indistinguishable from the dominant white eminence of Beachy Head when viewed from one of our short excursions out to sea.

Over the decades chalk has increasingly fascinated me. How is it that a rock tough enough to build the bastion of Beachy Head is also quite vulnerable to solution? When we strolled on the springy turf of the cliff-edge downland that adorns this striking promontory I was now old enough to ask for someone to explain why there were shallow concrete dish-like structures scattered at intervals across the landscape. These, I learnt, were termed 'dewponds' and, as their name suggests, were located to collect atmospheric moisture due to condensation, and also rainfall, in order to supply water for grazing livestock. Apparently, Sussex, despite its maritime situation, is one of England's driest counties but its higher chalk headlands are often blanketed with Channel fogs, thereby providing an important source of moisture to replenish the dewponds during periods of drought. This is necessary because chalk, like all limestones, is porous and surface streams are few and far between. It was to be many years before I understood the processes of solution, underground streams and aquifers, but I was later to spend several years living on the 'Chalklands' where I learnt that the term 'bourne' was common in their place names. For instance, the River Pang joined the Thames at Pangbourne, a village that I knew well, and I was able to witness how this particular bourne ceased to flow on the surface during lengthy periods of drought.

Britain's south coast sea cliffs, chiselled from the Chalk, were destined to become quite iconic in the British psyche as war clouds began to gather. A few months before our Eastbourne holiday Hitler had invaded Austria and the Prime Minister was just about to fly to Munich on a mission of appeasement. The newspapers were full of rumours and we read that trenches were being dug in the London parks. Apprehension prevailed and little did I think at the time that this part of the Channel coast was to become the 'Front Line' in 1940 when we 'stood alone'. Our shoreline was thought of as a bulwark against a possible Nazi invasion and the 'White Cliffs of Dover' came to be seen as a symbol of our resistance. Moreover, this was not the first occasion on which we had felt beleaguered; for centuries our continental neighbours had posed threats from the sea and in Eastbourne we were reminded of the Napoleonic wars by the so-called Martello Towers along its seafront, built to withstand French invaders. The most prominent had been quaintly titled "The Wish Tower" and it is anyone's guess as to what that wish would be. I remember that my sister and I simply wished that our father would not be 'called to the colours' because of the family's casualties sustained in World War I.

Despite Eastbourne's popularity with the Royal Family, following the summer of 1780, when George III's children spent their holidays there, the resort seems not to have attracted many famous writers, poets or artists. As far as I can ascertain, its major claim to literary fame was when George Orwell spent his preparatory school years in the resort, leading to his essay "Such were the Joys", published posthumously in 'The Partisan Review' (1952). This article discusses the bewilderment that he felt at the crimes of which he was accused by his class mates. From my own viewpoint, I had no feelings of bewilderment because I was in Eastbourne to enjoy myself. Old enough now to go off unsupervised to swim, play tennis, visit the shows and participate in the annual carnival. Those were the carefree years, never to be forgotten, but after hostilities had ceased my childhood was over and my life was to be directed almost entirely towards scholastic aims; a period when exam followed exam and a career had to become uppermost in my mind, once my National Service commitment had been fulfilled.

2. NEPTUNE

"The natural bravery of your isle, which stands
As Neptune's park ribbed and paled in
With rocks unscalable, and roaring waters".
(Coriolanus, William Shakespeare, 1607)

Rømø Island, Jutland, Denmark, showing IGU scientists learning about coastal management in 1960

Red Wharf Bay, Anglesey, where caravans had been 'hidden' in a coastal quarry (1965)

Unplanned coastal housing that also gave cause for concern

Since those carefree pre-war days spent in Eastbourne, time has rolled by – twenty-six years to be precise. In that time my scholastic career had taken me to academic posts in Ireland, East Africa, California, Australia, Oxford and finally Reading. Of these only the Irish and American sojourns could be said to have been in coastal environments, but such a variety of experiences has endowed me with a widespread knowledge of the complex physical processes that have shaped the various landforms throughout the World. Over time I have tried to explain to generations of students how the scenery of the British Isles has evolved and especially how their coastlines have slowly been created. At first, I was concerned only with physical phenomena but, as my career progressed, I began to understand that the landscapes which we see today have, in addition, been fashioned largely by the intervention of humanity. There is virtually nowhere in our islands that does not bear the imprint of people. Even the apparently pristine Old Man of Hoy sea-stack in the remote Orkneys has been ascended by intrepid climbers. Is there anywhere in the British Isles that has survived such intrusion?

In this respect Professor A. S. Woodward, President of The Linnaen Society, made a cogent statement in the Foreword to R. L. Sherlock's book "Man as a Geological Agent" (1922). He stated that "Man … ever since his appearance, has progressed in adapting surrounding nature to his needs". He goes on to say that, in a coastal context, "Harbour works and protective structures on one part of the coast may have disastrous effects on another part and, even with our present knowledge, it is not always possible to predict what those effects will be". He concludes by stating that "Man has, indeed, learned to be cautious in altering the balance of nature in the world of plant and animal life.

He may be approaching a stage when he should pause to consider whether his use and alteration of the crust of the earth itself are for future as well as for present advantage". These beliefs are even more pertinent today than they were in 1922 and have led to the founding of numerous environmental and conservation bodies by like-minded people. I was certainly aware of such sentiments when I stood on a Danish sandhill in 1960 to learn the effects of coastal erosion. I have already stated that it was this particular event which led to my involvement in the National Trust's Enterprise Neptune campaign but we shall see that this was not so much a concern with the physical effects of coastal erosion but with the increasing degradation of our shores by the impact of people.

By the Autumn of 1964 I had been married to Diane for seven years and we had a four-year old daughter, Fiona. I had returned to a lectureship in my old 'Alma Mater' of Reading University and we had just moved into a picturesque Thameside village in South Oxfordshire. After years spent in overseas posts it was good to be back in England and I was looking forward to a new challenge in my career. Little did I suspect that the postman, on that fateful September day, was bringing me a letter that would change my lifestyle. It came as something of a surprise to discover that it was from the National Trust inviting me to a meeting at their London headquarters in order to discuss a topic on coastal conservation. "Would I be interested in participating in one of their projects?". By now I had written a handful of scientific papers on British shoreline evolution but it appeared that the Trust's project was intending to deal with a different aspect, that of coastal preservation. On the 7th of October 1964 I arrived at the handsome park-side mansion of Number 42, Queen Anne's Gate with a certain degree of trepidation, a feeling that was not dispelled when I was ushered into a room full of formally dressed gentlemen not one of whom was I able to recognise. Then I caught a glimpse of Professor Steers from Cambridge, who gave me a sympathetic smile. Now I knew why I had been invited for, not only had he remembered our meeting on the coastal dunes of Denmark in 1960, but he had also included some of my coastal publications in his Second edition of "The Coastline of England and Wales" (1964).

It had been pointed out by the eminent historian, G. M. Trevelyan, some thirty-five years earlier, in his book "Must England's Beauty Perish?" (1929), that our coastline was under threat of over-development. Despite new planning legislation in 1932 and 1935, 'ribbon development' and other impacts on the coastal environment were manifestly on the increase, especially during the war years that followed, when large sections of our shores were draped with military installations. All of these threats were summarised by the National Trust Chairman, Lord Antrim, before introducing the Agenda for the 1964 meeting, which was entitled "ENTERPRISE NEPTUNE: A National Campaign to Save the Coast". I have retained a copy of this historic document and can well recall the vital topics that were to be under discussion:

1. How much remains to save?
2. To what extent is it already protected?
3. What contribution can the National Trust make to the permanent preservation of the coast?
4. How has the National Trust's project been received?
5. The scope, aims and policy of the campaign.

It transpired that Item 5 was the one which engendered the most discussion during the remainder of the meeting. So far as

Scope was concerned it was agreed that the campaign was "To be promoted on a regional as well as a national basis". In terms of the campaign's duration it was thought that the period April 1965 to April 1966 would suffice, with a possible extension. (some fifty years later this 'estimate' appears risible). I was surprised to learn, some twenty years later, that the Trust's Council had had serious reservations about both the time and the expenditure that should be spent on the Neptune campaign. After agreeing a sum of £75,000 for the launch-year of 1965 "...the Executive Committee was still concerned about the cost and, in October, there was a move to apply a further brake. Earl De La Warr, Field Marshall Sir Gerald Templar and Peter Scott...all, in their different ways, formidable adversaries, are all recorded in the minutes as having expressed their concern about the expense of the appeal". Significantly, it was this apparent concern that upset Conrad Rawnsley to such an extent that he was quoted as saying at a later meeting "The National Trust is not bankrupt in that (financial) way. But there are other ways of being bankrupt. You can be bankrupt in ideas, bankrupt in the common touch, bankrupt in your sense of what people need, and in your alacrity to provide it". Such an altercation was to lead to Rawnsley's dismissal (See below).

On turning to the Aims of the campaign it was thought desirable "To acquire control over the coastlands deemed most worthy of preservation either: (a) by gift, devise or, as and when they fall into the market, by purchase of freeholds, or (b) by gift, or purchase, of restrictive covenants". Most significant was the decision "To raise the sum of £2,000,000 by voluntary subscription".

At the outset the Central and Local Government Departments offered to pay 24% of the initial expenses whilst National Trust individuals and legacies contributed a further 28%. It was the next section of Item 5, however, that was to become the most important contribution to the conservation of the British coastline and was hereafter regarded as a 'Landmark' in the history of the National Trust. It stated that "In accordance with the National Trust's Acts, coastlands acquired for their natural beauty as a result of the campaign will be preserved unspoiled for the benefit of the nation". Moreover, "Wherever it has the right to do so, the Trust will give public access and provide facilities for enjoyment, recreation and scientific study, provided such access and facilities are comparable with the preservation of the landscape". These two sentences would become, in the lives of future generations of coastal visitors, the most fundamental aspects of the entire campaign.

The remainder of the Agenda dealt with minutiae of fund-raising, advertising literature and personnel. The Trust was hoping to recruit some 8,000 volunteers to run the fund-raising and advertising and, furthermore, to appoint a "…field force…which will comprise a Campaign Director, three Regional Directors, County Organisers, Municipal and County Borough Organisers, Urban and Rural District Wardens, Parish Stewards and Local Events Organisers wherever volunteers can be found". After several hours of discussion, I was beginning to wonder what my own contribution was to be and I became bewildered when the meeting began to break up. It was at this point that Professor Steers interjected and asked a very pertinent question: "Gentlemen, I agree with everything that has been said so far, but there is one fundamental omission in the discussion, namely, the meeting has failed to define what parts of the coastline are to be purchased. How do we know what is there? How do we know what state our coastline is in?". He then proposed that it was essential to carry out a detailed mapping survey of the coastlines of England, Wales and Northern Ireland and that I should be the Director of that survey. After this intervention and as the participants began to disperse, Lord Antrim invited a small group to stay behind to discuss this proposal and I shall never forget what transpired in the next few minutes. Professor Steers admitted that he himself was too old to conduct this onerous survey; Lord Antrim then invited me to submit a proposal as soon as possible; Conrad Rawnsley (Director of fund-raising) suggested that he wished to be involved; Reginald Hookway (National Parks Commission) offered to assist in any way possible, and it was he who, in a whispered aside, warned me not to let Rawnsley interfere "…because he was a loose cannon" (an appropriate analogy in view of his naval background). Sufficient to say that Commander Conrad Rawnsley (grandson of one of the Trust's three Founders) did try to interfere at subsequent meetings, speaking to me "as if he was on the Quarter Deck of a ship" (to quote something that I later recorded for the National Trust archives) but forewarned was forearmed, so to speak, and in a few years' time Rawnsley had been replaced by Captain Barlow. Such troublesome interventions such as this had already caused the Secretary of the Trust, Jack Rathbone, to resign. It is recorded that, despite of warnings, Rawnsley was likely to prove troublesome. (Merlin Waterson, 2011).

Before I left this historic assembly, I was hailed by yet another participant who turned out to be Dr E. C. Willatts from the Ministry of Housing and Local Government. He suggested that my proposed survey would be a unique opportunity to carry out a simultaneous photographic survey of the coast in order to identify the detail of its post-war condition, as Steers had earlier suggested. I rapidly accepted this challenge and he arranged for hundreds of colour films to be sent to me to distribute amongst my chosen volunteers. Sadly, I have to report, that despite an enormously successful completion of this task, the thousands of colour slides, illustrating the state of the entire coastline in 1965, have disappeared into the gigantic maw of the Department of the Environment, a unique archive that subsequent searches have still to discover, Even more sadly, those five gentlemen (Lord Antrim, Mr Hookway, Dr Willatts, Commander Rawnsley and Professor Steers) whom I regard as my mentors, have long since passed away, leaving me as the only survivor of Neptune's founding committee.

Within a month I had drawn up the required proposal and had returned to Queen Anne's Gate to present it to the rest of the Neptune committee on the 19th November 1964. After we had had a lengthy discussion of the details I was asked to go away and revise certain parts of its structure. After a further meeting on the 15th January 1965 the revised scheme for the survey was finally approved in February 1965. The final question had at last been resolved after lengthy discussions: How far inland should the survey extend? It was agreed that there should be no fixed rule but would depend on the character of the terrain. In undulating terrain, it would be fixed at the skyline; in flatland an arbitrary figure of one mile was adopted; if in doubt the surveyors were requested to stop at an easily identifiable feature such as a railway or road. in the case of estuaries, it was decided that that the limits should be taken at the lowest road bridging-point or vehicle ferry. Unfortunately, this latter rule meant that large stretches of coastline above the Severn Bridge were excluded from the survey. Nevertheless, the Trust accepted that this vast undertaking would provide a "...fundamental underpinning of the entire Neptune Campaign". Thus, at this juncture it is essential to summarise the major details of the revised scheme.

At the outset I made it clear to the Trust that the survey must be totally factual (i.e. objective) and that no attempt should be made to make qualitative assessments or recommendations on aesthetic (i.e. scenic) grounds. This was at variance with some of the Trust's documentary statements which spoke of "outstanding beauty". Unfortunately, such strictures proved to be impossible to regulate and the surveyors included their own personal scenic judgements on numerous occasions. I have to admit that I, too, broke my own rules a few times.

In terms of costing of the survey I suggested that "...the amount would probably be not more than £400 (including the cost of the maps)". Today this sum appears derisory but this was some fifty years ago! Moreover, my team of graduates, postgraduates and academic staff were all happy to work for basic expenses only, an altruistic approach that may not be reflected in present day society. It is important to point out, however, that such comparisons are invidious because modern day university scholars are saddled with monumental fees. On turning to the type and scale of the maps to be used, I decided that the so-called 6-inch maps of the Ordnance Survey, although offering ample space for annotations, would be too unwieldy to handle in the field to say nothing of the considerable numbers involved. The so-called 1-inch maps were too small to accommodate the detailed information so it was decided to use maps at a scale of 1:25,000. In the case of Northern Ireland, I discovered that most of their 1:25,000 maps had been destroyed by fire and that the survey would have to be carried out using 6-inch maps. At this juncture it became obvious that the Northern Ireland survey would benefit from being overseen by another person, because of possible overload. Thus, I was delighted to welcome my academic colleague, Ian Fenwick, who was pleased to accept this task, especially since he had recently been in an academic post in Ulster.

The time had now arrived for me to draw up the detailed list of categories that would have to be recorded and how to annotate and colour the field maps. This item had already undergone a great detail of discussion with National Trust officers and the final guidelines agreed. In terms of the colouration of the chosen categories I was influenced by the philosphy of my former academic colleague, Terry Frost (1915–2003), one of the Royal Academy's leading painters. He had always been consumed by the desire to communicate emotion through colour and form. In an attempt to follow his principles, I hoped to persuade my volunteer force to envisage a linkage between the chosen colour and the landscape that they were viewing. Thus, the urban scene was to be coloured grey; the industry to be shown red, using the analogy of the furnace; the woodland an obvious dark green; the 'managed' land that had not been built over, such as parks and golf courses, was to be depicted as light green; semi-permanent wooden coastal structures (pejoratively termed shack-settlement) were to be coloured brown; caravan and camping sites (some of which were only transient features) were to be depicted as white crossed by diagonal blue stripes in an attempt to illustrate the stark white 'intrusions' against a blue seascape; the land occupied by the Ministry of Defence was to be coloured orange (a rather limp analogy with the flash of gunfire); finally, the remainder of the landscape, which included all the non-built-over scene (generally farmland, rough grazing, moorland and heaths) was to be coloured an eye-catching yellow, largely because I had run out of colours! This latter category was to prove by far the largest of the land uses and the one on which the Trust would focus their interest.

The overall strategy required by the National Trust was agreed as follows: "An up-to-date survey of land-use and amenities was necessary in order to establish, in terms of land-use, those areas which remain free from the spread of urban and industrial expansion, and the development of poorly planned caravan sites, shack developments and the like. At the same time such a survey would help to ascertain which areas might be cleared of rural 'rubbish' e.g. derelict gun emplacements, by the use of voluntary labour. It was noted that not since 1943 had a coastal survey of this kind been conducted, by Professor Steers and Dr E. C. Willatts, and they were the first to admit that it had been a very rudimentary exercise. Ours was intended to be considerably more detailed.

The proposed 1965 survey was of such magnitude that it could not be carried out without a pilot study which was intended to iron out any discrepancies that might arise. Since time was running out, I decided that the western shores of The Solent, in Hampshire, would be a suitable venue in view of its short distance from Reading. Negotiations began with both the Hampshire County Planning Authorities and with the Regional Officer (South) of the Nature Conservancy. In this respect I must express my appreciation of the ongoing advice that had been given from the outset by another of the Conservancy's officers, Dr A. P. Carr. It seemed that there was growing enthusiasm for our proposed survey and in this respect, mention must be made of an offer from a philanthropist, who wished to remain nameless, to fly an aerial photographic survey (obliques) on the south-central coast of England on selected Bank Holidays in order to identify the degree of tourist density on beaches, car parks, etc. For reasons which now escape me this generous offer was declined by the National Trust as was the proposed pilot survey on The Solent. Instead, I decided that the Dorset coast, to the west of Swanage would be a more suitable venue (I hope that I wasn't swayed by its scenic beauty or its geological attraction). Thus, in May 1965, a coachload set off from Reading University's Geography Department en route to the Purbeck coast, comprising 4 staff members and 33 undergraduates and postgraduates. I had ascertained that the total length of the coastlines of England, Wales and Northern Ireland was of the order of 3,500 miles and that it would be essential to recruit a force of at least 35 volunteers. Admittedly some coasts would be simpler to map than others, Lancashire as opposed to Essex for example, but each student agreed that they would be capable of surveying about 100 miles in the given time. And the given time, they assured me, had to be in the summer vacation of 1965 because by then they would have graduated and would be starting their careers shortly afterwards. So, in a couple of months, the survey was completed on a coastline that has subsequently been accurately measured at more than 8,000 miles (excluding Scotland which was never included in the Neptune campaign because the National Trust for Scotland is a separate body). In retrospect I wonder if we would have baulked if we had known about the true distance. I think not.

The 'field' maps that were distributed amongst the volunteers, in most cases just after they had graduated, came to a total of 350, including those for Northern Ireland. I recall that for most parts of our far-flung coastlines the summer weather remained fine and that the surveyors made very good progress. Some of them kept in touch by letter: a question from Rosemary Burton regarding the maze of Essex creeks; an appeal from Richard Tazewell who wondered if he should claim ferry costs when mapping the Isle of Wight; an announcement from Rodney Gunson and Veronica Webb that, after completing the Pembrokeshire survey, they were intending to get married; a similar decision was made by David Pinder and his fiancée, whilst they tramped along on the intricate coast of south Cornwall, a picturesque area in which they eventually chose to live, in nearby Devon.

The completed field maps arrived sporadically at my university office, with the notable exception of those covering the coastal section from Neath to Amroth in South Wales, including the important peninsula of the Gower. An apologetic note came from Colin Williams: "I'd completed the exercise, rolled up the maps, tied up my tent and went for a much-needed drink in a nearby pub. When I returned I discovered that my tent and all its contents had been torched, probably by some yobs from Swansea. I'm very sorry but I shan't be able to repeat the mapping because I'm just about to start a job." I, too, was restarting my new term's lectures and was unable to take time off, but two of my postgraduates, Tony De Souza and David Pinder, kindly offered to repeat the mapwork. Tony had just returned from the Northern Ireland survey, which had been supervised by my colleague, Ian Fenwick, who himself had spent a month trudging the shores of this Irish outlier. David went straight from Cornwall to the South Wales coast and in due course their maps reached me. It seemed that they had thoroughly enjoyed the extra challenge, to such an extent that they had named the summit of the highest of the Gower's sand dunes "Pinder's Peak". Included with the maps were requests for expenses, ranging from £10 for Pembrokeshire down to 10 shillings for the coast of Glamorgan. Partly to set an example and partly to familiarise myself with the methodology my wife and I spent weeks of that summer mapping the North Wales coast, from Rhyl (of distant memories) to the attractive resort of Aberdyfi, on the border of Cardiganshire.

The latter county was itself mapped by another of my departmental colleagues, Dr Peter Wood.

By October my office was almost overflowing with hundreds of field maps and at this point I had to find time, single-handedly, to check the results, write short reports for each of the counties and begin the painstaking task of producing carefully drawn copies of each sheet. Thank goodness that I had some assistance, first from Ian Fenwick who dealt with the Irish maps and then from Sheila Dance, our senior technician, otherwise the last of these three assignments would have taken several months longer than the time agreed with the National Trust. The latter had requested that each County Report would be accompanied by a set of statistical analyses which, together with my conclusions on the "state of the coastline", would form the basis of the Trust's policy on future coastal acquisitions. It has to be remembered that by 1965 the Trust had already acquired 187 miles of coastline but their aim was to acquire a total of 900 miles. My job was to recommend the areas in which the Trust should concentrate its efforts.

In order to provide an overall foundation, on which their policy could be based, I classified the results into three broad categories:

1. Coastline Developed beyond Normal Redemption.
2. Coastline Partly Developed.
3. Coastline Relatively Undeveloped (which the Trust chose to call "Pristine").

The detailed classifications of land-use employed in the survey and the broad categorisation were based on the following criteria: Category 1 included an amalgamation of urban, rural built-over land, industrial and industrial spoliation and transport installations (docks, airfields etc.). Category 2 included 'shack' settlement, caravans, tents, holiday camps, military occupation and 'cared-for' but unproductive land (golf courses, parks, etc.). The third category included all farmland, heathland, rough pasture and woodland etc.

Not surprisingly, the Trust was to concentrate very largely on the third of these categories, although there were to be some surprises in store. It was rather reassuring to find that of the 8,000 miles of our coastline no less than 3,342 miles could be classified as 'pristine' in 1965. A few cases will serve to illustrate the contrasts in the amount of 'pristine' coastland still surviving in different counties: North Devon and Anglesey, for example, had some 80% classified as "Relatively Undeveloped" whilst Flintshire, Cheshire (The Wirral) and Sussex had less than 40%. It is perhaps significant that it was the high degree of coastal development in Sussex which alerted the National Trust in 1964. It remained to be seen to what extent the tracts of 'unspoiled' coastline would be whittled away by development over the succeeding decades. It will be recounted below how the Neptune Campaign progressed over the next half-century.

Once all the 'fair copies' of the maps had been completed in 1966 my next duty was to deliver both the maps and the accompanying reports to the National Trust in London where I was greeted by a charming young lady, Gillian Raikes, who turned out to be the Director of Fundraising for the Trust. We immediately struck up a rapport and Gill was to prove a staunch supporter of Neptune over the succeeding decades. She explained to me that the maps were regarded as such a valuable archive that in the future they were to be housed in an air-conditioned chamber at Heywood House, a Trust property in Westbury, Wiltshire. There they could only be accessed by officers of the National Trust (and of course by myself).

She took the opportunity to ask if I would be happy to remain as an unpaid consultant to the Trust in the event of Enterprise Neptune continuing into the future. Fifty years later I was still offering advice on coastal acquisitions and Huw Davies, Head of Conservation Information at the Trust, was able to conclude that: "Since its launch (during which time it has been renamed the Neptune Coastline Campaign), it has become the National Trust's most successful and enduring fundraising campaign, thanks to overwhelming public support which has so far raised £65 million" (Mapping Our Shores. H. Davies (Ed.), 2015).

It was not long before the Neptune funds were used to make their first purchase, namely Whiteford Burrows in the remote north-west corner of the Gower, widely regarded as one of the finest sand dune environments in the United Kingdom. This imposing landscape had suffered a wretched experience during World War II when it had been used as a military artillery range after which it became a bomb disposal site. On 12 March 1965, however, this virtual wilderness had its moment of celebrity when it became Neptune's first purchase.

The donations and gifts continued to roll in over the years enabling the Neptune Campaign to acquire mile after mile of coastline and to continue its aim of giving "…statutory landscape protections in conserving the very things that often bring us to visit the coast" (H. Davies, 2015, *op. cit.*). It is noteworthy that the Trust had changed its earlier use of the word 'preservation', used in its initial publicity, to that of 'conservation' which is much more appropriate in terms of its landscape management aims. The bold initiative taken by the National Trust appears to have been a signal for other conservation bodies to set in train a number of similar initiatives, although the National Trust for Scotland failed to launch a coastal survey of its own. When one examines the incredibly convoluted

Scottish coastline and its numerous islands, it is quite understandable why the task must have appeared to be far too daunting. If invited, I certainly would have had to decline, but the situation never arose.

One of the first bodies to respond to the coastal challenge was the National Parks Commission who, no doubt at the urging of Reginald Hookway, arranged a Regional Coastal Conference that was held in Exeter on July 22nd 1966. A whole series of Regional Reports resulted from this important meeting in which "The local planning authorities were asked to identify… any derelict or unsightly buildings, whether of wartime or other origin, and sites of incompatible unauthorised development" (National Parks Commission. The Coasts of South-West England. 1967). The Commission's brief did not extend to an appraisal of the state of the coastal flora and fauna, an omission which resulted in an official request to the Nature Conservancy, in a letter dated 1st June 1967, in which it was asked to produce an annex to the Commission's final report. In turn, the Conservancy instructed their own officers to:

1. Provide an appraisal of the coastline of England and Wales (N.B. not Northern Ireland) in relation to its value for scientific research, wild life conservation and education.
2. Identify all areas of the coast which have special importance from the above points of view.
3. To describe the extent to which these areas are protected and to assess the need for further protection.
4. To suggest that planning and management of the coast should be based on a proper understanding of the ecological and physiographical processes taking place and the impact of man's activities upon them.

The detailed forms provided for the field mapping were distributed by Dr F. H. Perring, Director of the Conservancy's Biological Records Centre, and required the officers to identify not only the types of 'scientific users' but also, most importantly, the various habitats, namely: maritime grassland, saltmarsh, mud flat, sand bank, sandy shore, sand dune, shingle, sea-cliff or rocky shore, brackish lagoon and marsh. Such an intricate inventory would prove to be an invaluable addition to the findings of Enterprise Neptune and of the National Parks Commission which, taken together, would act as a spur to the Government, pressurising it to introduce legislation in the fields of conservation. A political party booklet entitled "A Better Country" (Conservative Political Centre) was quickly published in 1966. It resulted from the brief of a committee (set up to examine recreational impact on the countryside) and chaired by the MP Christopher Chataway. It concluded that the country needed a number of "Sea Parks" in order to control the "Misuse of Leisure" and stated baldly: "Without careful planning…the more intensive use of leisure [on the coast]…will render this a wretched country in which to live".

Within a year the results of the Neptune Survey had reached the Press which, by and large, sang the praises of the National Trust's initiative. One newspaper article will suffice, that written by David Green in The Sunday Telegraph for 2nd January 1966, under the headline "How long will Britain's coasts stay beautiful?". He stated that some 20 million people will holiday at the seaside in that coming summer but would they find their favourite spot unspoiled? He exemplifies his statements with two cases, Land's End and Portland Bill. So far as the former was concerned he believed that Land's End "…has a desolate, hang-dog air about it; a few gaunt buildings slopping out cups of tea to the thirsty masses; innumberable paths scarring the cliff-tops with the passing of shuffling thousands and a startling lack of grass". When he turns to describe Portland Bill, Green becomes even more pejorative for he was saddened "...to see the cafes, built as though for temporary use but clearly set for a lifetime of serving chips with everything; the litter of ice-cream wrappers and cigarette cartons: the battered brow-beaten vegetation". It was these types of indictment that were mirrored by some of the personal comments that had been written by the Neptune volunteers on their maps, notwithstanding my strictures to be entirely objective. From my own findings on the North Wales coast in 1965, I can hardly blame them! How long will we have to suffer the way in which parts of the British coast have become massive 'dumping grounds' both from the land and the sea?

Some of the individual annotations by the Neptune students expressed personal sentiments when they were confronted by what they perceived as despoiled coastal landscapes, similar to those expressed by David Green (above). Subsequent writers, many years later, drew attention to those subjective comments. For example, Merlin Waterson, a former Trust Director for East Anglia, writing in the National Trust's Magazine (Autumn 2015) states that "Apart from being a unique and nationally important record of coastal land use, these maps provide a fascinating insight into attitudes at the time. Comments such as 'picturesqe harbour sullied by caravan camp' and 'deplorable cliff top development above fine chalk cliffs' provide an invaluable commentary on 1960's social mores. The team was perhaps overly concerned about the visual damage caused to some stretches of coast by holiday shacks and the presence of the Ministry of Defence in other areas. Both of these obstacles have in some cases proved temporary and have not stood in the way of acquisition by the Trust". In fact, such an example was to take place in 1995, when

Orford Ness, in Merlin Waterson's 'territory' of East Anglia, proved to be the largest Neptune purchase (see below). In so far as the 1965 survey had mapped this stretch as "Beyond Redemption" I can see his point. And this was to prove not to be the only example.

It must not be forgotten that, whilst this mid-1960's frenzy of conservation activity was being given enormous publicity, another national survey was ongoing, in order to assist with national recovery after World War II. The Second Land Use Survey of Britain, conducted by Dr Alice Coleman of London University, had been collecting data, since 1950, on the state of the entire town and countryside. It was charged by the Government to produce hundreds of maps indicating the areal extent of land utilisation, using similar categories to those later to be used in the National Trust's coastal campaign. The great differences lay in the considerably more detail that was required by the 1950 survey, where every single field-crop, type of grassland and woodland species had to be mapped. The First Land Use Survey had been carried out in pre-war years, under the Directorship of Sir Dudley Stamp, one of Britain's leading Geographers. The second 1950 replication of this extraordinary achievement was currently taking place when I was invited to undertake the Enterprise Neptune exercise, indeed, I personally contributed by mapping part of west Berkshire. Dr Coleman, on hearing of my own survey, offered to let me have copies of the few coastal maps that had been completed in the intervening fifteen years. These proved useful as a final check on my own maps when I came to make the fair copies and it was encouraging to discover that there were few if any discrepancies.

I often wondered if the British initiative was being followed by other countries but some perfunctory enquiries discovered only one, a coastal survey carried out in France in 1977 by an agency which produced a report entitled "Inventaire Permanent du Littoral". The land use was interpreted from 1977 aerial photography and transcribed by the use of automated methods of thematic mapping. I feel sure that Professor Andre Guilcher, of The Sorbonne in Paris, would have been involved in the French mapping scheme. He was one of the scientists whom I had first met on the Danish coast in 1960 and whom I was to meet again in Ireland (See chapter 6). The resulting 147 land use maps (at a scale of 1:25,000) were accompanied by an additional set of 23 maps (at a scale of 1:100,000) which illustrated the legal status of the French coastline. The idea behind the latter data-base appears to have been of such significance that some years later (1990) the National Trust invited me to conduct a similar review of the legal status of its own coastal properties in England and Wales. My mentor at the National Trust during all of the somewhat frenzied activities of the 1960's was an extremely supportive officer, Richard Offen, who was in charge of Enterprise Neptune and all coastal affairs. It was rather curious that he was based not on the coast, as one would have expected, but at the Trust's Shropshire property of Attingham Park. This location was greatly appreciated by me because I was later to live a mere hour's drive away. It came as a great blow when, during a period of in-house reorganisation, the Trust decided to phase out this position, whereupon Richard emigrated to Australia to inaugurate a coastal conservation scheme based largely upon the Neptune Campaign structure.

From its outset the Duke of Edinburgh had kindly agreed to become The Patron of Enterprise Neptune, for it was well known that he had a keen interest in most environmental and conservation issues. In 1963 he had launched a 'National Nature Week' conference in conjunction with the equally dynamic figure of Max Nicholson, Director-General of the Nature Conservancy. As stated by Michael Dower, of the National Parks Commission, in an article in The Observer, 14th November 1965, there was a pressing need for a second countryside conference at which all British planning and conservation bodies would "…take a hard look at immediate (environmental) problems – the rapid growth of industry, the shameful heritage of industrial dereliction, the growing demands upon the countryside by weekend trippers, the future of the countryman himself". These remarks were to be endorsed by the Duke of Edinburgh, when the planned 1970 Conference took place, which he described as "The biggest group-think ever attempted for the countryside". Although, the coast itself was not specifically targeted, several speakers spoke about the threats posed to our coastal scenery, including those stretches still held by the Ministry of Defence; the impending location of nuclear power stations on our shores and the siting of an oil refinery within the bounds of the Pembrokeshire National Park. In this respect it was later to become a national concern that Britain's maritime environment would be under constant threats of future oil spillages. A paper by Neil Hailey, from the Freshwater, Marine and Pollution Policy Branch of the Nature Conservancy Council of England, drew attention to such potential impacts. He announced that The Department of Transport [had] commissioned the then Nature Conservancy Council to produce an atlas of the GB coastline showing sensitive wildlife areas vulnerable to oil pollution to assist their contingency planning procedures. The total of 77 maps (at a scale of 1:100,000) showed the location of wildlife habitats, together with concentrations of seabirds, marine mammals and other fauna and highlighted the sites that should be designated because of their nature conservation importance. This new data-base would not only complement the maps of Enterprise Neptune, despite their smaller scale, but also, of much greater significance, draw everyone's attention to the fact that the marine environment extends well beyond the 'edge of the land'. In later years the National Trust became increasingly engaged in monitoring the zones below the high-water mark.

For the next decade or so the coastal acquisitions went steadily ahead and although I continued to give advice, from my own viewpoint National Trust affairs were put temporarily 'on the back burner' so to speak. A secondment for a year to an Australian University not only broadened my knowledge of very different shores from those in the British Isles, but also gave me a chance to supervise a Higher Degree on a Coastal Conservation topic based on part of the coastline of New South Wales. This was also the period when Penguin Books invited me to write three books on "Geology and Scenery". It began with a re-write of Arthur Trueman's well known book on England and Wales (1971), followed by Ireland (1974) and finally Scotland (1977). Moreover, it was during those same years that I became seriously involved in a geological survey along the coastal fringes of North West Wales, the results of which were to be published as a chapter in a forthcoming book (See chapter 3). Yet another onerous but rewarding task, undertaken for the Forestry Commission (1973), gave me wonderful opportunities to explore the Scottish coasts (See chapter 7)· Meanwhile, between 1967 and 1975, I continued as Chairman of the Landscape Research Group in London, during which time, amongst other things, I helped to devise and test the "Isovist" technique that assisted the Central Electricity Board in the measurement of the visual impact of large power stations on the surrounding landscape. This also provided information on the location of sites for the possible 'undergrounding' of transmission-cables in areas of high scenic value. Coastal sites in Snowdonia and Anglesey were cases in point. It will be realised that I was seriously involved in conservation exercises in addition to those of the Neptune campaign.

It was now time for me to return to Enterprise Neptune affairs, especially since twenty-five years had elapsed and the National Trust had started to organise a Silver Anniversary event. It transpired that my contribution to the celebration would be the production of a large-scale map to illustrate the location of all the coastal acquisitions that had been made since 1965. I suggested that in order to produce a more striking visual impact it would be important to add photographs to the map itself. Such an undertaking would be expensive but it was agreed that, for future publicity and for educational purposes, this idea should be adopted. Thus, after seeking commercial estimates for its production, some of which were extortionate, I decided to design it myself in the Geography Department's cartographic laboratory. After several visits to the National Trust's photographic library in Queen Anne's Gate I was able to make a suitable selection and these were added to the map itself. The university's cartographic laboratory, under the supervision of Sheila Dance, was able to construct an impressively attractive image, thereby undercutting the lowest commercial estimate by no less than £500. The finished article measured some five feet by three feet and had to be transported to London in the departmental minibus. Shortly afterwards I was gratified to receive an invitation to the celebration itself at which Enterprise Neptune's Patron, the Duke of Edinburgh, was to be present.

On a bright sunny morning the celebration commenced in an impressive building not far from the National Trust's headquarters. I took up my allocated position alongside the large map of Neptune acquisitions and awaited the Duke's arrival. In due course he entered the room and gave a few introductory remarks about Enterprise Neptune before proceeding around the room to meet various dignitaries. Imagine my surprise when he was led over to peruse the map and, after an introduction, he asked me several pertinent questions about its production before stooping down to look more closely at its southwest corner that depicted Devon and Cornwall. "I am very pleased to see that many of your coastal acquisitions are in this region because it is England's finest stretch". Such a remark was not really surprising when one considers that he commenced his naval career at Dartmouth Naval College. He went on to tell me that he had just come from a meeting with Neil Kinnock, leader of the Labour Party, at which one of the points of discussion had concerned the coast. After the Duke had moved away I was besieged by a flock of paparazzi asking me to enlighten them on the Duke's remarks about Neil Kinnock. Not to be caught unawares I was quickly reminded of "royal prerogative" by an equerry and my mouth remained firmly closed.

After returning to Reading, following this memorable meeting, I looked up the List of Acquisitions that had been compiled by the Trust before the advent of the Neptune campaign and I discovered that the Duke had been quite correct. Of the 140 miles of English coastal holdings in 1965 no less than 89 miles were located in the South-West. A later examination of the Register revealed that during the early years of Neptune (1965–1989) no less than 189 new coastal properties had been acquired, including such well known places as Worm's Head and Rhossili Down in the Gower (1967) and Lundy Island (1969), thereby adding a further 325 miles to the existing coastal properties in England, Wales and Northern Ireland. One has to remember that the majority of the work involved was carried out by the Trust's Regional Directors and Land Agents who worked assiduously to discover where and when suitable properties had come on the market. Their policy was aimed largely at 'infilling' gaps between existing holdings and discovering whether there was already 'protection' by other conservation bodies over their potential purchases. In addition, large stretches of coastline were being given to the campaign in the form of legacies, gifts and covenants from the growing membership.

The Silver Jubilee celebration appears to have produced quite a boost to Neptune and it was given widespread press coverage. Very soon afterwards I was interviewed by the producers of Television Southwest to assist them in a film about the particular coastline that had so intrigued the Duke of Edinburgh. It was then that the Trust discovered that the fair copies of these very maps had been mislaid. I still have the original letters which flew back and forth between Gill Raikes and myself and I was delighted to inform her that our map curator, Bob Parry, had retained all the field maps. Having taken part in the 1965 survey as an undergraduate, Bob had played a not inconsiderable part in the whole operation of both supplying, collating and delivering the precious fair copies to the Trust in 1965–6. He was now to come to our aid once more and allow me to produce a new set of maps to replace those that had been mislaid. By the autumn of 1991 the matter had been resolved and the maps transferred to their venue, Heywood House in Westbury, Wiltshire. A visit, by Bob Parry and myself, to this impressive old house, from which all the Trust's fund-raising affairs had just been relocated, satisfied me that the complete 1965 archive of maps and reports would, in due course, be safely stored in an airconditioned unit. Gill Raikes, as Head of Fund-raising, had also been transferred from London to Westbury and she was able to explain that "...the first stop for the maps would be to the National Trust Estate Office at Cirencester, where Jo Burgon will ensure that they will be properly collated, catalogued, repaired and fixed with proper storage attachments prior to them being placed in the archives here". It seemed to me that during the intervening twenty-five years the maps must have undergone a great deal of handling and damage. Little did I know at the time that when Heywood House itself was sold, some years in the future, the maps would be sent for storage to an underground site in a cave near to Bath. Perhaps it was as well that I was never informed. I was much later given to understand that photocopies had been made!

By the early 1990's I had been introduced to Jo Burgon, mentioned above, who turned out to be The Trust's 'Advisor on Coast & Countryside' from his office in Cirencester. The first meeting with Gill and Jo, in the Senior Common Room at Reading University, proved to be of enormous significance for not only did it kick-start a renewal of Neptune acquisitions but it also marked a point at which I was asked if I would be prepared to give advice on future coastal purchases. The invitation happened to coincide with the final years of my academic career at Reading University: I was still Deputy Head of Department but had at last relinquished my position as Chairman of the School of Earth Sciences (Geography, Geology, Meteorology and Soil Science). Although I was due to retire in 1994 I felt fit enough to take up this challenge and renew my relationship with old colleagues and friends at the National Trust.

Throughout the next twenty-five years I devoted much of my spare time to Neptune affairs. This entailed attending numerous meetings, first in London and later in a purpose-built edifice termed Heelis, erected in Swindon, following the Trust's Executive Committee's decision to move out of London. My attendance at such meetings gave me excellent opportunities to meet most of the Trust's senior officers, foremost of whom were: Fiona Reynolds DBE (the Director General); Peter Nixon, (Head of Conservation); Gill Bolton (Patrons and Bequests) and last but not least Phil Dyke

(Coast and Marine Adviser). These were the main people at the forefront of the 're-launch' of the Enterprise Neptune campaign and I felt privileged to work with them. The coastal purchases continued to grow and in the period from 1994 to 1999 a further 137 new properties were added to the list. Notable amongst these was Porth Dinllaen in Caernarfonshire (which included the Trust's first purchase of a public house) in addition to substantial shorelines in North Yorkshire and Northern Ireland.

All this flurry of activity in the early 1990's had probably been spurred by another 'landmark' meeting of the Trust's Executive Committee in November 1990, who were asked by its Chairman not only to "...reflect on what has been achieved over the last 25 years but also to address its future coastal acquisition and management strategies". It was announced that the National Trust at that stage, was protecting 521 miles of coastline, through ownership (469 miles) and by covenant (52 miles). One of the most important points on the agenda concerned "...the many new threats to the coastline, unperceived at the time when Neptune was launched and Heritage Coasts [first defined] by the Countryside Commission". These included:

1. The prediction of rising sea levels and the place of sea-defences in dealing with these.
2. Proposals for tidal barrages affecting several large estuaries.
3. Increasing concern over the environmental quality of inshore waters and beaches as a result of industrial pollution and seaborne litter.
4. Proposals for extraction of marine gravel, off-shore oil developments and fish farming which fall outside the scope of normal planning controls.

I realised that most of the above concerns had been beyond the brief of my 1965 survey but that they were causing such current disquiet at a national level that they could no longer be ignored. It was agreed that the Government should be made aware of such threats and their attention drawn to another significant National Trust initiative, namely an ongoing "...study of renewable energy schemes, tidal barrages and wind farms, and their likely impacts on coastal landscapes". One immediate outcome of this meeting was a letter sent to me by Jo Burgon in which he sought my advice on future acquisitions in the light of the above recommendations.

At a subsequent meeting in 1993, with Jo Burgon and Gill Raikes, they brought the news that the Ministry of Defence had no further use for Orford Ness in Suffolk and were willing to sell it to the National Trust. It appeared that the asking price was £5 million and my thoughts on this matter were invited. The 1965 survey had mapped it as "Beyond Redemption" so the discussion ranged about its value to the Neptune campaign because from a visual viewpoint it still looked like a derelict eyesore. One must remember that in 1965 the Neptune surveyors would have been refused access and could only make an assessment from the 'mainland' shore. However, its value lay not so much in its defunct yet historic military and scientific buildings but largely in its ecological importance. A survey, on behalf of the Trust, had been carried out by the Suffolk Wildlife Trust and their findings reported that "The Ness is the largest vegetated shingle spit in Europe [and that] the shingle flora...still retains a number of nationally rare species and rare plant communities of significant size". The report also highlighted the ornithological value of Orford Ness because it included the breeding sites of four endangered birds, namely marsh harrier, little tern, avocet and barn owl, in addition to several other rare species. Its overall importance in all these respects had led to the Ness being listed as a Grade 1 Site of Special Scientific Importance. It must not be forgotten that the Ness was also of considerable historic interest because it was here that experiments in radar, defence systems, bombs and atomic weapons were carried out, many of which "…affected the course of world history". The National Trust concluded that here was a unique opportunity to fulfil both of its twin obligations of preserving "…places of historic interest or natural beauty". Furthermore, it would put an end to a coastline previously judged as "Beyond Redemption" and which even the Trust believed remained "…open to the devastating effects of the triple forces of Easterly gales, scrap metal merchants and vandals".

So, what was to be my own contribution to the ongoing negotiations, because the case for acquisition was overwhelming? I made two critical points: First, from a geological viewpoint, the Ness was extremely dynamic, for not only was the spit moving southwards at an average rate of some 15 yards per year but also, due to geophysical sinking of the North Sea Basin over the millenia, the viability of the shingle spit could be at risk. Secondly, I pointed out that (as the Trust's Executive Committee had already noted three years before) rising sea levels, resulting from global warming, posed a further long-term threat to its survival in its present form. I laughingly suggested"…that it was an awful lot of money to pay for a feature that may end up in Essex by the next century". Gill Raikes responded that "Neptune donors would certainly think that such a large amount of money should not be risked if in this sort of doubt". Thus, it seemed that my views may well have been regarded as very significant, in terms of costing, especially since the Trust would be faced with an enormous amount of clearing-up of the widespread clutter. I suggested that such an operation ought to result in a major price reduction, despite the attraction of such a unique acquisition. In the end it was agreed by the MOD that a reduction would be acceptable and finally "The total cost of acquisition, clearing ordnance and restoring some of the buildings amounted to £3,500,000, of which £2,300,000 came from a Countryside Commission grant, £587,500 from the Trust's Enterprise Neptune appeal and £389,000 from the National Heritage Memorial Fund" (The Times. 6 June 1995). I understand that the five miles of extra coastline represented the largest single outlay from the Neptune funds.

It must have taken at least two years for the MOD to clean-up the site, for the official opening did not take place until the summer of 1995. I was gratified to receive an invitation from the Natural Trust Chairman, Lord Chorley, and the Regional Chairman, Lord Hemingford, to attend the event at yet a third peer's home, that of Lord Bridges, at the imposing "Great House" in Orford village. It was interesting to recall that Lord Bridges had been the Chancellor of my own University of Reading between 1959 and 1969, thereby spanning the launch of the Neptune campaign; quite a coincidence. The celebratory luncheon, held in a very large marquee in the grounds, provided me with a delightful opportunity to chat with Libby Purves, the journalist, who lived in Suffolk, but the most amusing conversation ensued with the blazered gentleman seated on my left. He courteously enquired why I was present at the event and, after explaining my role in Enterprise Neptune, I returned the question. His reply was somewhat startling: "I am here as the Bomb Disposal Officer and, much as we have tried, I cannot guarantee that all the ordnance has been removed. Some of the bombs may still be hidden at depth below the muddy salt-marshes. If you'll take my advice you should keep to the paths". I certainly bore this advice in mind when we crossed to the Ness by ferry-boat later in the afternoon, but all the time remembering the old warning given to tourists "Beware of Adders", in order to stop them from trampling the vulnerable vegetation. I had already witnessed this ruse when visiting parts of The Lizard Peninsula in Cornwall.

Even on a summer's day Orford Ness is a bleak place, and the ever-present dereliction only added to a general feeling of uneasiness, as if the ghosts of former occupants were still lingering in this forlorn coastal landscape. Its military history began in 1915 when the Experimental Flight of the Royal Flying Corps tested machine guns, bombs, bomb sights and aerial photography. Such activity continued throughout the Thirties but the next significant instance came in 1935–6 when Watson-Watt and his team visited the Ness to work on the development of RADAR in three dilapidated wooden huts. During World War II many fresh scientists came to the Ness in order to improve techniques of bomb-aiming and the increased protection of allied aircraft to enemy fire. But some would say that the most important military use of Orford Ness did not occur until 1959 when the Atomic Weapons Research Establishment (AWRE) moved on to this isolated shingle spit. In order to test these frightful new devices several enormous concrete bunkers were erected at intervals along the coast. Although there was no fissile material present, there was sufficient high explosive in the atomic fuses to create a catastrophic explosion in the event of an accident. The bunkers were designed to prevent such a mishap from affecting nearby Orford village and their gaunt shapes, nicknamed "pagodas" still stand silhouetted against the North Sea. They reminded me of the ancient Martello Towers of Eastbourne and the Channel Coast and, like them, they have been given the status of 'Listed Buildings'. Having experienced at first hand this extraordinary coastline it was not difficult to understand why such a bizarre scene was classed as "Beyond Normal Redemption". But because of the invaluable work of the ordnance removal officers and the enormous ecological importance of the site it became easier to understand the reasons why the Trust persisted with its acquisition and why it was considered worth changing the image that had been perceived in 1965.

Such a brave decision by the National Trust to invest in what appeared to have been a derelict coastline was a further indication of a 'wind of change', because a few years previously the National Coal Board had offered a stretch of sullied shoreline in County Durham for little more than a token fee, after its mining operations had ceased. The challenge was to win back a short stretch of coastal cliffs below which the beach had been overwhelmed by decades of colliery waste from a local coal mine. Not only had the beach turned into a scene of unbelievable desolation but also the sea itself had become polluted by a scum of black filth. Little wonder that the 1965 surveyors had written it off as land that would be of no value to the Neptune campaign. Yet attitudes were already changing at the National Trust and these types of challenges were being re-examined, after the offer had been accepted in 1990. The Trust rapidly joined a local project termed "Turning the Tide" in which the Durham authorities, together with landowners and interested conservationists began the seemingly hopeless task of winning back such spoliation within the Durham Coast AONB. In less than a decade this public spirit, aided by the erosive waves of the North Sea, had brought both the beach and the rare limestone grasslands above the cliffs back to a "pristine" state. Henceforth, the National Trust was able to showcase this paradigm as an example of enlightened management. More than a decade later, as I was being interviewed by the BBC News, as part of the 50th anniversary celebrations of the Neptune campaign, despite giving my views on different coastal acquisitions, the presenters chose to concentrate on this remarkable feat of reclamation on the Durham shoreline.

The Millenium was rapidly approaching and the National Trust was anxious to mark the occasion by producing a 'snapshot' of the state of the coast in order to ascertain the rate of change that may have occurred since 1965. Apparently, such a 'snapshot' was needed to justify continuing coastal acquisitions under the Neptune campaign. Jo Burgon was soon in touch and in 1995 he asked me if I could produce such an analysis for what came to be called the "Millenium Report". My response was somewhat incredulous: how could I singlehandedly replicate something that had taken an army of volunteers to produce thirty years previously? It fleetingly crossed my mind that I was still only an unpaid volunteer (as were thousands of others) but, having given my promise to Gill Raikes of my ongoing commitment to Neptune, and remembering the sterling efforts of the volunteers 'winning back' their stretch of Durham's disfigured coast, I was quick to respond in the affirmative. Jo Burgon knew that the task would be extremely onerous but suggested that he would lend me all the reports on the coast that had been recently commissioned by the National Trust during the 1990's. These had been compiled by their Regional Directors and Agents and it seemed that my job was to scrutinise their data and make comparisons between their 1995 results and those of the 1965 survey. I pointed out that this could only be a 'broad brush' exercise because it would be impossible to look in much detail at the current land use. Having received the promised bundle of regional reports I was immediately struck by two things: firstly, the Trust were still talking in terms of "Landscape Quality" and it appeared that 'beautiful scenery' had been the main criterion in the preparation of the 1995 coastal reports; secondly, there were no reports for South-East England or for Northern Ireland and I found that the report for North-West England had been designed in such a way that any comparisons were quite impossible. Thus, any data that I was able to produce would not give an accurate comparison of coastal changes throughout the country.

It transpired that the surveys produced in the 1990's were based on a qualitative grading system as follows:

> Grade I. National or international importance. Natural beauty or historic interest of the highest order, often with international designations.
> Grade II. Regional/local importance. Important but less exceptional.
> Grade III. Unspoiled and undeveloped but unremarkable; areas only worth acquiring as buffer land or land capable of restoration or assisting access or management.
> Grade X. Unsuitable for protection by the National Trust.

Thus, I was faced with the difficulty of comparing subjective data with objective data but a final resolution was reached by comparing Grades I, II and III (1995) with categories 3, 5, 6, 8 and 9 of the 1965 survey. Overall it appeared that some 6.8% of the "pristine" land, in which the Trust would be interested, had disappeared under 'bricks and mortar' in the intervening thirty years, although it has to be reiterated that the figures could only be regarded as rough estimates. The press were quick to seize upon the results, especially in the regions that appear to have suffered greatest 'losses'. I was almost overwhelmed by requests for radio and other media interviews although I tried to point out that the results could not be regarded as accurate as those of the 1965 survey because of the 'broad brush' approach. The newspaper reports exhibited various degrees of hyperbole but the Sunday Telegraph (4th June 2000) came closest to an accurate outline of the major findings of the Millenium Report. It was stated that "North Wales was the worst hit, with Flintshire losing 44% and Denbigh losing 36% of its coastal land". Furthermore, it reported that "Somerset has suffered badly too with 20% of its coastline disappearing under concrete since 1970 (sic) mainly because of industry at Avonmouth, Hinkley Point power station and 'sprawl' between Burnham on Sea and Clevedon". I was also quoted as saying that in general "The introduction of designated protected areas had increased protection for some stretches of coastline but may have put added pressure on unprotected areas". It echoed my 1995 findings that a few areas had actually returned to their former 'pristine' state. Cornwall, for example, showed that 4% of its coastline had benefitted from the decommissioning of military occupancy and a decline in the quarrying and mining industries. In conclusion the newspaper reported that in my warning for increased vigilance, I had stated that "...the 'gains' were encouraging but are very small compared with the 'losses'. We have to guard against the less scrupulous developers who will exploit any weakness shown by the planning authorities". From a present-day standpoint one can conclude that since that date (1995) both central and local government planning authorities have been under almost unending demands to allow different degrees of intrusion into relatively undeveloped land. But one also has to bear in mind that an expanding economy and a growing population have placed increasing pressure on all our landscapes. Some parts of the unprotected coastline have not escaped the development. One only has to think of wind farms, tidal barrages, harbour extensions, oil and gas terminals, the massive container port near Felixstowe and the destruction of coastland near Folkstone during the construction of the Channel Tunnel, to name but a few.

It was not long before the 40th anniversary loomed large in the minds of the Neptune fundraising officers. Although the income had been fairly steady it had become clear that an impressive event was needed, not only to raise more money but also to gain renewed press publicity. The brave decision was taken "…to hold a fundraising dinner to celebrate the 40th anniversary of the Neptune Coastal Campaign on board Cutty Sark on Tuesday 26 July 2005 in the presence of HRH The Duke of Edinburgh KG, KT". Thus, read the invitation to Diane and myself to attend this prestigious event, as having been major contributors to the success of the forty-year enterprise. We were gratified to be two of the eight guests at the Duke's table and we only learnt later that the other eighty guests were happy to pay £1,000 per head for the black-tie occasion.

A private-hire riverboat took us from the Festival Hall Pier downriver to Greenwich, all the while being serenaded by a jazz band and plied with cocktails and canapes. I have always found it difficult to make polite conversation whilst holding a glass and consuming delicious tit-bits at the same time, and it did not help when a strong sea breeze buffeted the boat enough to make all of us sway dangerously at times. Nonetheless, at Greenwich we were ushered aboard the Cutty Sark where we learnt that, having been launched in 1869, some 26 years before the National Trust itself was founded, "…she occupies a unique place in maritime history as the world's sole surviving Tea Clipper". After waiting amidst the packed guests on the Main-deck we were invited down below to take our seats at the Duke's table on the 'Tween Deck'. We were formally introduced, although he remembered our previous meeting in London and his interest in the acquisitions along the South-West coast. He jokingly said that "…after all the intervening years he would now find it difficult to stoop to his knees to view the bottom left-hand corner of the large map that I had presented". Other guests at the table were Fiona Reynolds (Director-General), Gillian Raikes (Fundraising), Nicholas Soames (MP), two American guests (who raised Neptune contributions in the United States) and last but by no means least a charming old lady, Miss Battersby who, I was informed, was by far the largest donor to Neptune funds. I had a lively discussion about fund-raising, when I had the privilege of being seated next to her, in which she recounted that, since she had no relatives, she was more than happy to carry on supporting such a worthwhile cause. The banquet was intended to reflect a totally British coastal theme and who better to host the event than Rick Stein OBE, who brought the entire staff from his Cornish restaurant to prepare the meal aboard the venerable sailing ship. I recall that the lobster, langoustine, sea bass, salmon and salt cod were washed down with large glasses of Chapel Down Reserve wine. Prince Philip himself much preferred a pint of beer, but for the rest of us the wine glasses must have been quite large for the conversation and jokes at our table continued apace and with much hilarity. The occasion concluded with a full-throated chorus, as we all sang the sea shanties and the Duke banged his empty tankard in time to the music. These have remained treasured memories. Once the cabaret (Isla St Clair) had finished at 10.30 the royal equerry came to escort the Duke away from the event and we all believed that he had only to return to Buckingham Palace. Much to our astonishment it was announced that he was in fact travelling back to Sandringham. A private coach sufficed to convey the main guests back into London and Rick Stein sat at my side, insisting that I recounted the jokes that the Duke and Nicholas Soames had exchanged and which had caused such mirth. Not many months later the Cutty Sark was engulfed in flames and very badly damaged but sufficient time had elapsed so that no finger of suspicion was ever pointed in our direction.

We had hardly recovered from our Cutty Sark experience when a further invitation arrived requesting us to be present at the formal opening of Greenway, the former home of Agatha Christie, which had been gifted to the National Trust in 2000. Set in magnificent terraced gardens descending to the River Dart, the ancient house had an almost theatrical backdrop of exotic trees and plants that flourished in the mildness of this sheltered Devon estuary. This was the sort of environment that stirred atavistic memories within me, of wooded creeks and tidal mudflats, whose peace was disturbed only by the cries of seabirds. This frisson had occurred on other occasions, notably on the Helford River in Cornwall (See chapter 8) and on the Eastern Cleddau River in Pembrokeshire (See chapter 4). Yet another memory surfaced during the entertainment at Greenway when we were introduced to the lady who had given to the Neptune campaign a beautiful stretch of coast in Start Bay, including the cove at Blackpool Sands where my father had almost lost his life some seventy years before.

It was not many years prior to my retirement that I had been appointed External Examiner to the Geography Department at the University of Plymouth where, to my amazement, I met up with David Pinder who had played such a prominent role in the 1965 Neptune survey. We had not communicated over all the intervening decades and we were able to reminisce at our tiny hotel in Stoke Gabriel, upstream from Greenway on the Dart. It transpired that David was now a Professor at Plymouth and that he was one of the prime movers in the negotiations which led to the important National Trust's acquisition of Wembury Point near Plymouth. This World War II naval-gun fort and training establishment, at the mouth of Plymouth Sound, had recently been released by the MOD and at the formal opening, immediately after the Greenway event, we were able to appreciate the importance of this coastal acquisition. Offshore was the prominent sea stack of the Great Mew Stone and the views stretched from the attractive estuary of the

Yealm across The Sound to the Heritage Coast of Rame Head in Cornwall. Below Wembury village itself, David showed us a coastal woodland that he was later to persuade its owner to sell to the National Trust. As we stood on the concrete standings of the former naval establishment at Wembury Point we reminded ourselves that this was a further example, like that of Orford Ness, that would have been mapped as "Beyond Redemption" in 1965. Yet another symbol of the ever-changing coastal dynamic of our islands over the decades. It also crossed my mind that these attractive rock-bound and tree-hung bays and estuaries of South Devon were the absolute antithesis of the low-lying, wind-scoured shingle of Orford Ness. Two contrasting environments but both now safeguarded and able to offer countless opportunities for both tourism and conservation/research for the futures of countless generations. As Adam Nicolson, the author and journalist, had recently written for The Guardian, following an interview with me for the 40th anniversary: "Previous visits to the coast (The Lizard, Golden Cap, Lundy, the Gower and Pembrokeshire for example) had been such treasured experiences, which seem in retrospect so fragile and private, scarcely to do with public policy or fundraising campaigns, [but] will be repeatable by your children and their children for ever and the rest of time". In the same article (26 May 2005) he further quoted that Neptune "…is an achievement on a world level but there is a real conflict of freedoms involved here. In a sense, as Whittow says, 'You might see Enterprise Neptune as grandees nationalising the coast for the good of the rest of us. But in my view, this is a good worth having. It is those memories of times on a beautiful coastline which are the most precious things you can have. You don't want to own it. You can let them [the National Trust] own it. But you want to see it. In fact, for all of us, the coast is better visited than occupied".

It was to be several years before we re-visited Plymouth but we were intrigued when we received an invitation from the National Trust to visit Devonport to attend a reception on board HMS Albion, at that time the flagship of the British navy. This was something entirely new and we arrived on the dockside full of anticipation and curiosity. An armed marine ushered us aboard this highly unusual vessel, known as a Landing Platform Dock. Its role was to act as a floating command platform for the commander of an amphibious task force, together with its troops, weapons and supplies. The 37 guests included several important donors to Enterprise Neptune, and the Trust's Deputy Chairman, Sir Laurie Magnus, introduced us to the ship's Captain who had kindly agreed to host the event at the behest of his father, a member of the National Trust Council. During the meal, served in the Officers' Wardroom, I remember thinking that the event exhibited a very different ambience to that enjoyed below decks on the Cutty Sark. Amongst the guests I was especially pleased to make the acquaintance of an eminent British artist, Maggi Hambling, who had brought along the 18-inch bronze maquette of her latest sculpture "The Wave" which she intended to donate to the Neptune campaign to be auctioned at a future event. I well remember seeing one of her best-known sculptures, a gigantic scallop shell, standing alone on the shingle beach at Aldeburgh (See chapter 9).

Over the next few years the coastal acquisitions grew steadily towards the ultimate goal of 900 miles and the Neptune fund itself surpassed £50 million. So much had been given in cash and kind that the Trust decided to show their gratitude by offering "…an exclusive Benefactor & Patron lecture and reception entitled 'One Man's Vision – The Neptune Coastal Campaign'". I was invited to give this prestigious lecture in February 2006 at the distinguished Trinity House, Tower Hill, London, headquarters of the Lighthouse

Service. I spent a great deal of time preparing this important lecture but owing to a sudden illness was unable to deliver it personally. Instead of cancelling the event my old friend David Pinder kindly gave the lecture on my behalf and I believe that it was well received.

It has to be remembered that the Trust's ownership of these lengthy stretches of coastline carries with it the concomitant requirements of stewardship and access. In 2007 I heard once more from Jo Burgon who sought my advice on the latter of these points because Natural England had asked for the National Trust's perspective on coastal access, following the very significant Act of Parliament (2000) known as the CROW Act (Countryside & Rights of Way). This Act declares that there should normally be public access to land mapped as open countryside (mountain, moor, heath and down). Quite clearly such a 'right to roam', as it was dubbed by the media, had serious implications both for the National Trust and for Natural England. The latter is a non-departmental body sponsored by DEFRA (Department of Environment, Food and Rural Affairs) which was formed in 2006 to oversee England's natural environment. Jo Burgon had drawn up a paper in response but wished for my comments before submitting it. It stated that the Trust guarantees "The provision of access to, along and around National Trust coastline is secured through:

1. The inalienable status of NT coastline.
2. Rights of Way (some of which are designated as National Trails).
3. Additional promoted routes that are not rights of way but enable access to the shoreline.
4. Permitted open access due to long-standing custom."

I pointed out that wherever access was given on Trust land that is tenanted, it would have to be in close consultation with the tenant farmer. Equally, who would be responsible for car parking provision, footpath maintenance and litter clearance on CROW land? Would it be DEFRA or the National Trust? Some of these problems, at a wider level, would not be resolved without opposition, as demonstrated by a lengthy press correspondence launched by some 5,000 indignant English coastal landowners. One Suffolk landowner, for example, stated that "This is all about privacy – a fundamental human right". He continued, that on his estate: "There are six pairs of nightingales nesting along the shore. Marsh harriers are further along the river. These birds are not going to hang about if they are disturbed by people and dogs. And what about the vegetable growers? This area is a big supplier to supermarkets. If a buyer sees a dog in a field of cauliflowers that would be enough to cancel an order" (The Times June 9 2008). This coastal example was not part of the Neptune acquisitions but conflicts such as this were bound to arise after the Government had set aside £50 million to create a 2,500-mile coastal trail in England. The battle was soon to be joined between Natural England and the Country Landowners Association with DEFRA as the referee and the National Trust as an interested spectator.

These were the years when my own mobility was seriously impaired by twin hip replacements and advancing age. Too much coastal walking perhaps. Nevertheless, my spirits were greatly revived when we had a surprise visit from our long-standing friend Gill Raikes. After chatting at length about National Trust affairs she handed over a mysterious package. Imagine my delight when I discovered that it contained a framed photograph of a boat that the Trust had named "The Whittow" and that this vessel had been given to the Warden of Blakeney Point Nature Reserve as a replacement for one that had progressed beyond its 'sell-by date', so to speak. Needless to say, I regarded this as a great honour and, in a later chapter, I will describe my subsequent sea trips on this sturdy little vessel.

The year 2012 marked the centenary of the death of Octavia Hill (1838–1912) one of the three founders of the National Trust. With the support of John Ruskin, she "…is credited with starting the social housing movement as well as housing management. [Moreover], one of Octavia Hill's most passionate beliefs was the importance of beauty and open space to people's welfare and equilibrium". I quote these words from the introductory address given by Dame Fiona Reynolds (Director General) at a Service in Westminster Abbey to dedicate a Memorial to Octavia Hill and to give thanks for the work of the National Trust. I was privileged to be invited to be present at the service in the Abbey on the 22nd October 2012, at which the readings were given by such celebrities as Julia Bradbury (Broadcaster), Robert Macfarlane (Writer), Gillian Darley (Biographer of Octavia Hill), Simon Jenkins (Chairman of the National Trust) and Peter Nixon (Director of Conservation at the National Trust). At the close of the impressive service I was able to converse with the latter gentleman because I knew that Peter Nixon was someone who had a considerable interest in the Trust's coastal campaign. It was in the illustrious surroundings of Westminster Abbey that I was able to broach the subject of a second coastal survey to commemorate the 50th anniversary of Enterprise Neptune. He seemed to be genuinely interested in such a suggestion and asked me to phone him at his home to discuss the details. From our subsequent discussions the Trust's Council appointed a new Director of the coastal campaign, Catherine Weaver, whose first duty was to produce a scheme entitled "The year of the coast 2015". Another very important member of the 'coastal team' was Phil Dyke, Head of Marine Conservation at the Trust. It was a delight to meet and work with these two officials (and others) at numerous meetings in London and in Swindon, where we attempted to set up a new programme to replicate the 1965 coastal survey, in order to discover the changes that had taken place over fifty years. So much detailed planning was involved that I have decided to describe this momentous 2015 event in chapter 11. Another reason for such a postponement of any discussion relating to the progress of the new Neptune campaign, was the news that Dame Fiona Reynolds was going to retire from the National Trust a mere fortnight after the Octavia Hill Service at Westminster Abbey. Personally, I was saddened by the news, because in some ways it marked the end of an era and my feelings were exacerbated when Gillian Raikes also intimated that she, too, was retiring. Both had been stalwart friends throughout the most successful Neptune years and much of its success was due in no small measure to their assiduous work.

At Spencer House, St James's Place, overlooking London's Green Park, a farewell reception was held on a chandelier-lit evening. The palatial rooms of this mansion were packed with family, friends and celebrities and once more I was pleased to be invited to such a glittering occasion. I spent much of the time talking with Fiona's mother who told me that she was leaving the Trust to become Master of Emmanuel College Cambridge and I'm delighted to say that we have kept in touch. An even longer friendship, with Gill Raikes, was also at an end but I was pleased to discover that she was to be appointed as fund-raiser at one of London's major hospitals. Thus, in many ways, I was disappointed that they might not be there to celebrate the 50th anniversary of the National Trust's most successful campaign – Enterprise Neptune.

Believe it or not there was life before and even during the Neptune years. Thus, the next ten chapters will chronicle my life through the post-war decades until the beginning of the new Millenium, during which time I had matured from teenage angst to confident manhood. It seems to have been a time when almost every opportunity was seized to visit the coastline of the British Isles either for pleasure or for work. Or so it seems in retrospect, because the seaside memories were those that have survived longest in my mind's calendar.

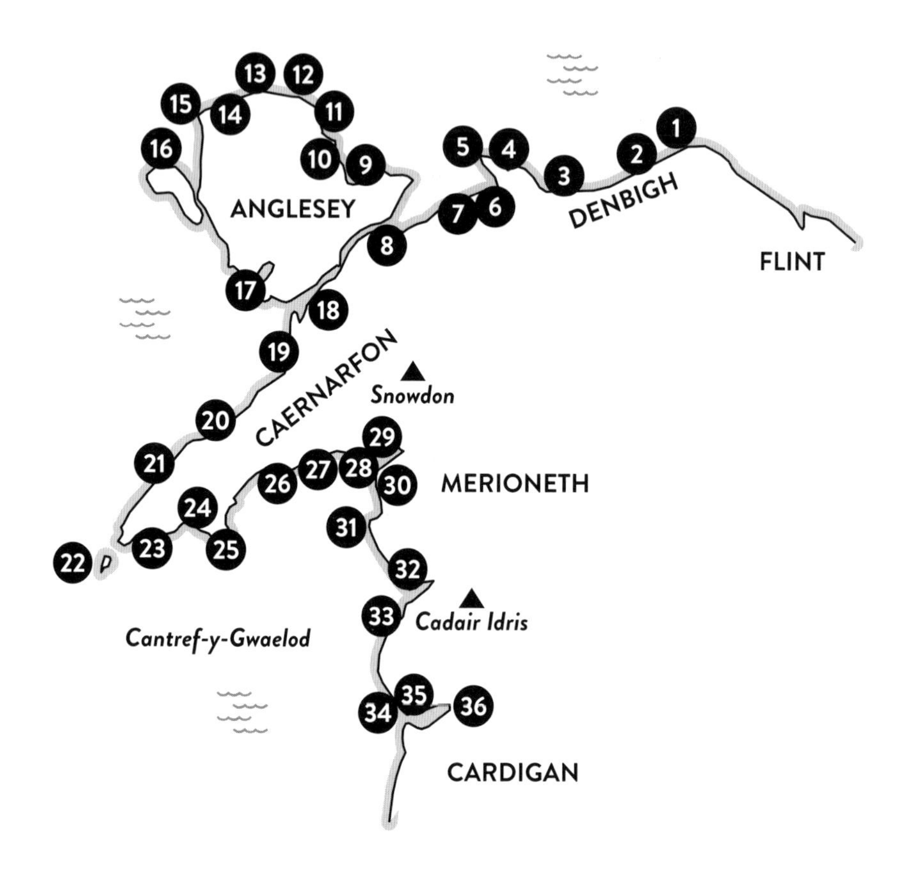

1. Prestatyn
2. Rhyl
3. Colwyn Bay
4. Llandudno
5. Great Orme
6. Conwy
7. Penmaenmawr
8. Bangor
9. Red Wharf Bay
10. Moelfre
11. Porth Wen
12. Amlwch
13. Wylfa
14. Cemlyn
15. Carmel Head
16. Holyhead
17. Newborough Warren
18. Caernarfon
19. Dinas Dinlle
20. Nefyn
21. Porth Oer
22. Bardsey Island
23. Aberdaron
24. Hell's Mouth
25. Porth Ceiriad (St Tudwal's)
26. Pwllheli
27. Glanllynau
28. Criccieth
29. Porthmadog
30. Harlech
31. Mochras
32. Barmouth
33. Fairbourne
34. Tonfanau
35. Aberdyfi
36. Ynyshir

3. NORTH WALES

"Evening on the olden, golden seas of Wales,
where the first star shivers and the last wave pales".
(James Elroy Flecker 1884–1915)

Conwy Mountain, North Wales, the location of my First Degree research camp site – *See plate section for colour version*

Braich-y-Pwll headland, near Aberdaron, Llyn Peninsula, North Wales with Bardsey Island beyond. This coastline was one of my 'special places' – *See plate section for colour version*

Wylfa Nuclear Power Station, Anglesey, showing 'landscape' planting on conical hills intended to replicate drumlins

The derelict brick works at Porth Wen, Anglesey (1965)

Criccieth beach showing boulder clay cliff-section. This was the first site to be recorded in our glacial survey of 1969 (See C. A. Lewis 1970)

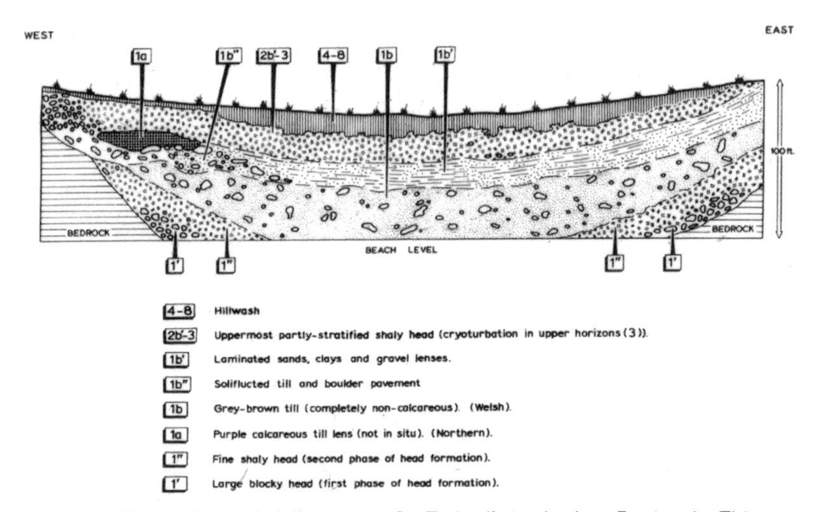

Diagram of Porth Ceiriad cliff-section, St, Tudwal's in the Lyn Peninsula. This was where we discovered the so-called 'collison zone' between Welsh and Northern ice-sheets that defined their spatial limits (See C. A. Lewis 1970)

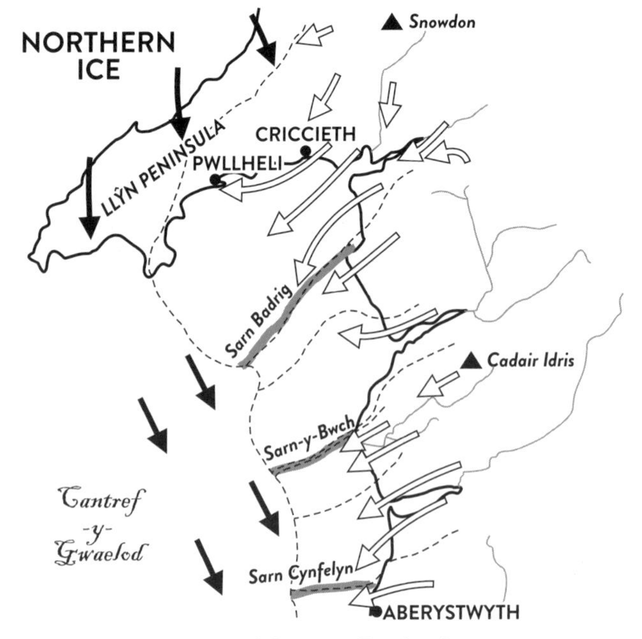

The formation of the sarn features of Cardigan Bay by glacier streams

Caravans making use of an abandoned World War II military site near Barmouth (1965)

Dinas Oleu hill, Barmouth. The first coastal acquisition of the National Trust, given by Fanny Talbot in 1895

I must now return to those much earlier years when not only the war but my childhood was over. In the first year of 'Peace' my family had moved house away from the smoke-laden air of the Potteries' outskirts and settled in a leafy suburb on the western hills overlooking the old market town of Newcastle under Lyme. Here, much to my delight, was open countryside so that the visions of Octavia Hill, referred to above, were as true in 1946 as they were in Victorian times – people had a right to fresh air and open green spaces. I must confess, however, that at the time I had never even heard of Octavia Hill.

By then I had entered the 6th form and was enjoying my chosen subjects of Geography, Geology, History and Fine Art, an eclectic combination that John Ruskin would have admired but left my Classics-trained headmaster seriously underwhelmed. I well remember his annoyance when he had to arrange my Geology tuition at another school because his own school lacked the facilities. Furthermore, as I sat alone in the examination room, as the school's first and only candidate in Geology, how I was sneered at by the supervisor. Moreover, the Latin master went out of his way to state that I would never be accepted at a university with such a disparate combination of subjects. If anything, such attitudes simply spurred me on and those subjects were to become the foundations of my training as an 'environmentalist', a word that was not in common parlance in 1946.

One of the greatest advantages of the family's recent move was the chance to join a local youth club run by a group of enlightened people at the church. Imagine my delight when they announced that in that first post-war summer the club would holiday under canvas on the coast of my beloved North Wales. In due course a couple of dozen teenagers piled aboard a dusty, musty LMS railway train at the equally grimy Stoke station. This excursion was really a landmark in my life: the first time that I had camped out; the first holiday away from parental control and the first time that I had packed a rucksack rather than a suitcase. As we journeyed slowly westwards we hazarded guesses as to the whereabouts of our 'secret' location because the majority had holidayed on this coastline in previous years. Was it to be Prestatyn, Rhyl, Colwyn Bay, Rhos or Llandudno? No, we left all these resorts behind and our bewilderment mounted as we rattled across the River Conwy by means of Stephenson's ingenious tubular rail bridge (which denied everyone a unique view of Conwy castle). The train then plunged into a tunnel through a high rocky headland before emerging into a coastal vista that, in my mind at least, was a 'worthwhile' shoreline where mountains are cliffed by the sea, very unlike the miles of low-lying sandy beaches that we had by-passed en route. To most of my collcagues this was 'terra incognita' but I was fortunate enough to have been here before the war. The train ground to a halt at the little station of Penmaenmawr, right on the seafront. We all tumbled onto the platform and stood marvelling at the view, as the train steamed away towards Bangor and Holyhead. This memorable episode, to my mind, was something of a catharsis, banishing the dreariness of wartime (when our home had been damaged by bombs) and the gritty atmosphere of the Potteries. To misquote Sylvia Plath: I also felt my lungs inflate with the onrush of scenery – air, mountains, seashores, and young people. I agree with her sentiments that the experience created a feeling of the utmost happiness. ("The Bell Jar". S. Plath 1963).

Pemaenmawr, a self-effacing little seaside town gazing across the notorious Lavan Sands to Anglesey, is embowered in a narrow curving bay between two stark headlands of tough igneous rock – Penmaenbach and Penmaenmawr. Apart from its short promenade, overlooking its shingle beach, this modest shoreline remained unspoiled for decades until the coastal dual carriageway of the A55 ruined its foreshore. But some would claim that the ambience of this embayment had already been ruined by the overhanging stone-quarries high on the summit of the larger of the two headlands. More than a century ago it was discovered that the hardness and durability of the rock were such that it was widely sought after as a roadstone. I well remember the 'stone boats' loading at the jetty and the way in which the domed summit was gradually reduced to a tableland, thereby lowering its height by some 400 feet. The quarrying destroyed a well-preserved prehistoric fortress whose importance had been enhanced by the adjoining Neolithic axe factory whose shattered debris littered the mountain slope. The stone axes of this site at Craig Llwyd were traded all across the land of Britain and were of such durability that they could be flaked and fashioned almost as well as a flint. Simply as a matter of report this disfigured coastal slope was much later to be classified as 'Beyond Redemption' in the Neptune survey whereas it should really have been preserved as an historic site. These were some of the stories that were relayed to us during our holiday but to be quite frank prehistory was far from our minds when we could spend our time cavorting in the sea, visiting the milk bar, playing rumbustious games and scaling the surrounding coastal peaks, to say nothing of the outrageous flirting that was carried on away from prying parental eyes. After all, the boys were out for a fling before the burdens of National Service loomed in 12 months' time. Many years later I came across a poem by Charles Tennyson Turner (1808–1879) which I thought was almost uncanny for it described the very episodes that we had all experienced in 1946:

"That first September day was blue and warm,
Flushing the shaly flanks of Penmaenmawr;
While youths and maidens, in the lucid calm
Exulting, bathed or bask'd from hour to hour".

He even commented how "...evermore the jarring trains went by" so he too must have holidayed on this very stretch of coastline a century before.

Many of those glorious sunlit days were spent roving on the beach or along the narrow country lanes. After having been persuaded not to climb up the dangerously loose screes in search of remnant stone axes, my favourite ramble was through the village of Dwygyfylchi on the mountain road to Conwy. This led steeply upwards into a narrow and steep-sided valley known as the Sychnant Pass which, according to the principles of Geomorphology, should have held a stream descending rapidly to the sea. A Welshman would have explained that 'Sychnant' meant 'dry valley' and that was exactly what I saw. But dry valleys are normally found only in limestone and chalk lands in this country so it set me wondering about the origin of this remarkable feature. It was to be five years later before I returned and was able to decipher its genesis.

Some of the time, of course, was spent in carrying out all the chores associated with life on a campsite but the one that I remember most was the initial hoisting of the bell tents and of the massive dining marquee, tasks that were the responsibility of the boys. These were tasks quite foreign to me and the rough hemp ropes caused blisters on my hands. The first night in such unfamiliar surroundings meant that I lay awake staring at the diffused moonlight through the canvas and suffering discomfort from a burst blister. In the early hours of the morning I crept quietly from the tent, crossed the railway bridge and dropped down to the beach. The seashore at night is an ethereal experience in which sounds are magnified and the swish of wavelets shuffling the pebbles was the only thing which broke the stillness. A few streetlights in Penmaenmawr itself, the red and green railway signal lights, when adding their twinkling reflections to that of the moonlight glittering on the Menai Straits, were the only reminders of civilisation. Matthew Arnold, although he was writing about The Straits of Dover (Dover Beach, 1867), must have experienced similar feelings when he penned the lines:

"The sea is calm to-night,
The tide is full, the moon lies fair upon the straits...
For the world, which seems
To lie before us like a land of dreams"

By the end of the holiday we were all genuinely sad to leave the camping field, even though sheep had left enough evidence of their former presence to soil our shoes. Three of us were so entranced with this stretch of coast that one month later we took a smaller tent and cycled back to Wales in order to renew our happy memories but this time camping at several other coastal venues before finishing at Dwygyfylchi itself at the foot of the Sychnant Pass.

After completing National Service and commencing my University degree course at Reading it was incumbent upon me to choose a region upon which to write my dissertation. North Wales had still retained its magnetism and I informed my tutor that I would like to make a study of the Conwy Valley and its adjoining coastline. At last I would be able to spend more time in the Sychnant Pass and seek an explanation for its formation. Once the location had been agreed with my tutor I took the train to Conwy station and set off with rucksack and tent to the top end of the Pass to find a dry camping spot on a patch of sheep-grazed turf sheltered by the gorse. That evening I wandered to the top of Conwy Mountain, an eminence carved from brown and yellow volcanic rocks known as rhyolites, outpourings from volcanoes that had existed here some 500 million years ago. Similar rocks had helped to build the high rugged peaks of Snowdonia which I could see to the south and west. But it was the seaward view that was the most beguiling. Away to the north-west the rolling lowland of Anglesey stretched as far as the eye could see; below were the Lavan Sands across which travellers had to be ferried en route to Ireland before Telford built his famous bridge across the Menai Straits; to the north across Conwy Bay was the Carboniferous Limestone hump of the Great Orme overshadowing the resort of Llandudno that I knew so well; nearer to, behind the estuarine mussel beds, was the tiny resort of Deganwy crouching beneath its old Welsh castle; and finally the view to the east spanned the towers of Edward I's castle at Conwy that reared loftily above Telford's first suspension bridge. The view encapsulated all the features that had played so large a part in my persona and where my parents were destined to live a decade later. In the future I was fortunate to be able to buy a picture painted from the very same spot where I was standing that evening in 1950. The oil painting by Robert Fowler (1853–1926) was completed in the 1920's and depicted the sandy coastal foreland of Conwy Morfa as a deserted waste surrounding the local golf course. The view that stretched in front of me in 1950, however, was quite different, for all I saw was nothing but a sea of regimented caravans stretching to the shore. I lingered long at this picturesque spot until the sun began to dip towards the ocean. On a separate occasion I had bought another watercolour of that very scene, looking westwards across the northern flanks of Snowdonia by a lesser known artist named simply

J. Mills. The poet Robert Southey must also have marvelled at such a scene when he wrote, over a century ago:

> *"The sun goes down…*
> *far off the light is on those native crags of*
> *Penmaenmawr and Arvon's ancient hills".*

Little wonder that I too was bewitched by the same unforgettable coastal scene that lulled me off to sleep, after thinking of the work programme that lay ahead.

The following morning, I awakened to a pale sunrise threatened by grey clouds marching in from the west. After a perfunctory breakfast I hastened back to the top of Conwy mountain, aware of the capricious nature of Welsh weather. I was able to make notes on the summit hill-fort, dating from the Iron Age, before the drizzle set in. By now I had worked out the genesis of the Sychnant Pass and went to photograph it in the rain. Soon I was becoming wetter and wetter so was forced to retire to my tent where I set about drawing a sketch map of the local terrain. It became quite clear that during the Ice Age a large glacier, surging from the heart of the Snowdonia mountain mass, had pushed northwards along the valley of the Conwy before meeting the enormous ice-sheet that had ploughed down the centre of the Irish Sea basin. This was the same ice-sheet that had brought the erratic pebbles that I had discovered on Llandudno beach many years before. As in modern Antarctica the edges of ice-sheets and glaciers are always in a state of melting on their forward fringes and the 'Conwy Valley glacier' would have acted in the same way many thousands of years ago. Its 'meltwater' would have been unable to escape northwards because of the blocking northern ice so it was forced to overflow at the lowest dip in the ridge and would then have torn out a deep gorge-like valley.

Once the ice cover had melted away the valley would have been left high and dry. Problem solved!

By late afternoon the rain was hammering on the canvas and showed no sign of easing. It was going to be a long lonely night on this windswept mountain. Part of me thought about keeping a 'stiff upper lip' and retaining my self-discipline, learnt in my Army days, but another part reasoned that a warm dry bed awaited me if I could stagger down to a Conwy hotel before dark. Just then a voice hailed me and a friendly head popped through the tent flap. "Did you know that this hollow will be uninhabitable after a few hours of rain. You had better move to a drier spot but, better still, why don't you come to our cottage, dry yourself off and sleep on the sofa in front of the fire?" Such an invitation was really a 'no-brainer' (although I don't think that such an Americanism was current in those days). This gentleman helped to dismantle the bedraggled tent and carry my few utensils several hundred yards to his pretty white-washed cottage perched on a nearby hillside overlooking Conwy itself. His wife helped to dry my clothes and asked me to share their evening meal. "We had seen you walking around mapping and note-taking and wondered what you were up to". After lengthy explanations and a welcome glass of beer we discovered that we had a lot of common interests and a strong love of mountainous coasts.

My saviour turned out to be Alf Sharrocks, President of the Royal Cambrian Academy of Artists, teacher, ornithologist, artist and a well-known naturalist. After a good night's sleep, he suggested, much to my relief, that I should forget camping and spend the rest of my stay at their tiny cottage. He proposed that he would be pleased to accompany me on my perambulations for he was retired and eager to help. Over the next few days we walked the coastal hills and he showed me hidden chough's nests on the sea cliffs, rare Alpine flowers, talking incessantly about the local pre-history and the other aspects of natural history. I must place him as one of the three most important mentors of my life: the other two were my History master, Eric Warne, at my old school, who taught me how to write acceptable prose, and my former University Warden, Tom Creighton, who gave me the confidence to venture into the upper echelons of the academic world. The latter always addressed me as J. M. S. Whittow, an anomaly which puzzled me until we became great climbing friends and he explained that J. M. S was his soul-mate at Cambridge University. But it was Alf Sharrocks who opened my eyes to a different world, the world around us, and he must have played a great part in my future development as an environmentalist because he viewed the world as one vast ecosystem. Moreover, he was already aware of the changes that were beginning to impact on the fragile shoreline habitats on his own coastline. During my stay I realised that he and his wife were the centre of a wide group of friends, for this was 'open house' to a great number of artists, writers, botanists, archaeologists and zoologists. Indeed, in later years, I discovered that it was virtually a microcosm of a university Senior Common Room, and as a callow young scholar, it was a privilege to make their acquaintance during the long evenings of dialogue around the welcoming fire. I especially remember the ornithologists and their enthusiastic tales of the nearby Lavan Sands where they constantly watched enormous colonies of birds, both over-wintering and birds of passage. In addition to the gulls, terns, ducks and oystercatchers, they said that they had also recorded dunlin, redshanks, and the occasional greenshank. I was impressed both by their knowledge and by their diligence in all weathers, and there was I, prepared to give up at the first drop of rain. It was a salutary lesson for the future – I would have to be prepared to suffer hardships on storm-bound coasts if I wanted to progress in my chosen career. Most of these are birds that I had never knowingly encountered but they began to feature more commonly in my vision when I later began my postgraduate research on the shores of the Llyn Peninsula of North Wales.

After my graduation, much to my surprise, my Head of Department, Professor Austin Miller, suggested that I stay on to read for a Doctorate. The financial aspects were solved by the award of a scholarship and a University Demonstratorship, whilst my father kindly gave me a car to allow me to conduct the future field work. This old but tough pre-war canvas-topped Morris Tourer was to become my beast of burden for the immediate future. However, the most important decision still had to be made: What and where would be the region on which I would be set to work? In the 1950's a cabal of senior Professors of Physical Geography, known as the 'kingmakers', not only had an influential say on who should be short-listed for particular appointments but also on the location of individual areas open for research projects in geomorphology. The External Examiner for my first degree, Professor David Linton, now suggested that there was an important gap in the field of Welsh Denudation Chronology (how certain landforms had evolved) and Professor Miller agreed that he would supervise my Doctorate and Linton would be, once more, my External Examiner. Therefore, I was allocated the Llyn Peninsula in North Wales, a region of which I had virtually no knowledge.

This lengthy promontory certainly has a broken and rocky coastline, which appealed to me. Tony Soper in his book "A Natural History Guide to the Coast" (1984) described it thus: "Its flattish plateau of croft-like farms punctuated by shapely mountainous features, and almost surrounded by the sea, makes one think of the Assynt part of Sutherland". The Scottish coast is one that I came to know almost as well as that of Wales and I believe that the Llyn is nowhere near as spectacular as that of Assynt with its peaks towering above the bare and rugged coastline (as described in chapter 7). Soper further believes that the Llyn Peninsula "...exudes that same Celtic fringe atmosphere found in Ireland, Anglesey, the St David's part of Wales and Cornwall". In this respect I would agree with his sentiments because I too discovered great similarities when I worked on their shores. But I was also to discover that some residents in such remote places, especially in Scotland, were far more pragmatic and much less idealistic than a visitor, like myself, who entered into their world only on a temporary basis. For example, the modern Welsh poet, R. S. Thomas, saw it in a very different light. From his home on the Peninsula he wrote that the region is beautiful to the tourist but bleak to the farmer. For him "Beauty is glimpsed only fitfully, beyond the realities of plough and tractor, of fluke and foot-rot and fat maggot". Be that as it may, I was not there on this occasion to investigate its ancient culture or its farming hardships, despite their marginal interest which would become of paramount importance during my subsequent Neptune survey a decade later. No, my current concern was only with its landforms which, up until then, had not been described from a geomorphological viewpoint. It was true that the geologists had made a pretty good job of mapping the layout of the solid rocks and my old friend Professor Steers had walked its coastline many years before, but for me it was a 'blank canvas', so to speak.

A blank canvas it may have been but there were certain rules which one had to follow before any detail could be added. In the early post-war years, the geomorphologist's 'bible' was a research monograph by Professors S. W. Wooldridge and D. L. Linton entitled "Structure, Surface and Drainage in S. E. England" (1939). These were two of the so-called 'kingmakers', mentioned previously, and woe betide anyone who challenged their views without reliable evidence to the contrary. The received wisdom was briefly as follows: Before the growth of the ice-sheets, during the so-called Pleistocene, there was a time when world sea-level was much higher; water abstracted from the oceans to form the ice-sheets caused a dramatic drop in sea-level of the order of some 600 feet; the highest sea-level had left sandy shoreline deposits on the chalk downs of South-East England at this height; because the latter region was never glaciated the deposits had survived in a deeply weathered state; in western Britain such coastal shingle and sand would have been swept away by the advancing ice; the ancient 600-foot wave-cut platform itself, planed across a variety of rock types, should have survived, albeit in a much denuded and dissected form. Patently, it could be seen by all how present-day waves are currently fashioning similar rock-platforms between modern high- and low-water marks.

It has to be realised that the ice-sheets would have been many thousands of feet thick, similar to those of present-day Antarctica, and because of their enormous weight those ice-masses would have caused the Earth's crust to buckle downwards, in response to the geophysical laws of 'isostasy' or 'crustal warping'. Towards the end of the Ice Age, however, as the ice-sheets began to melt, the land surface would begin to slowly recover and 'rebound', following the laws of isostasy, which would initially be at a rate faster than that of the rising sea-level. Thus, a slowly increasing amount of the Llyn Penisula's landforms would have begun to emerge and, what once had been a chain of former islands, would slowly become linked together into a staircase of expanding shorelines, increasingly exposed at lower levels, to create the present promontory.

The coastline that we see today is simply at a stage in geological time but scientists know that, what we perceive as a relatively static shoreline, is nothing of the sort. Over thousands of years this coastline will change inexorably and, although the geophysical rebound in Wales has now terminated and appears to have reached equilibrium, the same is not true of our dynamic sea-levels. The gradual rise of sea-level, resulting from the continuing melting of other world ice-sheets is, therefore, beginning to encroach on all shorelines and, even in my own lifetime I have witnessed changes in Britain's coasts, some of them quite catastrophic, but I shall consider this impact of rising sea-levels on British shores in later chapters.

Basically, my job was to search for the remnants of these former high shorelines and record their location on a map. One has to envisage what this region of Wales would have looked like some 7 million years ago when the ocean stood some 600 feet higher. The nearest analogy is present-day Cornwall, a peninsula of a much greater size than that of the Llyn. Today, the granite, tor-topped uplands of Cornwall descend in height as they are traced westwards, from Bodmin Moor to Land's End. From there onwards the granite heights descend below sea-level until their last forlorn tors create the tide-washed islands of the Scillies. At a smaller scale the Llyn Peninsula would have had a similar appearance, with its present-day isolated hills appearing as islands as they were seen to descend in altitude as they were traced westwards away from the mountainland of Snowdonia. The equivalent to the Isles of Scilly would have been the few scattered summits near to the tip of the peninsula and the present Bardsey Island mountain would have been the last of the archipelago. Consequently, it was the remains of these marine stages that I had to measure in order to build up a picture of the evolving Welsh coastline prior to the onset of the over-riding ice-sheets.

To be certain that any wave-cut platform was not simply a horizontal stratum of bedrock it had to be demonstrated that the horizontal planar surface had been cut across different layers of rock that had been folded or tilted by much earlier earth-movements. Since I would be the sole surveyor engaged in the measurements it would have been impossible to carry out a proper triangulation, so I was forced to resort to the use of an aneroid barometer to record the absolute elevations of the landforms. One might well ask why the current Ordnance Survey maps were not adequate, but their contour-interval was insufficient to record the requisite data. The literature suggested that aneroid barometers had an accuracy of plus or minus 5 feet which was satisfactory enough. I had just been elected a Fellow of the Royal Geographical Society which kindly loaned me two instruments in order to be able to calibrate one against the other. The necessity of carrying two barometers was soon found to be essential for it wasn't long before, on losing my balance on a steep hillside, one of these delicate instruments went bounding rapidly down the slope, thereby ruining its accuracy. But I laboured on, in all weathers, mapping the entire peninsula until I was almost seeing 'erosion surfaces' in my dreams. It is little wonder that I became obsessed with coastlines throughout my life because for the next three years 'marine benches' were the raison d'etre behind my research. I was later to learn that a few graduates from other universities were engaged in similar exercises elsewhere in the British Isles and it was this type of painstaking research that led to an understanding of the way in which Britain first "Arose from out the azure main". Such research was categorised under the uninspiring title of 'Denudation Chronology' and was believed at that time to be of fundamental importance in adding to the geological record. In future years, however, this tedious type of pre-glacial fieldwork has declined in importance, to be replaced by a more rigorous examination and explanation of the creation of glacial deposits and their influence on current landforms – a field in which I was soon to become seriously involved. But to return to those heady days of the early 1950's when I roamed the Welsh coastline in order to commence my research. This was not the first time that I had viewed the coast as a laboratory and it would not be the last.

As soon as my University demonstrating and marking duties were over and the undergraduates had gone down for the vacation I was free to travel to North Wales and start my mapping. At the outset my chosen base was the tiny picturesque village of Aberdaron at the westernmost tip of the peninsula. It comprised an ancient grey stone church, a cluster of white-painted cottages, a couple of shops and two hotels, all facing southwards in a tiny bay nestling between two headlands. I had had my fill of camping in the Conwy region a few years previously, so I used some of my limited resources to book a room at the seemingly welcoming and characterful Ship Inn. It soon became clear that my finances would not stretch to the requisite number of months necessary to complete my fieldwork. On explaining my dilemma to the owner, he came up with an idea to which I responded positively, namely that if I acted as a waiter for breakfast and evening meals the entire middle part of my days would be free to carry out my research. In return he offered me free board and lodging for several weeks during the high season. However, he admitted that he would be unable to tie-up a hotel room for such a lengthy period, so offered to rent a room on my behalf at a pretty little cottage right across the street, which backed immediately on to the beach itself. Here the old couple, Mr and Mrs Ellis, made me feel quite at home and, after coming back to Aberdaron, tired after a long day's work both in the field and in the hotel dining room, I would fall asleep to the sound of breaking waves beneath my bedroom window. In retrospect, I regard those weeks as something of an idyll and I thought of how, on two occasions, the local Welsh people had come to my rescue with their kindness. At the outset, I had mentioned that my coastal perambulations would be strictly concerned only with the physical landscape, but as the years progressed I found myself becoming increasingly involved in the lifestyles and histories of the local cultures. A true Geographer should not close his or her mind to the total environment, for these people that I met are as much a part of the landscape that we see before us, as are the rocks, soils and vegetation from which it is composed. Moreover, as I matured, I became quite fascinated with the human input into the scenery that I came to describe in my future writings. In many cases it was the local inhabitants and their stories that made the landscape to really come alive. I suppose it's termed 'local colour'.

Mr and Mrs Ellis talked proudly of their son's musical achievements. Apparently, he was about my own age but had already won a Bardic Chair at the Welsh National Eisteddfod. They showed me photographs of him in his regalia and today many thousands of people would recognise him as Ossian Ellis, probably the world's most famous harpist. I regret that I never had a chance to meet him but many years later I had the privilege of meeting one of his most eminent protegées, Catrin Finch. She was a former Royal Harpist to Prince Charles, Prince of Wales and became well-known in her own right as a concert harpist in which she played in the English Youth Orchestra and later in international concerts throughout the world, at some of which she accompanied such eminent tenors as Bryn Terfel. She told me how one of her most memorable tours had been to Patagonia to entertain a long-established Welsh colony in

Argentina. After another of her concerts in our own English village church I took the opportunity to ask her about the degree to which the Welsh coastline had inspired some of her recordings. She drew my attention to two of the tracks on the CD that I had just bought, suitably called "Tides", which she said were inspired by the weather when viewed from her childhood home at Llanon, in a cottage which is perched on the sea cliff of Cardigan Bay. This is a sanctum to which she still returns to see her parents and we laughingly postulated the future danger of this beautiful location after I had explained that the cottage stood on a crumbling cliff of glacial drift. But to return to the workaday 1950's.

Several weeks had rapidly passed by, when I suddenly became aware that the long summer vacation was coming to an end and only about one-third of the mapping had been completed. But at least I was beginning to perceive a general picture of the landform chronology in the Llyn. The penisula's far-reaching main plateau surface stood at an elevation of 200–240 feet from which its island-like summits rose. The latter had survived the many aeons of wave erosion which had created the so-called '200-foot' wave-cut surface across rocks of all types, many of which had been previously contorted by ancient earth-movements. The planation at this height is common all along the western coasts of Wales and implies that sea-level had remained stationary at this level for many thousands of years during a lull in the Ice Age. The residual hills, however, have been fashioned not from the less resistant sedimentary rocks of this low plateau but from the harder igneous 'intrusions' similar to granite. Thus, they had survived as what are known to geologists as 'monadnocks'. The term had been coined by one of the most famous of geomorphologists, William Morris Davis, an American whose principles of landform evolution underpinned all modern geomorphological thinking. It was only because I was working amidst Welsh-speaking scholars in North Wales that I learnt how the derivation of the American term 'monadnock' came from a combination of the Welsh words 'mynydd' (a mountain) and 'cnwc' (a hill), thus 'a high hill'. The Scots claim that the term is based on Gaelic but one only has to look at the author's name, William Morris Davis, to realise that this great man had Welsh ancestry. Even more importantly, I had discovered some limited remnants of a similar wave-cut shoreline at 600 feet, some 400-feet higher than the coastal platform. This was precisely what Professors Wooldridge and Linton had hoped would be discovered to fit into their own chronological pattern. Because it is manifestly clear that the west-facing slopes of Wales would have been open to the mighty marine forces of the Atlantic, it is not surprising to find that they exhibit such primeval coastal landforms. It also has to be remembered that, over time, the highest of the ancient wave-cut platforms would have been largely destroyed by the encroaching waves of a lower sea-level throughout later lengthy periods of tectonic stability, during which sea-level would have remained unchanged (termed a 'stillstand'). If one accepts this premise, it follows that the youngest platform, i.e. the 200-foot surface, ought to be the most extensive of all and that the highest and oldest would be the most eroded and dissected. This was precisely what I was able to discover and was further able to show their respective dimensions in both map and diagrammatic form; a chronology of extending shorelines that led to the peninsula's present shape.

Despite the somewhat humdrum fieldwork, the task proved to be extremely rewarding during those long summer days for it gave me endless opportunities to indulge in one of my favourite pastimes, that of scrambling on rocky hillsides and exploring hidden bays and beaches on this relatively unspoiled and sparsely populated peninsula. Sometimes I would walk for a whole day without seeing a soul except for a lonely farmer ploughing in the distance. The constant presence of the sea, the magnificent array of seabirds and the deserted shorelines, all combined to gratify the deep affinity which I felt for these wild Celtic landscapes. The most dramatic scenery lay on the north coast where, beneath the towering summit of Yr Eifl, the coastal cliffs plunge almost vertically into the sea. William Condry knew this site well and described how the great cliff of Carreg y Llam is the guillemot metropolis of North Wales (2,000–3,000 pairs). Additionally, there are hundreds of razorbills, kittiwakes, cormorants, shags, fulmars and gulls. (The Natural History of Wales. W. M. Condry, 1981). He also draws attention to a nearby oakwood, a rarity in coastal Wales, and, despite the fact that it is stunted, Condry believes that it gives the aura of a feature dating back without a break to the time of ancient Welsh forests.

Amongst my own 'special places' were the lonely coastal hills which rise at the tip of the peninsula to provide a wonderful view of the sacred Isle of Bardsey. This stretch of coastline boasts a fascinating outcrop of one of Britain's oldest rocks, dating from Pre-Cambrian times (2,500–3,500 million years ago), including exposures of contorted jasper, a semi-precious stone. In such an exposed site and with its acid soils, the vegetation is merely a heathland of gorse, heather and bracken amidst swathes of sheep-grazed turf. On calm sunny evenings I lingered long on these coastal summits, whose ambience could have been encapsulated in Shelley's lines "When west winds sigh and evening waves respond in whispers from the shore". But nearby Aberdaron can sometimes be a stormy place and has records of windspeeds approaching 100 mph. Fortunately, I experienced few days of strong winds although a trip to Bardsey had to be postponed due to inclement weather. The artist, Brenda Chamberlain, made her home there in 1947 and wrote of how, despite her love of the island, she was relieved to havc a sanctuary away from the shore itself and the booming of the winter waves. (Tide Race. Brenda Chamberlain, 1962). This small island is reputed to be the burial place of thousands of saints and pilgrims but to a bird-lover it is surely more important that its deeper soils provide shelter for several thousand pairs of Manx shearwaters whose cacophony breaks the stillness as they return to their night-time burrows. These fairly rare birds owe their survival to the fact that Bardsey is a rat-free island. Closer inshore, in Aberdaron's tiny bay, are the Gull Islands (Ynys Gwylan) where I landed on a calmer day. These flat-topped isles (although one has a protruding tor-like rock which is an ancient sea-stack now high and dry), can boast the largest colony of puffins in the whole of Wales. Like Bardsey these tiny islands exhibit deep soils for the burrows and are also free of rats.

As my mapping took mc eastwards along the penisula's southern coast, the scenery began to change into one of protruding hard-rock headlands interspersed with lengthy stretches of sand and shingle beaches, such as the dauntingly named Hell's Mouth. It became clear that this coastline was open to the maximum 'fetch' of the Irish Sea waves that had driven the bays far inland where they had found it easier to attack not solid rock but the more yielding layers of boulder clay that had been dumped by the enormous, southward-moving Irish Sea ice-sheet, mentioned above. By now, my mapping of the descending 'staircase' of wave-cut platforms had brought me down to present sea-level and gave me numerous opportunities to view the exposed glacial drifts that plugged the embayments, which in reality were pre-glacial river valleys. The waves continued to erode these relatively 'soft' sediments and open up clear sections of the glacial stratigraphy. It soon became clear that here was a completely new opportunity for future research, but it was a project beyond the present scope of my current undertaking. Nevertheless, I saw this as a challenge and I would spend several more years in the future attempting to unravel the even greater complicated chronology of Llyn's glacial landforms.

I have to acknowledge that the vast majority of visitors to Llyn would have no interest whatsoever in the origin of its landforms, simply that they offered a pleasant venue for a holiday. I have no doubt, that most would prefer to lounge on the beaches, happily unaware that the crumbling cliffs behind them held geological secrets that would be of great value to scientists trying to piece together the movements of former ice-sheets. Many of the holidaymakers would certainly value the scenery of this unspoiled peninsula and their children might be fascinated by the different coloured beach pebbles, as I had been in my childhood holidays in Llandudno. During my duties as a waiter in Aberdaron I had encountered scores of such visitors and observed that their activities ranged from sunbathing, sailing and angling to brisk walks along the rugged coastline. One or two enquired about my work but I suspect that few if any understood my explanations. An exception was the poet Stephen Spender, a friend of W. H. Auden, Louis MacNeice and Christopher Isherwood. This tall handsome gentleman spoke of his desire to cross to Bardsey to 'commune with nature' and find new inspirations for his forthcoming poetry (Collected Poems. Stephen Spender, 1955). Before he left for Bardsey, during his few days sojourn in the Ship Hotel, this rather taciturn and private individual enquired about the reasons for my research and its importance in the 'way of the world'.

The only other visitor to bring back memories was the Chief Constable of Caernarfonshire who, with his wife, was being entertained to dinner by the Manager of the Ship Hotel. It had been a long day in the field and I was rapidly tiring after serving countless evening meals in the dining room. All the other guests had left the room but the private party lingered later and later until well after 11 pm. The chef informed me that the kitchen was now closed, that he was going home and that the last savoury for the threesome was on the hotplate. Finally, I was summoned by the Manager who, like his guests, had indulged in a few bottles of wine. By then the serving plates were scorching hot and, despite being held by a napkin, were burning my hands as I hastened down the room. Serving the lady first I clumsily tipped the scalding and dried-up morsel on to her lap. "Excuse me Madam" I implored but she was blissfully unaware and carried on the inebriated conversation. Clearly, in their minds, I did not exist so, with a deft flick I transferred the item from her lap to her plate, and all was well, I hoped. A few moments later the telephone rang and I took the message to the Manager. It transpired that the chef had been involved in a road accident a few miles away. The three diners hastened away, driven by a police chauffeur, and the rumour the next day was, that on the unlit narrow lanes of western Llyn, the speeding police-car had run into the wreck itself. Fortunately, there appeared to have been no serious injuries and the chef himself recovered in due course. At the time it appeared to be a diversion from the 'tread-mill' of fieldwork and caused quite a flutter in this sleepy Welsh village.

My supervisor now informed me that my University funding was about to end and that I ought to be seeking employment elsewhere for the two remaining years before I was due to hand in my completed research in 1957. Although this news was not unexpected it meant that I was about to emerge into the real world, away from the closeted environment of Reading University. If I was to continue to visit North Wales I would have to discover a teaching post in a school not too far away from the field area. However, much to my surprise, I was persuaded to seek an appointment at a British university, although at the time only three posts were being advertised in my particular subject of Geomorphology. Two of the interviews proved abortive but I was delighted to be successful at the third, a little-known university in Northern Ireland, which would enable me to have long vacations in which to complete my Welsh research. My sojourn in Ireland will be described in later chapters and it is irrelevant to talk of my subsequent employment in Africa, Australia and California, before returning to my old 'alma mater' in Reading. Sufficient to say that I was awarded my doctorate and many years went by before I was invited to return to the coastlines of North Wales in order to work out the glacial chronology of the region as a contribution to a forthcoming book: "The glaciations of Wales and surrounding regions" edited by Colin Lewis. But before I become involved in a description of yet another lengthy undertaking of North Welsh landform mapping, there was the not inconsiderable matter of my field contribution to the Neptune survey which had to be completed during the summer of 1965. It will come as no surprise to learn that because of my considerable knowledge of the coastline of North Wales, I chose to carry out my own part of the Neptune survey on those selfsame shores.

The National Trust survey was, of course, a totally different exercise, and I would constantly have needed to remind myself that I must put rocks, pebbles, erosion surfaces, coastal processes and all that geological paraphernalia behind me. Diane and I had been married for eight years during which time we had toured North Wales on occasions. Indeed, we had bought our wedding ring in Conwy, so that the region had very many happy memories.

Therefore, I was delighted when she agreed to accompany me, and it would be good to have a companion to help me map the coasts of North Wales from Rhyl to Aberdyfi. Diane was equally enthusiastic (or at least she claimed to be) and we tramped the shorelines, maps in hand, for several weeks. Moreover, we vowed to turn the exercise into a protracted holiday. The first few miles from the Dee estuary westwards were quite familiar territory and, because of its string of towns, it comprised largely of 'developed land', in addition to the seemingly endless 'shack metropolis' on the dunes to the east of Prestatyn. This was the first occasion that I had encountered the contentious problem of chalets and beach huts which, in the National Trust's eyes, were considered, by and large, to be "Blots on the Landscape". For several years, in my Environmental Planning course at the University, I had tested student perceptions of such an impact on the coastal scene. In the majority of cases the responses had been negative, leading to the decision to map these 'temporary' dwellings in a pejorative sense during the Neptune survey. Notwithstanding such a decision, I became increasingly aware that these wooden structures, like 'static' caravans, were representative of countless numbers of holidaymakers' only chance of visiting the coast. Moreover, were not the 'shacks' of such places as Dungeness generally regarded as 'rather quaint' by many observers? But, having initially decided on this somewhat subjective category, we were forced to adhere to it in order to maintain overall uniformity of mapping. It certainly served to make me aware that, when the time came for me to present the final report to the National Trust, they too would have to be appraised of this type of controversial demand on our coastal resource.

When it came to industrial impact, however, the decision-making was much easier to resolve, especially when we reached the massive coastal roadstone quarry at Llandulas whose constant blasting rent the air. The 'undeveloped' areas were few and far between and even these short stretches were generally stuffed with caravans. To a lesser extent this was true of the coastline between Conwy and Bangor, where I retraced my steps on a well-known shoreline around Penmaenmawr. Here, during a pleasant break at a local pub, I learnt that Gladstone used to holiday here, a short distance from his Welsh home at Hawarden. Furthermore, the locals were eager to tell me that an equally famous personality also found Penmaenmawr inspirational for, in 1913, Elgar rented a cottage, Tan-yr-Allt, although both he and his wife found the house and the weather left a lot to be desired. And yet Elgar used his time in Wales to make final touches and revisions to his Symphonic Study "Falstaff", a work that he considered to be his greatest, and, into which he is said to have put most of himself (indeed, the work has been described as a "musical self-portrait" (Music in the Landscape. E. M. Marshall, 2011). Such anecdotes may appear to be peripheral to the job in hand but, as the weeks went by, they began to serve as a welcome relief from the increasingly mundane exercise of colouring maps. I decided to lighten the ongoing strictly objective account of coastal attributes by including several references to the ways in which other visitors perceived this wonderful coastline. Moreover, I also decided that I, too, would cast my artistic eye over these well-trodden shores, even though it would be purely from a subjective viewpoint, apart from continuing my inescapable pictures of its geology and scenery. Do I really have to apologise for giving potential readers such descriptions, for this is supposed to be a catalogue of all my coastal memories?

Beyond the attractive wooded shores of the Menai Straits the beautiful Isle of Anglesey beckoned, an island with a treeless and somewhat nondescript centre but with a coastline striking enough to be classed as an Area of Outstanding Natural Beauty. In this respect it matches the coastal AONB of the Llyn Peninsula and in some respects boasts a landscape similar to that of this neighbouring promontory because it has been carved from almost identical Pre-Cambrian rocks, with their sporadic cover of glacially derived soils. Anglesey, however, exhibits two major differences; first, its monadnocks are much lower than those of Llyn and, secondly, at intervals on its eastern shores, outcrops of Carboniferous Limestone enhance the coastal cliffs, thereby bringing into the scene a lime-loving vegetation quite distinct from the widespread cover of bilberry, bracken, gorse and heather on the older exposed rocks.

The cliff-bound limestone coast from Anglesey's easternmost Black Point (opposite Puffin Island) northwards to the resort of Moelfre is broken by the wide beaches of Red Wharf Bay and, whilst we were not really concerned with natural habitats during the Neptune survey, in this instance, one had to acknowledge that it was the underlying geology that had helped to shape the land-use that we were recording. First and foremost, the friable sedimentary rocks have weathered into wide sandy beaches, and beaches mean tourists. In the 1960's, hotel accommodation here was quite insufficient to meet the visitor demand so that this picturesque coastline had become overrun with caravan parks. Secondly, the limestone had been sporadically quarried for many years and although the industry had ceased long before our visit, the scars remained. And yet, in an attempt to shield the 'caravan explosion' from the wind and from 'disfiguring' the view, some entrepreneur had hidden dozens of them in the disused coastal quarries. I was so taken with this enterprise that I devised an entire category "Caravans in quarries" for the Neptune survey guidelines. Little was I to know that this Anglesey example was ultimately found to be the only case in Britain. In 1815 the artist William Daniell (1769–1837) visited Red Wharf Bay, as he travelled by sea around the coasts of Britain, where he recorded an outcrop of what he termed 'black marble'. This may have been a band of black chert in the limestone, although coastal erosion has destroyed the exposure during the intervening years.

Normally, Diane and I would have carried out the 1965 mapping by car and tent but, since my parents were then living at Deganwy, overlooking the Conwy estuary, we were able to use their home as a base for most of the North Wales excursions. As we progressed northwards on the Anglesey coast we came to the tiny village of Moelfre, once known for its fishing, then later became famous for the so-called 'Golden Wreck' when, in 1865, the "Royal Charter" foundered on its cliffs with the loss of 459 lives. The ship was bound for Liverpool with some £500,000 worth of gold bullion from the Australian goldfields, hence the soubriquet. To the holidaymakers that we met such tales gave the 'colour' that they had travelled to see. I don't suppose that the majority gave a thought to the ways in which the coast is being used or whether they might actually be adding to its possible 'degradation'. And, in one sense, why should they? After all, one of the aims of Enterprise Neptune was to discover where the 'honeypots' should be located, in order to earmark other coastal stretches for possible protection from over-development. Today, Moelfre sits amidst thousands of caravans and was our first example of a potential 'honeypot' on an attractive coastline. Moreover, I soon became aware of the reason why this island attracted so many tourists. Bearing in mind that Anglesey is within a day's drive of millions of people in Merseyside and the English Midlands, its appealing coastline bears few scars that we would have to classify as 'Beyond Redemption'. However, the tiny port of Amlwch, at its north-eastern corner, fell into that bracket. In 1965 we found that its narrow dock was almost derelict despite its remarkable 18th century history as the out-port for the world's largest copper mine at nearby Parys Mountain. It is difficult to believe that the harbour, squeezed into a chasm some 50 yards wide, could not only service more than fifty cargo ships to export the copper worldwide but also import more than 1,000 tons of coal per day. William Daniell gave a graphic description of this coastline in his 1815 visit: "As we approached Amlwch the country became still more barren and dreary: here all vegetation is blighted and tarnished by the poisonous fumes from the copper-works. [From]…a village of six cottages…it became the most considerable town in Anglesea. Nothing met our observation that bore the marks of cheerfulness and comfort". I had to admit that, in my opinion, little seemed to have changed since his visit. However, it was worth keeping an ear open in the local bar that lunchtime for I overheard visitors claiming that this derelict area was, in their opinion, a veritable attraction. Such an observation proved to be another salutary lesson, because it clearly illustrated that different people have very different perceptions of landscape to those of my own and possibly to those of my academic team of Neptune surveyors. It certainly poses the question: Do the so-called 'experts' really know best? Not very far from Amlwch we had to record another site of coastal dereliction at the deserted cove of Porth Wen. Here, a deeply weathered outcrop of white rock had been exploited to make a special type of brick. Now, the abandoned brick ovens and associated clutter sitting incongruously on the shore, were sufficient to merit, as at Amlwch, our use of the term 'Beyond Redemption', although a future entrepreneur might see a potential use as a site for 'caravans in quarries'. A thought lingered for a few moments in my mind: I wondered if those tourists in the bar would find this particular site attractive?

The beautiful northern coast of Anglesey is a succession of rocky headlands and tiny bays all of which exhibit wonderful exposures of the ancient Pre-Cambrian rocks. The geology of Anglesey is so important that UNESCO has designated it as one of only six "Geoparks" in the British Isles and therefore was quite heavily protected. The National Trust has also secured several properties between Point Lynas in the east and the imposing bastion of Carmel Head in the west, foremost of which is the peaceful lagoon-like bay at Cemlyn, impounded by its shingle bar, reputedly formed by the same storm that caused the 'golden wreck' at Moelfre. This was one of the first properties to be bought with Neptune funds and it is famed for its colonies of Arctic, Sandwich and common terns. But nearby there is a concrete intrusion that towers against the skyline of this peaceful and attractive environment. It was one that we were forced to record as "Beyond Redemption". I speak of the gigantic nuclear power station at Wylfa Head, midway between the National Trust's properties of Cemlyn and the pretty little beach of Cemaes Bay. Such a building poses something of a dilemma: clearly its environs would be beyond the interest of the National Trust yet it is claimed to be essential to the national economy because it produces power sufficient to serve not only the whole of North Wales but also the city of Liverpool. So great is its importance that it has recently been announced that a new structure will soon take its place. Moreover, like many other nuclear power stations in the UK, it needs a coastal location in order to obtain the immense amounts of cooling-water required during its generating process. My arguments are not with its location but with the feeble attempts by the landscape architects to plant trees on weirdly pointed artificial hills around its perimeter. Some years later I happened to be examining a prospective PhD student from the Central Electricity Board and whose External Examiner was the renowned landscape architect, Dame Sylvia Crowe. I took the opportunity to question her about the incongruous landscaping at Wylfa and she explained that one of her colleagues had tried to shield some of the surrounding industrial buildings with artificial hills meant to replicate the nearby tracts of 'drumlins'. Any geomorphologist, if asked, would have told the architect that 'drumlins' are natural whale-backed landforms created by ice-sheets passing over thick deposits of previously deposited boulder clay and would never be cone-shaped. Moreover, such a monumental structure as a power station, notwithstanding its coastal location, should be allowed to be acceptable in its own right without a festoon of artificial fripperies. But perhaps I am becoming too pedantic in my criticisms.

We moved on to the formidable cliffs of Carmel Head whose slopes of sea campion, thrift and vernal squills brought swathes of colour to the closely-grazed turf. Here we turned south at the National Trust property of Mynachdy. The next eight miles contain the sort of coastline that the National Trust would usually aim to acquire because not only is it attractive but is, in the main, so remote that it can only be reached on foot. Admittedly it has its occasional crops of caravans but, to date, I have discovered that in the thirty years up to 1995, only the small site of Church Bay had been purchased with Neptune funds. Further south, above the golden sands of Trefadog and Porth Tywyn Mawr, caravan parks had sprouted on the low headlands but I was pleased to note that the latter had been sited on a disused military base built, presumably, to guard the approaches to the port of Holyhead. It has to be pointed out, however, that long stretches of the Anglesey coast were found to be already well protected from development by other environmental bodies which explains the paucity of subsequent acquisitions by the National Trust. The finest and largest expanse of golden sands on this coast stretches southwards for over a mile to the estuary of the Afon Alaw in the bay of Traeth Y Gribin. I expected this to be packed with mobile homes but, apart from a small unofficial site at the northern end, this beautiful strandline was found to be completely undeveloped. I thought at the time that if there was no planning protection this bay could easily become a future honeypot. One must bear in mind that a change in ownership of the coastal farmland may result in a new owner wishing to grow tents and caravans instead of arable crops, notwithstanding the AONB status. But, in general, we found that the farmland of this 'pristine coastline' was quite easy to map. To discover such a lack of major development on a coastline that must be under quite heavy tourist pressure was quite reassuring, but we discovered that this was not the case once we had crossed on to Holy Island. There, it seemed that Angesey's major housing and industrial development had been purposely clustered along a great deal of its very attractive coastline.

Two centuries ago Holy Island must have been one of the most scenic jewels in the Welsh crown. This relatively small island has one of the most diverse of Welsh coastal landscapes: in the north is a 'mountain' that looks higher than its modest 720 feet because it rises vertically from sea level. Because of this attribute it is famous for its sheer sea-cliffs which provide some of the most severe rock-climbing in Britain; in the south the highly indented shoreline is an intricate mixture of low rocky headlands and tiny bays with postage-stamp sized beaches, that have induced hundreds of people to build their holiday bungalows sporadically along the shore. Such an environment was quite different from the Anglesey coastline that we had already mapped and therefore it took considerably longer to record because of its closed vistas and rapidly changing land-use patterns. In my opinion, few coasts of comparable length in rural

Wales have suffered such a noticeable human imprint as this small island. When we visited in 1965 the drab grey town of Holyhead appeared unwelcoming but I have to confess that it was on a wet Sunday with all the shops closed. Perhaps such a similar experience helped to influence the pessimistic writings of the poet R. S. Thomas who grew up in Holyhead. William Daniell found the harbour important enough to paint in 1815 but remarked that "The situation of Holyhead is singularly dreary and comfortless". Our artist friend, Jacqueline Piper, however, was lucky enough to discover a sunny day on which to paint a picture looking south from Holyhead Mountain along a relatively unspoilt stretch of coast, and this watercolour is now in our possession, to always remind us of our Neptune mapping exercise in North Wales. The picture doesn't show the rash of housing at Trearddur Bay or around Rhoscolyn to the south and would give the impression of a coast in which the National Trust might show an interest but, apart from a tiny purchase at Porth Dafarch, the Trust has chosen to look elsewhere.

Clearly, like Dover, Holyhead is a town of passage, where everything is geared to the business of shuttling people and their vehicles on and off the Irish ferries. Although it is an ancient town, built inside the remains of a Roman fort (Caer Gybi), it scarcely gives an image of antiquity because it is overwhelmed by the clutter and traffic of a ferry port, the largest port for Irish traffic from the whole of northern and midland England. Its maritime claim to fame is its breakwater (almost 2 miles long) built in the mid-19th century to protect the harbour from northerly storms, thereby creating one of Britain's longest artificial coastal structures. It became obvious that all of this development had to be mapped under the Neptune category of 'Transport', as did the nearby RAF station of Valley, whose screaming jets flew regularly over this well populated coastline. It seemed such a pity that the one reasonably sized sandy beach on Holy Island, at Llanfawr, had been chosen as the site of a gigantic aluminium smelter in order to utilise some of the electricity generated at Wylfa Point. Its 420-foot stack dominates the scene, together with another large jetty, built to accommodate the enormous ships from Jamaica and Australia carrying cargoes of alumina to the smelter. Long after our survey had been completed, I learnt that the owners, Rio Tinto Group, had closed their Anglesey production plant, although its surviving jetty has given safe anchorage for modern cruise liners which today generate a different but very needful source of local income. Thus, the landscapes of this small island were found to be a complete contrast to those that we had been recording only a few days previously. I had to keep reminding myself, however, that certain British shorelines could never remain pristine forever: there must be some that were destined to be zoned for industry, transport and other commercial demands, as other Neptune surveyors were to discover elsewhere. But this is why the Neptune project had been devised in the first place, as a means of identifying the likely extensions of these developments along the coastline and where the National Trust, and other bodies, could be constantly alerted in sufficient time to monitor future planned development and ensure that it is confined to specifically agreed zones of our shores.

As we travelled slowly down to the southernmost corner of the Anglesey coastline we found that its coastal scenery was very similar to that which we had already traversed, in which ocean waves had worked differentially on the contrasting rock types to produce a fretted shoreline of tiny coves and rocky promontories, all of which we mapped as relatively undeveloped farmland. It was from one of these sandy beaches that our good friend Jacquie Piper painted a very atmospheric view of the mountain of Yr Eifl on the Lyn Peninsula, looking across Caernarfon Bay. Because it illustrated not only the wonderful coastline but also the area where I had already spent many research hours, the watercolour was soon added to our picture collection as a further memento of Neptune. Two nearby features caught my eye on the lonely headland of Llandwyn Island: first, a fairly rare British example of a rock-exposure of so-called 'pillow lavas' has been exposed by the sea. They appear as a welded mass of large spheroidal rocks, formed when massive volcanoes poured lava into the ocean many millions of years ago, as can now be seen in present-day Hawaii; the second unusual feature is the tiny church on the nearby tidal island at Llangwyfan close to the ancient village of Aberffraw. I mention these features because these are examples of the phenomena that some tourists come to see and should therefore be protected by a conservation body. We found the setting to be a haven of peace in 1965 but Simon Jenkins came this way some 40 years later. He is a renowned author and former Chairman of the National Trust, and he encounterd a very different ambience. He spoke of how the church is a mile from the nearest parking place but, unfortunately, it is less than a mile from the motor-bike racing-circuit on the nearby cliffs, thereby ruining the ambience of both beach and church with the roar of their engines. (Wales: Churches, Houses and Castles. Simon Jenkins, 2008). Unlike the nuclear power station at Wylfa, this circuit may be only a temporary intrusion but why on earth does it have to be on such a beautiful coastline? It crossed my mind that our 1965 survey had no category for this type of latter-day land use. Perhaps it could be entered as 'Transport'.

Beyond this point the coastline changes dramatically, first into the enormous embayment of Malltraeth Sands that lead inland to

Malltraeth Marsh and mark the estuary of one of Anglesey's longest rivers, the Cefni. Curlews, shelduck and many other wading birds frequent this watery wilderness, creating an environment that encouraged the famous wildlife artist, Charles Tunnicliffe, to make his home on the shore. An even greater wilderness lies nearby, but this time characterised not by marshy mudflats but by one of widespread aridity which is a surprising occurence on a coastline of high rainfall. The extensive coastal National Nature Reserve of Newborough Warren is one of the largest expanses of sand dunes in Britain. History tells us that the coastline hereabouts has seen quite remarkable changes since the 14th century when its rich farmland and settlements were overwhelmed and buried by violent storms that swept enormous quantities of sand from the offshore sandbanks. Today many of the dunes have been fixed by the planting of marram grass, thereby allowing such plants as wild thyme, dune-pansies and orchids to gain a foothold. Not surprisingly, this type of environmental history carried my mind back to my 1960 experience on the coast of Denmark, as described earlier, and even further back in time to reflect upon the coastline of Nord Beveland in Holland from where my ancestors had been forced to retreat from floods and blowing sand. Even more striking in this sandy desert are the swathes of Corsican Pine forest planted by the Forestry Commission in an attempt to reclaim the dunes and create shelter. At first sight this seemed an admirable scheme and one that we happily mapped as 'pristine' coastal woodland. William Condry (*op. cit.*) begged to differ with the Forestry Commission when he lamented how the plant-rich dune slacks, beloved by nature-lovers have disappeared beneath the forest. Moreover, he claims that even the unplanted slacks have deteriorated because of the general lowering of the water table. So here we have a conflict in coastal management. Visitors like ourselves find the woodland a peaceful, sheltered refuge on a windy and exposed coastline. In addition, these trees provide a pleasant scenic contrast on a low-lying, rocky and sandy shore, bearing in mind that coastal woodlands are relatively rare in stormy Britain. In short, this is an excellent example of the type of coast in which the National Trust would have been interested in purchasing if it had not already been protected. Furthermore, it has to be said that, in defence of the Forestry Commission planting schemes, a 2017 report demonstrated that tree-planting in Britain has witnessed a progressive decline over the last fifty years. In this respect it is interesting to note that in 1858 Anglesey was described thus: "…the surface has, in most parts, a bare uninviting aspect. It was called by the bards 'the shady island' because it formerly abounded with groves and trees, but there is now little wood, except along the banks of the Menai" (Black's Picturesque Guides: Wales, 1858). The latter stretch of coast was now our destination and a few more miles along the shore of the tide-ripped Menai Straits and our weary 125-mile perambulation of this sea-girt isle would be completed. The final journey gave us an opportunity to take time out and visit Plas Newydd, an 18th century stately home designed by Wyatt, and marvel at Rex Whistler's enormous wall-painting of an Italian 'capriccio'. In 1976 the mansion and 73 acres of woodland were given to the National Trust by the Marquess of Anglesey. From the lawns, which slope down to the sea, it is claimed that one is privileged to enjoy one of the finest views in North Wales. The panoramic vista across the straits and the parkland of Vaynol Hall leads the eye onwards to the magnificent backdrop of the heights of Snowdonia. Few places in Britain can replicate such a stunning view, although I had to continue to remind myself that aesthetic appraisal was not part of our present brief. Regrettably, on this occasion we were denied this idyllic vista because the heavens opened and we were confined to the mansion's interior.

To summarise the coastal land use in Anglesey it is instructive to turn to the statistics in a report produced by the National Parks Commission three years after our visit. (It was interesting to note that both Professor Steers and Mr Hookway were members of the Commission at that time). The authors concluded that "Agriculture is still the county's most important industry and most of the coastline is given over to it (50.4%)". But they sounded a cautionary note: "The tourist industry has been expanding over the last 20–30 years, but only in the last decade has this trend rapidly accelerated…Traffic volumes are increasing by 10% per annum and the volume of traffic crossing the suspension bridge into the county suggests that almost one-and-a-quarter million day-visitors came during the holiday periods of 1966". Elsewhere in the report it was recommended that "…building of isolated houses in the coastal area should be prohibited…and that the existing caravan policy should be strictly enforced". (The Coasts of North Wales. National Parks 1968). Perhaps the Commission's officers had visited Holy Island. Such cautionary conclusions corresponded very closely with our own detailed findings in the 1965 survey but we had already confirmed that the Anglesey coast was reasonably well protected within its 110 miles of AONB designation and virtually unsullied by old military eyesores. But I too was aware that the influx of caravans was threatening to destroy some of the coastal beauty that the tourists had come to enjoy. There is, of course, the added problem of possible impacts on the shoreline vegetation both from trampling and from litter, but this is a topic that will be discussed in a future chapter. It is significant to note that in the recorded discussion of the National Parks Commission report, Dr R. Elliot of the Nature Conservancy, spoke of the importance of screening of caravans by tree-planting (much more appropriate than my example of screening in quarries). He stated that "The Dutch had been very successful in this field and were now able to accommodate substantial recreational pressure in attractively conceived afforestation. You can 'hide away' possibly a hundred people in a wooded area which as an open space would have been crowded with only twenty on it."

I left Anglesey with some regret because islands have a magnetism that draws me towards them. A feeling of insularity is a remarkable phenomenon and has been remarked upon by dozens of writers. George Orwell, for example, found peace and isolation on the Hebridean island of Jura, before he was able to write his famous novel "1984". In addition to the solitude, islands give a sense of both escape and security. An island the size of Anglesey, so close to the mainland, hardly meets such criteria although its earliest Celtic name, 'Mon', is said to signify "…remote, detached or insulated" (Black's Picturesque Guide, *op. cit.*). In 1188 Gerald of Wales (Giraldus Cambrensis) spoke of Anglesey as 'Mon mam Cymru', literally 'Mon, the Mother of Wales'. Such a description illustrated the fact that in those early days its fertility was such that its corn harvest could feed the whole of Wales in times of emergency. In a later chapter I will describe how this deep longing for experiencing an island life was finally fulfilled on a remote and uninhabited Hebridean island.

Time was now running out and there were still 165 miles of my allotted coastline to map as a contribution to the Neptune survey. There remained the peninsula of Llyn (136 miles) and Merionethshire (29 miles). I was very fortunate, therefore, when a postgraduate student of mine, Kathleen Simpkins, offered to survey the Llyn Peninsula, because this was the location of her postgraduate research. Such a kind gesture left us free to continue southwards from the historic town of Caernarfon where, in 1301, the first English Prince of Wales was crowned. It boasts one of the finest castles in Britain, whose towering waterside image has been painted by many artists from Turner to John Piper. I am very fond of Caernarfon and have walked its narrow streets on many occasions because of their redolent sense of history. It seems that North Wales' castles were almost all sited on the coast, ranging from Flint and Conwy to Beaumaris, Caernarfon and Harlech. And there was a very good reason for these locations. A position on the shore meant that they could always be supplied from the sea during the centuries when the native Welsh armies were often in control of the hinterland. Today these manifestations of English hegemony are all in ruins but still remain great tourist attractions. But try to visit Caernarfon in the winter or on a traffic-free evening, after the crowds have gone, and you will discover why that great Welsh traveller, Thomas Pennant (born 1726) says of it: "Carnarvon is justly the boast of North Wales, for the beauty of its situation, the goodness of its buildings, the regularity of its plan, and above all the grandeur of the castle, that most magnificent badge of our subjection" (Pennant's Tours in Wales, 1791).

One might wonder why I have dwelt so long on a description of an urban coastal landscape. It is simply because, in the Neptune scheme of things, such a picturesque coastal site would have been by-passed as land in which the National Trust would have little if no interest, except, perhaps for an occasional historic building. Like other elegant North Wales' coastal towns such as Llandudno, Conwy and Beaumaris, Caernarfon would have been coloured an anonymous grey on the Neptune maps, although the Trust does own the Roman fort of Segontium within the built-up area. Regrettably, it is this built-up area that has now overwhelmed what the Victorian guide books tell us was one of the finest viewpoints on the local coastline. My student, Kathleen Simkins, when she started her Neptune mapping, would have to traverse the lengthy Llyn coastline (which I knew so well and to which I would return once more in the future). Meanwhile, my wife and I continued south to the shores of Merioneth. Perhaps Kathleen would have marvelled, 'en passant', at the celebrated Gothic church of Clynnog Fawr, the prehistoric hillfort village of Tre'r Caeri on the summit of Yr Eifl, the deep cleft of Nant Gwertheyrn (Vortigen's Valley) or the former fishing village of Nefyn whose beaches are now a tourist honeypot. Whatever these suppositions, she finally produced, like all my other volunteers, an accurate land-use map of her allocated region and one where the National Trust was soon to make many coastal purchases along its delectable shores.

The 1968 report of the National Parks Commission stated that the Llyn AONB was "...one of the remaining outstanding lengths of coastline in the country". Praise indeed, and one of the reasons why the National Trust, by 1997, owned no less than 37 properties on its shores (1,811 acres) with 14 of them bought from Neptune funding. The Commission's findings tallied well with those of Kathleen Simpkins in which they both concluded that the major disfigurements of the peninsula's northern coast were the forsaken machinery in the granite quarries at Trevor and Yr Eifl, together with the "...worst kind of coastal shack development at Aberdesach and Pontllyfni" on the southern coastline. On turning to this less spectacular south-facing coastline, where the National Trust has few holdings, there are many sandy beaches and, not surprisingly, both the 1965 and the 1968 surveys discovered that it was these stretches which exhibited the greatest impact from tourism. Abersoch, Llanbedrog and Pwllheli were renowned sailing centres and the well-established holiday camp at Pen-y-Chain, when taken together, catered for much of the holiday demand on the peninsula. But both reports found that the caravan park at Morfa Bychan, near to Black Rock beach, left a lot to be desired in terms of its sprawling layout. Moreover, the National Parks Commission reported that at "Morfa Bychan a car park for over 3,000 vehicles had come into being and added to the [dune] erosion problems". Mr Pyne, the Planning Officer for Caernarfonshire, went on to say that "Because it was below the high water mark it was outside planning control. Moreover, this number of vehicles pouring off one site created a major traffic problem. It could take an hour and a half to drive two to three miles along the [narrow] road to Portmadoc. Coastal car parks should be kept small and well hidden". Such comments drew attention to some of the problems that had first motivated the Neptune campaign: Loss of natural habitats, exploited beyond their so-called ecological 'carrying capacity'; poorly sited caravan and shack development; major traffic problems on approach roads; and, above all the complexity of planning laws at 'the edge of the land'. It is instructive to note that just to the east of this caravan village the National Trust has subsequently bought the dunes that reach out to the rocky knoll of Ynys Cyngar in order to prevent further eastward encroachment. This is precisely the sort of advice that was highlighted by our onerous Neptune mapping campaign and in its small way gave me immense satisfaction.

Before we set off southwards towards Harlech we made time to visit the tiny village of Llanystumdwy, near to Criccieth and where the tumbling waters of the Afon Dwyfach reach the sea. Here was the former home of Lloyd George, one of Britain's most prominent Prime Ministers, in a house designed by Clough Williams-Ellis (see below). This beautiful mansion was redolent of his presence and resonant of his oratory. It seemed very appropriate to learn that 25 years after our visit, Ty Newydd was to become the most important Creative Writing Centre in Wales. More prosaically, in order to map the coast of Merionethshire Diane and I had to find a different base from which we could carry out our ongoing journeys. We chose the Queen's Hotel at Porthmadog, a smart little town which for some unknown reason was excluded from the Snowdonian National Park. The National Parks Commission's policy seems to have been to exclude all coastal towns (even historic Conwy) but it still included Harlech and Aberdyfi. Almost two decades later I re-visited our chosen venue, the Queen's Hotel, for a very different reason because I needed cye-witness accounts of a 'strong' earthquake that had rocked the region in 1984. In Porthmadog I was told how goods had fallen from the shop shelves but, more importantly, there had ben major rockfalls from the former sea cliffs that tower over nearby Tremadog. The 'quake had an intesity of a 'mere' 4.5 on the Mercalli scale but was the second most severe in British records (behind Colchester in 1884) but an earthquake of such magnitude is a rarity in Britain. In an article in The Geographical Magazine, (1985) I wrote how "The reaction of the public to the initial tremor was most dramatic in a tract extending from the Llyn Penisula north-eastwards to the Menai Strait, throughout Anglesey and along the north coast of Gwynedd as far east as the Conwy Valley. It was here that people spoke of being thrown out of bed or down the stairs, amidst the noise of breaking crockery and glassware. Within a 20-mile radius of its epicentre, between Pwllheli and Nefyn, there were many reports of structural damage to chimneys, roofs and windows, especially at Aberdaron, Pen y Groes and Llanllyfni. A church steeple on the shores of the Menai Strait was damaged, drain pipes were fractured in Holyhead and culverts disturbed on the

Ffestiniog railway. People living near to the nuclear power stations at Trawsfynydd and Wylfa, fearing a nuclear accident, had to be reassured that the power stations had been designed to withstand similar incidents. In coastal terms such severe shaking, for 20–30 seconds, would certainly have caused significant collapses of local sea cliffs especially where they were composed of unconsolidated glacial material. Such an event could have been equivalent to decades of wave erosion but, on the positive side, probably revealed new exposures for geologists to explore.

The coastline to the east of Porthmadog is a complicated configuration, for the joint estuaries of the Afon Glaslyn and the Afon Dwyryd meet in Tremadog Bay which forms the county boundary between Caernarfonshire and Merionethshire. Moreover, the joint estuary is itself split by a rocky, wooded peninsula on which the renowned architect, Clough Williams-Ellis, built his well-known Italianate village of Porth Meirion. This rocky promontory divides the coastline into two separate vales: the larger Traeth Mawr and the smaller Vale of Ffestiniog which debouches into Traeth Bach. It is in the picturesqe latter vale that the National Trust has acquired most of the natural woodland. Whereas the latter vale is enhanced by these ancient woodlands which descend to a winding river, that reaches the sea via a narrow glacial gorge and an array of glistening sand banks, the Glaslyn estuary is said to have been 'desecrated' by the works of engineers. The landscape of the Glaslyn estuary must once have appeared very similar to that of its neighbour and was then noted as one of the glories of Welsh coastal scenery at a time when tides would have penetrated far inland to the bridge at Aberglaslyn, almost to the foot of Snowdon itself. But no longer, because in 1807 a certain Mr William Maddocks received permission to build a mile-long embankment across

Treath Mawr and henceforth the Cob, as it is known, carried a road and the celebrated Ffestiniog railway, the world's oldest surviving narrow-gauge railway. Unfortunately, this once famous coastal view towards Snowdon, painted several times by David Cox, has now been truncated and has reduced a former seascape to some 10,000 acres of low-grade marshy farmland instead of gleaming low-water sands. Cledwyn Hughes (1949) summed up the regrettable effects on this otherwise attractive coastal stretch: "Here on the the shores of this bay once lived Shelley and once Lawrence of Arabia. The flat land of Traeth Mawr was stolen from the sea…Once the tides came in salty, and full of their own particular life, where now the land is tilled". One has to remember, however, that the causeway not only gave tourists the pleasure of a rail journey through wonderful mountain scenery but also provided motorists with a very acceptable short-cut across the Glaslyn estuary. Furthermore, the Central Electricity Board must have thought that the view had remained attractive enough to spend millions of pounds in burying their power-lines underground where they crossed Traeth Mawr. However, my Neptune rules forced me to ignore the aesthetics of the landscape of this part of the Merioneth coast, so that the grey pencil came out to delimit the built-up areas of Porthmadog, Minffordd and Penrhyndeudraeth settlements and the red pencil to pin-point the very intrusive stone quarry at Y Garth, facing across the marsh, and from which the stone was taken to build the Cob. It is worth recording at this juncture that to travel any coastline and ignore the attractive views or the historic associations is an almost impossible task, especially for someone like myself, well schooled in the seaboard nuances.

In 1965 we had to pay a toll to cross the rickety roadbridge that spanned the Afon Dwyryd but in 2017 we were lucky to be one of the first tourists to benefit from a new bridge now toll-free. The next section of coastline skirted the seaward fringe of the National Park and therefore had a fairly strict planning control all the way south to Barmouth. Our route took us up a slowly climbing road overhung by woodland, some of which is now in the hands of the National Trust, but it was the seaward view which held our attention, for the immense sweep of Morfta Harlech stretched its magnificent 'dunescape' far out into Tremadog Bay. On an overcrowded coastline this sandy desert is as near to a wilderness as anywhere on the Welsh seaboard and its flora and fauna have profited from the lack of intrusion. That is, except from the Forestry Commission who, as at Anglesey's Newborough, spied a few acres of 'empty' land and have begun some conifer afforestation. Botanists tell us that the Harlech dunes are very old and my good friend Professor Steers explained that they had become established on an ancient shingle spit that had grown northwards at a rate of some 450 yards in less than fifty years. We noted that the prevailing westerlies continue to blow sand constantly inland to overwhelm the poor-grade farmland that stretches back to the rocky former coastline, so that the links golf-course seems to be one of the most sensible and profitable land-uses on this sort of terrain. One of the most interesting stories relating to this coastline is the claim that Harlech castle once possessed a water-gate, allowing it, like most other medieval Welsh castles, to be supplied by sea in times of trouble. This must give some indication of the changing coastline over the centuries because today the castle crag stands some way from the sea. Steers found no evidence of such an architectural feature but also stated that a 1325 document in the Public Record Office demonstrated that Hardelowe (Harlech) was a port in those times "...into which the men of Flanders, merchants and others" brought their merchandise into that port. Personally, I found this information important insofar as it illustrated the ways in which my early ancestors might have been trading at this time along the Welsh coast from their base in Pembrokeshire (See the following chapter).

To the south of Harlech both the main road and railway leave the coastline in order to cross the Afon Artro at its lowest bridging point at Llanbedr. The river reaches the sea through a tidal lagoon held back by a line of sand dunes where the Trust has acquired a tiny piece of coast at the village of Llandanwg. The violence of the westerly winds is well illustrated here because the stone-built church is half buried by drifting sand and, despite the valiant attempts by the villagers, has had to be left to the vagaries of Nature. This lonely coastline is known as Morfa Dyffryn and has long been a National Nature Reserve with strict rules of conservation, so that its 'pristine' coastline proved very easy to map. To its north is the remarkable boulder clay mound at Mochras, known as Shell Island (although it is far from being insular). When we visited in 1965, following the simple track across the marshes, we found it virtually deserted apart from a scatter of campers' tents. I had been here, as a teenager, twenty years previously, and found that, on that breezy day the only visitors had been a few naked seabathers. Today it is a well known accredited but crowded camp site, where children happily 'gather sea shells along the seashore'; it is reputed that there are some 200 varieties of shells but because we had so little time we failed to gather any to add to my collection of fossils, rocks and pebbles.

It will be seen, later in the chapter, how Mochras is of special significance to the geomorphologist because it stands at the edge of the so-called Cantref-y-Gwaelod, a legendary expanse of land reputedly drowned by a marine incursion in the 7th century. Stories abound about submerged ruined buildings and lines of ancient streets but these have been shown to be nothing more than stony reefs. The legend is probably related to the rising post-glacial sea-level which pushed the Welsh coastline inexorably inland, as it did on other low-lying coasts in our islands. But back to the land-use mapping. We discovered that the deserted track to Mochras, across the flat coastal plain, had to skirt around the perimeter of a large military airfield, a remnant of World War II but later to become a Royal Aerospace Establishment. It divides the unspolit coastline to the north from what can only be described as a blizzard of caravan and camping sites that fringe the sandy beaches almost as far south as Barmouth. Such a complex not only took our eyes off the scenery but also brought the blue pencil into constant use.

It was here that I began to pause for thought, because it was mid-August and, as in Anglesey, we saw many hundreds of people thoroughly enjoying their holidays in the sun. And why not? The entire concept of Enterprise Neptune was to discover coastlines worthy of preservation but, as a corollary, other shores must be seen as open for recreation and/or development. Therefore, such caravan and camping sites as these must not be viewed in an over-critical state of mind, especially as they serve to concentrate the land-use into a limited stretch of coastline. In 1965, however, some planning authorities had noted that this type of usage was growing exponentially in a series of stages as follows: (1) Mobile caravan. (2) Static caravan (3) Conversion to permanent bungalow. Such a progression was already becoming commonplace, usually before the provision of such amenities as water supply, sewage, electricity, road access, etc. had been formally installed. I even heard it whispered that "Here are the rural slums of the future". Nevertheless, the final word must remain with Adrian Robinson and Roy Milllward (1983): "The coastal sand-dune belt to the south of Shell Island is a favourite site for caravan parks which somehow seem less offensive here than do the larger sites along the north [Wales] coast". Was this because they were concentrated rather than sporadic? Unfortunately, they give no reason for such a distinction. If I was asked to give my own thoughts on the matter, no matter how subjective, I would have to agree that a large aggregation is considerably better than an indiscriminate scattering at intervals along the coast. Moreover, it would be able to offer planned and well managed facilities in place of unauthorised camping and the concomitant dangers of litter and other pollution. Having said this, however, I am aware that restrictions are anathema to hikers and some scientists who wish for freedom of movement along Britain's coastal footpaths and are sometimes dependent on 'free camping'. There was, of course, a sense of irony that during the present mapping exercise we had spent one or two nights under canvas, although we had always sought permission and had moved on after one night. Nevertheless, both camping and parking caravans on unlicensed sites will remain a contentious issue, especially on farmland. I will return to this problem on many more occasions throughout the remainder of the text.

Our next stop was Barmouth which one guide book describes as "a typical seaside resort: chip shops, dodgem cars, donkey rides and crabbing – catering to thousands from England's West Midlands", whilst another speaks more demurely of "A small but lively holiday town huddled between the sea, the Mawddach estuary and the steep flanks of a craggy-peaked hill". But this is no ordinary hill for it was the first coastal acquisition of the National Trust, given in 1895 by Fanny Talbot. This rocky, gorse-clad eminence, Dinas Oleu, was gifted by this wealthy lady because she wished the public to enjoy it by giving it to a society "…that will never vulgarise it, or prevent wild nature from having its way". It was a fine exemplar of the Trust's tenets and especially those of Octavia Hill, one of the Trust's founders, who believed in the importance of providing "...open sitting rooms for City dwellers to have a place to breathe". We shall never know whether Charles Darwin, who visited Barmouth in 1828 and again in 1829, came for these reasons or, more likely, if it was simply to study its natural history. Those times are well illustrated in David Cox's contemporaneous paintings which show Barmouth as little more than a small fishing village clinging to a hillside above a tiny harbour. But to really capture the atmosphere of modern Barmouth one must turn again to Cledwyn Hughes's pre-war description of it as "...grey-stoned and little-harboured. A sea-wall on the one side and the rising height of the cliff at the back [where] streets pushed up and built on ledges on the cliffs...old stone cottages and fairyland sugarloaf houses with bright brass knockers and flower-potted windows. Early travellers tell of the pigs which slept in the Barmouth streets. Now, where children clank spade against gay bucket and the ladies walk in peach and pink in bathing costumes". No matter what this colourful atmosphere conveys, my own rules dictated that this delectable built-up area has perforce to be coloured grey on the map. It would be of no interest to the National Trust despite its historic hill. But just around the headland there lay an estuary that would prove of considerable interest.

The Mawddach estuary is one of the 'crown jewels' not just of coastal Wales but of the entire British shoreline. It was the home of Cledwyn Hughes who spoke lovingly of "This wonderful estuary, changing its moods and its colours; pliable to every wind, every change of sky". This was exactly how we saw it for the first time, when cloud shadows chased each other across its surrounding peaks. In 1965 I was very conscious that the strict Neptune rules would have excluded this extraordinary section of coastline from the survey if the lengthy wooden bridge, that spanned the estuary mouth, had carried a road instead of a railway. I was mindful of how the Severn road bridge had robbed the survey of miles of attractive coastline, because of my survey strictures, but here in Merionethshire we were able to indulge in very little complex mapping as we travelled along its beautiful 'pristine' shoreline.

The Afon Mawddach meanders for miles along its broad estuary which burrows deeply into the Snowdonian National Park. Its gleaming low-tide sandbanks are flanked by thick hanging woodlands which rise up into the steep slopes of the surrounding mountains. It has long been celebrated by John Ruskin's famous adage "That the only walk in Britain more beautiful than the one from Dolgellau to Barmouth is the walk from Barmouth to Dolgellau". Indeed, it is the epitome of the 'picturesque', a description summed up by Thomas Roscoe in his book "Wanderings in North Wales" (1836) as "The dense wood, the wild overhanging precipice, the large gloomy rocks…all blended in a series of rich and varied prospects which could not fail to please the eye and charm the imagination of even the coldest observer". Surprisingly, the National Trust has no properties here but it could remain safe in the knowledge that virtually no development will take place. This is because not only have the National Parks Commission's controls long held sway but also because such bodies as the Woodland Trust and the Forestry Commission own many miles of the hinterland above the shoreline. Moreover, apart from the tiny stone-built hamlets at the stream outlets, the terrain is far too steep for development. Since we had virtually no actual mapping to distract us from our admiration of the scenery we vowed that we must return someday for a holiday. This intention, however, was delayed for more than fifty years before we stayed in a delightful converted watermill the gardens of which looked across the vale to the crags of Cadair Idris.

I had stayed near here many years previously, in my student days, as a guest of my old Professor, Austin Miller, whose ancient stone cottage boasted an entrance to a gold mine in its garden, although he assured me that the gold had long been worked out. My most abiding memory was of ascending to the summit of Cadair Idris with both Professor Miller and my external examiner, Professor Linton, where we sat and discussed the geomorphology of this very region on which I would soon begin my research. I recall that the discussion also ranged about the origin of the summit rock pinnacles known as 'tors' which are most commonly found at lower levels in such places as Dartmoor. Linton was engaged in writing his seminal paper on "The origin of tors" (1955) and I felt privileged to have been involved in his nascent thoughts in this field. We were very lucky with the weather, unlike the Reverend Robert Kilvert, the indefatigable curate of Clyro near Hay on Wye. He climbed to the summit on a day of wind and rain that led him to conclude that "Cader Idris is the stoniest, dreariest, most desolate mountain I was ever on".

Cadair Idris, although not the highest Welsh peak, rears its lofty summit only a few miles inland from where it can be seen from the open sea. Although not strictly coastal its foothills descend to the Merioneth shore. It has always fascinated me, ever since I saw the oil painting of Llyn Cae by Richard Wilson (1714–1782), Wales's most famous artist. I have recently acquired two watercolours of its craggy image, one by Cornelius Varley (1804) and one by David Cox (c. 1820). When the first Victorian tourists came in awe to ascend what they thought was Wales's highest peak, they were forced to take a guide. I cannot resist recounting an amusing story by Thomas

Roscoe (*op. cit.*) about one of these guides, "Robert Edwards, second son of William Edwards, ap Griffith, ap Morgan, ap David, ap Llewellyn, ap Cadwaladar…He was dressed in a blue coat with yellow buttons, a pair of old boots, and a cocked hat and a feather of enormous size. Nothing could be so amusing as to see the guide, with a long white rod in his hand, like another Merlin, setting out at full canter from the door of the inn, on his Welsh pony, followed by a little cavalcade, who could scarcely keep their seats for laughter. He talked much of 'curiosity-men', meaning naturalists; and enumerated among his followers some eminent names in science and literature; among the rest, Sir Joseph Banks and the late Earl of Bristol". This region must have been regarded as a 'research area' even in those far-off days.

The westernmost flanks of Cadair Idris constrict the coastal plain south of the sandy coastal spit at Fairbourne, a seaside hamlet comprised of a rather unprepossessing scatter of caravans and post-war chalets and bungalows. From there southwards the coast road is forced to run 'en corniche' along the cliffs all the way to the headland at Tonfanau with its coastal quarry. I had visited this site in my army days just after the war, because it was a heavy artillery gunnery school, although I was actually stationed at the field artillery camp further inland at Trawsfynydd, an isolated spot in the Snowdonia National Park. I never fired a shell at Tonfanau and some of those that I fired at Trawsfynydd fell so far off target that they scattered a flock of sheep! (There was one gunner worse than me, for he landed a shot almost on the 'forward observation post' which housed the Colonel). In 1965 we were forced to map the Tonfanau camp merely as miltary land-use but Cledwyn Hughes saw it otherwise when he fulminated about the intrusion of the military onto his homeland: "Flat fields have had their hedges taken away, and old houses have been surrounded by stark, red-brick buildings and black, round-roofed shanties of galvanised iron… The towns of the coast have the English troops, good natured and joking at taffy and the song of his voice". One of those towns must have been Aberdyfi which would mark the end of our own Neptune itinerary in Wales.

Aberdyfi's situation is very similar to that of Barmouth, tucked into a narrow strip of land between the mountains and the sea. Since our visit in 1965 the small town has become rather an exclusive centre with a smart yacht club. It is noteworthy that the sailing club's insignia of a black bell was inspired by "The Bells of Aberdovey" from Charles Dibden's 18th century opera "Liberty Hall". It tells how the sound of bells ringing beneath the waves may be yet another reference to the reputed lost land of Cantref-y-Gwaelod out in Cardigan Bay. The estuary of the Afon Dyfi was recognised by UNESCO as of such importance that it was designated as a 'Biosphere Reserve', one of only six in the whole of Britain. It is considerably wider than that at Barmouth and seems to have caused great consternation several centuries ago when medieval travellers approached its shores.

That doughty coastal rambler, Nicholas Crane (2007), describes how the chronicler, Gerald of Wales (Giraldus Cambrensis), came that way with his fellow travellers several centuries ago and how they arrived at "a dark gulf" (The Welsh word 'Dyfi' means 'black' or 'dark'). "Beyond the water rose ominously gloomy forested hills…In Gerald's eyes, the far shore of the Dovey symbolised the untouchable interior of Wales. It was wilder and less accessible than other [Welsh] regions and the rudest and roughest of all the Welsh districts. Culturally, this was a foreign country, inhabited by Welsh men and women who had never been subjugated by the Normans and who therefore spoke no [English] or Latin". Significantly, these 'intruders' were meeting the same hostility that had been encounterd by my ancestors when they had come to settle in Pembrokeshire a few decades previously (See the next chapter). When I viewed the magnificent coastal scenery of North-West Wales a mischievous question crossed my mind. Was it simply a strategic decision by the War Office to place its wartime military establishments in these parts of rural Wales in relatively safe areas, or had their decision-makers previously read Gerald's commentaries and placed their airfields and firing ranges in the 'rudest and roughest' parts? I very much doubt that the latter surmise was the case, but I bet that Cledwyn Hughes would have thought so.

This fleeting thought led me to recall a story related to me by Professor Steers who, with Dr Willatts, had been making a coastal survey during the early years of World War II (referred to in chapter 2). He told me how they had been arrested as suspected spies on the beach of Hell's Mouth in the Llyn Peninsula. It transpired that they had been on the verge of one of several new airfields sited on the coasts of North Wales to provide cover for the port of Liverpool and as a precaution against a possible German invasion via Ireland. However, they were not told that they had, in fact, been walking across the firing range, where newly recruited air-gunners were being trained to fire live ammunition seawards from mock aircraft turrets. Such a tale was a stark reminder of the large number of even remote coastlines, like that in question, which had been taken over by the military in order to maintain utmost secrecy. These now deserted and forlorn coastal 'footprints' simply remained for the Neptune surveyors to depict with their orange pencils.

By now I had begun to realise that this detailed Neptune mapping was becoming very tedious and that many of my volunteers in other parts of the United Kingdom may have been coming to similar conclusions. But of course, in my case, I had the compensation of travelling along very attractive coastlines, much better, perhaps, than other less attractive parts of the surveyed areas. This is probably the reason why I have spent so many words extolling the virtues of the landscapes as well as hinting at their geological, literary, artistic and even musical attributes.

Before we finally left this part of Wales we felt that we had to witness something of its wildlife, especially its rich variety of birds which flourish in the coastal estuaries. A visit to the RSPB centre at Ynyshir, on the estuary of the Dyfi, allowed us to enjoy the sight of thousands of waders, mallard, teal, wigeon, shelduck and many other wildfowl. Here, in the absolute tranquility of cloud-dappled mudflats, we began to relax and watch the curlews pulling lugworms and ragworms from the marshy shore, while the oystercatchers searched for the cockles and mussels further out on the sandbanks. One is able to understand, when experiencing such bliss, why the conservation bodies must never relax their vigilance in attempting to protect such coastal environments. But, the well-known Welsh red kites in those days had their range somewhat further further inland, so we were unable to spot a single one.

Our concluding journey was along a tortuous single-track road, superbly driven by Diane, to visit the remarkable rocky pinnacle known as Bird Rock (Craig yr Aderyn) that stands some 4 miles inland. Centuries ago it was recorded that the tides washed the foot of this former sea-stack when it became the home of numerous cormorants. Records go back to 1695 when the naturalist Lhuyd records that a "number of corvorants, rock pigeons and hawks breed upon it". We had learnt that the cormorants were still there but, as in the case of the kites, we never sighted one. My own share of the

Neptune mapping was now over and it remained for me to return to Reading to receive, collate and hand-colour the hundreds of maps from the other volunteers who had been working diligently in all corners of England, Wales and Northern Ireland.

The final word on this stretch of coastline must be with the 1968 Report of the National Parks Commission who noted the growing pressures of tourism on the shores of North Wales. Even fifty years ago, more than 34,000 day-visitors came to the coast of Merionethshire and the conclusions were that future holiday centres will be promoted inland near to Lake Bala and Llyn Celyn "...as more coastal caravans and camping sites are regarded as undesirable". (More than 80% were then located on the coast). The report drew attention to the rapidly increasing numbers of touring-caravans: "Every year more are turned away by the owners of permanent sites who prefer the steady income from resident caravans, once the area allocated in the site-licence for touring caravans is filled. The result is that certain lay-bys along the coast are filled nightly during the peak period with touring caravans, a very undesirable state of affairs from a public health standpoint". At that time in the 1960's, as the Neptune campaign was about to be launched, it appeared that there was something of a national fixation by Britain's planning and conservation bodies concerning the location of caravan and camping sites, and the cult of 'Nimbyism' was soon to become widespread.

One might think that my obsession with the coastline of North Wales had been satiated but, as I mentioned earlier, within a few years of finishing the Neptune survey an invitation arrived asking if I would like to contribute to a forthcoming book entitled "The glaciations of Wales and adjoining regions". This would be a great opportunity to utilise many of my PhD research findings and also to make use of the detailed knowledge gleaned during our Neptune perambulations. On my acceptance I was allocated the entire region of North-West Wales and, fortuitously, I had recently met Dr David Ball from the Soil Survey who had just completed the official map of the soils of this very region. What better than to join forces for this major undertaking? Our fieldwork would entail a detailed description and analysis of every exposed section together with any borehole data in the region and then to work out a chronology of the various ice-sheet advances that had fashioned the landforms. Not surprisingly, thanks to the incessant marine erosion, the vast majority of the exposures were to be found along the shoreline, so here we go again – yet another coastal trek.

Once more the coast would become my laboratory and this time there would be no time to eulogise about its scenery, its literature, its art or its musical associations. This was to be a time of hard graft, hard hat and a geological hammer. It would entail miles of scrambling across landslips and on crumbling cliffs of unconsolidated glacial sediments, refreshed by every high tide. Such sediments were exactly those that had for countless centuries been carried away by the waves to create the pebble beaches and the shingle spits and forelands that we had traversed during the Neptune survey in previous years.

One may question the significance of asking a number of scientists to plod along the Welsh coastal cliffs at this time, arrayed with soil-testing kit, trowel and notebook. The answer lay in the great importance of these particular shoreline drift deposits in deciphering the complex history of the Ice Age in Britain. Other geomorphologists were carrying out similar surveys in many other parts of Britain and Ireland so that by the Millenium a fairly clear pattern of Ice Age events had begun to emerge. North-West Wales, our allocated region, was of particular importance for it was here that "Louis Agassiz (1842) was one of the first to describe the effects of glaciation in Britain (and) to include the valleys of Snowdonia among the localities in which he saw evidence of former glaciers" (J. B. Whittow and D. F. Ball, 1970). Later work by the eminent geologist, A. C. Ramsay (1860 and 1881) confirmed these findings and, in 1909, another geologist, T. J. Jehu made a rudmentary glacial survey of the Llyn Peninsula, to be followed in 1919 by Edward Greenly's monumental Memoir for the Geological Survey on "The Geology of Anglesey" (1919).

I apologise for the following digression but one that I believe is marginally relevant. In 1945 John Piper, the celebrated modern artist, having read Ramsay's ground-breaking book "The Old Glaciers of Switzerland and North Wales" (1860), produced a magnifcent painting of "Cwm Graianog", one of the ice-scooped hollows on the flanks of the glacial trough of Nant Ffrancon. Such hollows are termed 'cwms' in Wales and 'corries' in Scotland and this picture epitomises the forces of glacial excavation in a mountain region. I am the proud possessor of one of the few 1978 prints of its monumental depiction of glacial erosive landforms. I also own another of his equally important prints of a different Snowdonian glacial feature, that of a so-called 'roche moutonée', an unusual term derived from the French which describes an ice-smoothed dome-shaped rock that resembles a recumbent sheep. Many people believe that it was in Snowdonia that Piper made his finest pictures in the immediate post-war years. (John Piper: The Mountains of Wales. D. F. Jenkins and M. Munro, 2012). Henceforward, I realise that I must refrain from being side-tracked into artistic eulogising instead of concentrating on the work in hand, a detailed examination of exposures of glacial material on the coasts of North Wales.

I have already described how a massive ice-sheet had driven down the basin of the then waterless floor of the Irish Sea, dredging up many of its abyssal deposits and grinding their incorporated marine shells into a mélange before dumping them on the coasts of North Wales together with 'erratics' from Cumbria and Scotland (in what is termed a 'shelly boulder clay'). The thickness of this Northern ice-mass may be gauged by the fact that some of these calcareous clays and sands have been discovered at a height of 1,400 feet on the slopes of Moel Tryfaen, not far from Caernarfon. Like others before him Charles Lyell, a leading geologist, visited the site in 1863 and declared that this particular deposit was indeed of glacial origin but had been deposited by floating ice-bergs. It is more than likely that the Geological Survey's adoption of the term 'glacial drift' was derived from such beliefs. Initially, the term was used to describe glacially derived clays, sands and gravels but was later expanded to include such superficial materials as peat and blown sand. Hence the two types of maps produced by the Geological Survey: a "Drift Map" and a "Solid Rock Map". Lyell went on to claim that such "...shells show that Snowdon and all the highest hills which are in the neighbourhood of Moel Tryfaen (i.e. in the Llyn Peninsula) were mere islands in the sea at a comparatively late period". It has been cogently argued by another geolgist, F. J. North, that this early claim would imply a marine submergence of some 1,500 feet (that would have coincided conveniently with Biblical stories of The Flood). Finally, F. J. North concluded that a movement of such magnitude was impossible in the relatively short time-span of the Ice Age. (Snowdonia, F. J. North, 1949). Indeed, my own mapping of ancient shorelines in the Llyn Peninsula (described above) estimated that marine oscillations of some 600 feet took more than five million years before they reached today's relative equilibrium at the level of the present shoreline, not merely a few tens of thousands.

To begin our survey of 'coastal drift deposits' David Ball and I set off on a sunny July day in the late-1960's to start our meticulous investigation of the coastal cliffs of the Llyn. This was very familiar ground and we chose to start near Criccieth and work our way westwards. Here, at the extensive beaches around Black Rock, renowned for their car-parking on firm sands below high-water-mark (as described in a previous chapter), we picked our way through hundreds of tourists who must have been puzzled at our behaviour. They may well have asked "What on earth are these two doing hacking at the cliff face instead of enjoying the delights of swimming or sunbathing?" At a place called Merlyn, at the end of the Criccieth promenade, we slithered and tottered as we attempted to dig into a low unstable cliff amidst a crowd of curious children. "Are you looking for buried treasure?" they hooted and we realised that it would be useless to try to explain, on both this and on many future occasions, as to what lay behind our seemingly useless delving. What we did find, however, were layers of boulder clay of Welsh origin, almost certainly derived from the slatey and volcanic rocks of western Snowdonia. Because there were no Northern erratics present we could confidently conclude that this exposure was totally derived from a local Welsh ice-cap. It may not have been buried treasure but at least we were up and running.

On further days, as we progressed towards Pwllheli, we recorded, at Glanllynau, what turned out to be one of the most significant glacial coastal sections in the whole of Wales. Because it contained layers of interbedded organic muds, capable of being dated by their fossil pollen content, we believed that it could prove to be of immense importance to the Pleistocene chronology of Wales. I immediately asked one of my postgraduate students, Kathleen Simpkins (mentioned above in the context of Neptune), if she would like to carry out an in-depth examination of the section, for which she could be awarded a doctorate. In fact, her findings became of great geological importance. Subsequently, scores of scientists visited this iconic site which was in reality a cross-section of a so-called 'kettle hole' in which ancient flora and fauna had decayed in a water-filled hollow in the glacial outwash sands. Such hollows are formed when large blocks of buried glacier ice slowly melt, thereby causing subsidence of any overlying materials into the void. The very placename of Glanllynau (llynau = lakes) implies that there must have been several of these waterlogged depressions hereabouts and their hummocky landforms had resulted from a slowly decaying ice-sheet at the termination of the Ice Age in Wales. In later years we were profoundly grateful to the land owner, a sheep farmer, who allowed countless parties of university students to tramp across his land. I, for one, brought my own students from Reading every year for decades. It is to be hoped that wave erosion does not destroy this important site, but this section is only one example of a paradox. Geological scientists depend on coast erosion to expose such valuable sections but can do little to safeguard their future survival.

As we tramped slowly westwards, following the established scientific principles of recording: sketching, measuring, sampling, analysing and synthesising, our primary intent was to define the westernmost limits of the local Welsh ice-advance. To what extent had it been able to fend-off the mighty Northern ice-sheet which we all knew had once been powerful enough to reach as far south as the Isles of Scilly? We also knew that earlier geologists, such as Edward Greenly, had established that the centre of the Welsh ice-cap had been located in the uplands between present-day Harlech and Bala. From this central 'ice-dome', radially outflowing glaciers were able to reach eastwards as far as the Shropshire/Cheshire Plain until they had encountered a branch of the Northern ice-sheet ploughing southwards through the 'Cheshire Gap'. It seemed clear to us that the Welsh glaciers, driving northwards from the quite impressive 'ice-dome', would have been faced with the formidable unbroken barrier of the highest Snowdonian summits rising to elevations of more than 3,000 feet, and that they must have been powerful enough to tear out gigantic breaches in this former pre-glacial watershed. Today, tourists marvel at the deep ice-gouged troughs of the Nant Ffrancon, the Pass of Llanberis and that to the west of Snowdon. A present-day analogy is that of Greenland where glaciers flowing radially outwards from a massive central ice-dome have succesfully breached the coastal mountains to reach the surrounding occan. Our present mapping exercise was later to establish that the Snowdonian north-flowing glaciers came to an abrupt halt in the vicinity of the present-day Menai Straits when they encountered the Northern ice-sheet. The question remained: where was the outer limit of Welsh ice on the Llyn Peninsula? It was essential for us to establish this boundary with some accuracy because former geologists had never been able to agree its location. By then we had reached as far west as St Tudwal's Peninsula, near to Abersoch, at which point we found that Northern erratics and shelly boulder clay had begun to appear in the drift sequence, suggesting that Welsh glaciers had finally met their match. It is difficult to convey to the layperson how such an apparently trivial discovery caused us to be filled with a degree of exhilaration. It was, perhaps, similar to that of a rock climber, standing at the foot of a previously unclimbed mountain wall, and full of adrenalin-charged anticipation, although, in truth, ours was only a 100-foot cliff.

I well remember that on a cool autumn day, when a brisk north-westerly wind drove rain into our faces, we were glad to find shelter beneath the sea-cliff in the lonely south-facing bay of Porth Ceiriad at the tip of St Tudwal's promontory. This was a deserted cove rarely visited by holidaymakers so that our muddy scrambling and recording remained unobserved. Imagine the scene: David, the soil expert, noting the exact colour of each layer and the derivation of the included rocks and pebbles; myself being responsible for measuring and sketching of the exact relationships between the strata; all of this with cold fingers and a wet notebook. It was times like these when one began to question the relevance of the whole enterprise. However, there appeared to be the likelihood of a significant final result that would render the discomfort worthwhile. Almost all of the exposure comprised a thick layer of a grey-brown Welsh boulder clay, almost identical to that we had recorded at Criccieth and Glanllynau. But imagine our delight when we discovered, high up in the western corner of the highly unstable cliff, an isolated lens of calcareous Northern boulder clay that had been caught up in the eroded and contorted surface of the Welsh deposits. Here was the 'collision zone' of the two distinct ice bodies. The discovery was not exactly on the scale of the boundaries between global tectonic plates, but the principles were the same and, quite importantly, so far as Welsh glacial history is concerned this was quite important. Such a discovery may appear to be irrelevant and unimportant to the reader but to two wet scientists on a forlorn shore it was something of a 'Eureka' moment. After such a discovery, it was a relief to retire for a well-earned drink at a nearby hostelry. Henceforth, we were satisfied that this marked the last gasp of Welsh ice that had forced its way westwards into the Irish Sea basin against a gigantic opponent, something of a David and Goliath situation! Subsequently, all the way to Aberdaron, along Llyn's southern coast, every cliff section was found to comprise only of Northern drift stuffed with far-travelled erratics.

It was time to take stock and ask ourselves the question: If St Tudwal's Peninsula was the western limit of the Welsh ice-sheet, where was its southern limit? For centuries local folklore had claimed that there was a lost region of Cantref-y-Gwaelod beneath the waters of Cardigan Bay (see above) and that the sunken walls of its former buildings and field boundaries could be traced for miles westwards along the seabed, as described above. It seems quite clear that in reality these bouldery causeway-like ridges (termed 'sarns'), which uncover at low tide, are nothing more than wave-eroded end-moraines marking the termination of the Welsh ice-sheet. The northernmost, 'Sarn Badrig' (St Patrick's Causeway) can be traced seawards from Mochras (Shell Island) as far west as the longitude of St Tudwal's promontory, thereby fitting nicely into our own spatial scheme of things. The fact that it is the largest moraine reflects the greater volume of the glaciers that once flowed down the Glaslyn and Ffestiniog vales. To the south the combined flow of ice from the Rhinog mountain massif and the Vale of the Mawddach became terminated seawards by 'Sarn-y-Bwch' which runs offshore at Tonfanau Point. I wonder how many rusting unexploded shells, once fired by the coastal artillery, lie amidst its boulders (see above). The combined flow of Welsh ice from the vales of Tal-y-Llyn and from the Dyfi estuary is marked by the third of the sarns, 'Sarn Cynfelin', stretching offshore at Clarach just north of Aberystwyth. It is noteworthy that, northwards from this point, all the coastal sections on Cardigan Bay exhibit only Welsh glacial sediments, indicative of the fact that the ice-centre was in fairly close proximity, thereby giving the glaciers significant momentum as they descended steeply from the high plateau around the modern Arenig mountains. Not until one reaches as far south as Aberporth can Northern drifts be found in the record, implying that Welsh ice had been thick and active enough to fend off the great ice-mass that had once bulldozed its way southwards from Scotland and Cumbria down the floor of the Irish Sea. Other geomorphologists, employed to write different chapters of the same book, have chronicled the limits of this Northern ice as it swept across Pembrokeshire and The Gower before colliding, at the western end of the Vale of Glamorgan, with glaciers from the South Wales ice-cap (centered on the Black Mountains and Brecon Beacons).

Our brief, however, was not concerned with South Wales, no matter how interesting its contribution was to the intricate jigsaw of British Ice Age events. Thus, we had to soldier on mapping the northern coast of the Llyn peninsula. Here, the much rockier coastline offered fewer sections of exceptional interest and we found all of them to be composed entirely of Northern drift. To be true, there occurred a single 'frisson' of stimulation when we reached the sandy beach of Porth Oer, whose curiously shaped sand grains have given rise to its title as the "Whistling Sands". Thousands of visitors have taken immense pleasure from scuffing their feet across the beach surface to evoke a very audible squeaking sound. But it was not this phenomenon that we had come to observe. On the northern headland of the bay my Irish friend, Francis Synge, a member of the Ireland Geological Survey, had discovered what turned out to be one of only two remnants of what is termed a 'raised beach' in North Wales. He had recently told me of this discovery so we hastened to examine this rare example. It has to be explained that during the Ice Age there were several advances and retreats of the ice-sheets owing to periodic climatic ameliorations that were termed 'interglacials' or 'interstadials' according to their relative time-spans. During such episodes the partial melting and retreat of the ice, resulted in rising sea-levels which, if sufficiently prolonged, would create beaches at various elevations. In southern Britain such ancient shorelines have been virtually unaffected by 'post-glacial isostatic uplift' of the earth's crust, resulting from pressure release during the unloading of the enormous weight of the former ice-sheets (most notably in Western Scotland and Northern Ireland).

We soon reached the resort of Nefyn with its sandy beaches, holidaymakers and their happy but inquisitive children, escaping from their parents who sat dreaming in their deckchairs seemingly bemused at our cliff-face exertions in the summer heat. We muttered to ourselves that at least some people had time to take a proper summer holiday at the seaside. We laboured on and trudged northwards to examine what proved to be the most complex coastal section that we had so far recorded; it was a solitary hump of heavily landslipped glacial material at a place known as Dinas Dinlle, where an Iron Age hillfort's ramparts have been partly destroyed by the waves. And how fortuitous that marine erosion has created such a wonderful cross-section at the expense of this large fortification. Like the section on the St Tudwals' peninsula, we found remarkable evidence that this too marked the 'collision zone' of the two ice-sheets. Sporadic lenses of purple-grey calcareous boulder clay at beach level were found to be overlain by several layers of grey-brown Welsh stony clay and outwash sands and gravels. We quickly realised that the multiple layers of Welsh derived deposits were not indicative of multiple ice advances but that they illustrated the finest example of glacial tectonics in North Wales. Enormous overfolds and 'thrust-faults' demonstrated that the site had been over-ridden and churned about by an ice-sheet driving from a north-easterly direction. Such a discovery suggested that the over-riding thrust could only have been from Snowdonian ice fending off the Northern ice mass and crumpling all the existing sediments. Because marine erosion is constantly attacking and undermining the cliff-face there was much evidence of slumping and landslipping, making this the most complex of all our recording sites. Thank goodness that the weather stayed fine because it took hours to record this remarkable site. At last, although we worked systematically all the way to Llandudno we found little that merited any further description in this chapter and we still were faced with the lengthy Anglesey coastline to examine.

The coastal sections that we recorded on Anglesey, although time-consuming, added very little to Greenly's Geological Memoir (*op. cit.*) published fifty years before our visit. We already knew that, before the Ice Age, Anglesey was part of the mainland and that the Menai Straits appeared quite late-on in geological time, carved out by glacial meltwaters coursing along the expanding gap between the withdrawing Northern and local Snowdonian ice-sheets. It was this narrow channel that was ultimately to be flooded by the rising post-glacial sea-level and we had already wondered whether this same post-glacial sea had ever broken through from coast to coast at the narrowest part of the Llyn Peninsula between Nefyn and Pwllheli as the two massive ice-sheets finally parted on the peninsula. No marine deposits have been discovered in this low depression and yet we know that for a short time the post-glacial sea did rise above the present shoreline, at the time when the aforementioned Cantref-y-Gwaelod was inundated because I had discovered evidence of a relict shore-deposit lying only a few feet above high-water-mark, at the western end of Porth Neigwl (Hell's Mouth) as a wave-eroded example of a raised beach formed long after the ice-sheets had disappeared. Expert paleontologists have confirmed that its marine-shell fauna was not derived from the calcareous Northern boulder clay and that the various post-glacial molluscs, incorporated in the shingle, had become cemented together into a concrete-like beach-deposit surviving in a wave-cut notch in the boulder-clay cliff, marking a slightly higher sea-level than that of today. Indeed, it seems very likely that the calcareous waters which created the matrix must have emanated from the existing boulder clay. Similar slightly 'raised beaches' of post-Glacial age are to be found in The Gower in South Wales in positions very close to high-water-mark. One has to remember that such strandline phenomena as these must not be confused with the very much older 'raised beaches' of interglacial age such as that at Porth Oer.

Finally, our mapping and recording 'mission' was over. David and I retired to his home in Bangor to indulge in a much-appreciated afternoon tea during which we discussed our results and drew up the outlines of the diagrams and maps for the relevant book chapter. It would be inappropriate to include all of those diagrams in the present volume, but the lengthy episode, notwithstanding its importance to Welsh Pleistocene chronology, still remains one of the most laborious and fatiguing of all my coastal memories. Nonetheless, we were gratified when our results were eventually accepted by no less a body than the Nature Conservancy Council and were published in full in their Geological Conservation Review (Quaternary of Wales. S. Campbell and D. Q. Bowen, 1989).

Never before or since have I spent so many weeks investigating every nook and cranny of a lengthy coastline, but the latter experience in North Wales proved to be salutary. Never again would I be enticed to spend so much of my time in my beloved coastal environment by regarding my task as being restricted to a singularly exclusive research programme; never again would I visit a coastline with nothing but a notebook and geological hammer in my hand; never again would I treat the shoreline as a laboratory. Henceforth my visits to the shore would prove to be more hedonistic, although I have to admit that I continued to take generations of students to those very special research sites in North Wales (my 'special places') in order to inculcate them into the principles of coastal processes and also of environmental management. In this respect, when I regarded the coast as a sort of 'classroom', it must have felt like a sort of reward for all the painstaking years of research that I had spent in such environments, although I don't remember any sense of personal satisfaction at the time. Perhaps I had managed to inspire some of my graduates because, over the years, several of them proceeded to commence their own research into glacial events in different regions of the British Isles, and some of which I was invited to supervise when they submitted their findings for the award of higher degrees.

Such were the thoughts that whirled around in my head as I drove back from North Wales, vowing that my next coastal visit was going to be a leisurely holiday. These musings were probably due to tiredness, but I finally reasoned that such research was, after all, essential in my chosen career if I was to collect up-to-date material for my lecture notes. Moreover, as I have already explained, in my field of interest it was necessary to use the 'real world' as a type of classroom.

There was another matter, far more essential than all these introspective reflections, and this was my fundamental duty to my family. Our daughter, Fiona, was now ten-years old, and deserved to see the seaside as I had first viewed it, as a magic world of endless wonderment. This was the world that I had recently witnessed, being enjoyed by scores of children of a similar age; they were the children who had cheekily questioned our motives on the beaches at Criccieth and Nefyn, after having scampered inquisitively across the golden sands. Did I really want Fiona to grow up with a blinkered approach? We did, of course, take her on wonderful seaside holidays during which I was determined not to allow her to view the marine environment simply as a 'research workshop', even though I might have given her that impression during her formative years. As I hope to describe in the next few chapters, I wished to demonstrate that our shores are one of our greatest assets and offer bountless opportunities to enrich our sensitivities in a variety of ways. However, most importantly, I hope also to indicate how care should still be taken to ensure that one should never lose ones sense of enquiry. In many ways such questioning and perception of ones surroundings will be found to be extremely rewarding, insofar as it leads to a clearer understanding of the 'spirit of place'. It remains probable, however, that one can develop a liking for a special place without giving much thought to such matters of perception and cognition. But, in my own opinion, it follows that any lack of understanding of and 'feeling' for any environment might lead to a thoughtless degradation of that environment, which in turn could lead, for example, to an increasing amout of litter. It was with these sentiments in mind that I moved on from researching landforms to researching my family history which proved to be a very different undertaking. In order to carry out this quest it was essential to move on southwards and leave behind the well-trodden coast of North Wales in order to visit the glorious but lesser-known shores of South Wales.

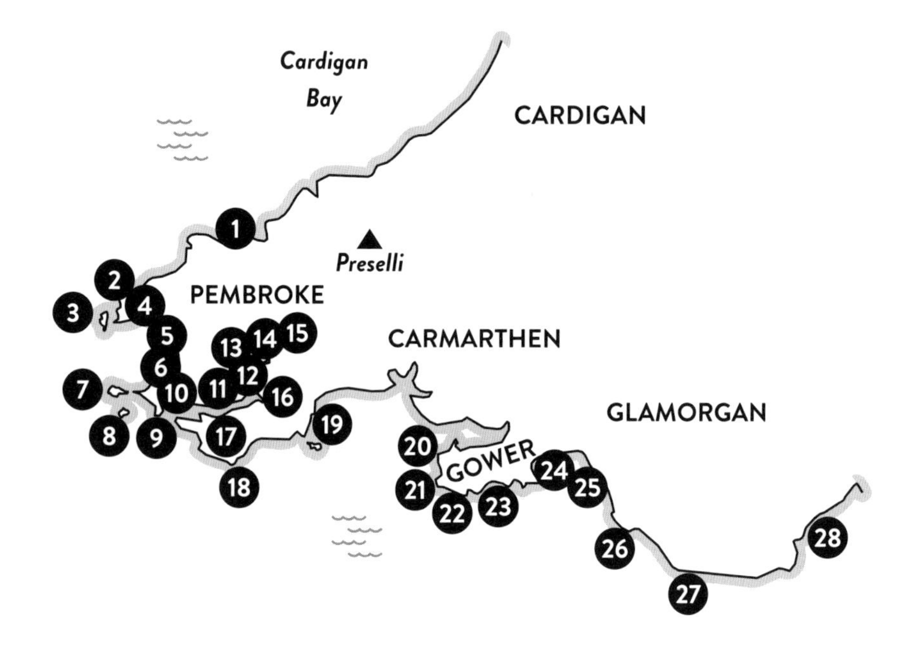

1. Fishguard
2. St David's Head
3. Ramsey Island
4. St David's
5. St Brides Bay
6. Talbenny
7. Skomer Island
8. Stokholm Island
9. St Ann's Head
10. Skerryback
11. Milford
12. East Hook
13. Haverford West
14. Picton Castle
15. Wiston Castle
16. Pembroke
17. Castlemartin
18. St Govan's Head
19. Tenby
20. Whiteford Burrows
21. Worms Head
22. Paviland Cave
23. Three Cliffs
24. Swansea
25. Port Talbot
26. Porthcawl
27. Southerndown
28. Cardiff

4. SOUTH WALES

"Half to forget the wandering and the pain
Half to remember days that have gone by
And dream and dream that I am home again"
(James Elroy Flecker 1884–1915)

Wiston Castle ruins, Pembrokeshire. The ancestral home of the Whittow family for some two centuries (c. 1100 to c. 1300). (From a painting by Leon Olin) – *See plate section for colour version*

Whittow Wharf, Milford Haven, showing modern development (1990's) – *See plate section for colour version*

St Govan's Chapel on the limestone cliffs of South Pembrokeshire

Whittow Wharf looking across to the old port of Hakin, birthplace of my father in 1900. Note the Belgian trawler, the only fishing boat in the harbour and the distant oil refinery (2005)

St David's Cathedral, North Pembrokeshire, where we discovered a family gravestone

Worm's Head from the limestone cliffs of The Gower

Whiteford Burrows, The Gower. The first coastal purchase with 'Neptune' funds (1965)

The midday sun was beating down from a cloudless sky, sharpening the shadows of the gravestones. Below the cliffs a dead calm sea endeavoured to push its tiny wavelets fitfully onto its sandy shore that stretched endlessly away to a hazy skyline of distant hills and promonteries. I was standing on a clifftop in the tiny churchyard of Talbenny looking northwards from this inauspicious hamlet along the expanse of St Brides Bay. Children were whooping as they cavorted at the water's edge of nearby Little Haven; a dog barked incessantly as it chased the seagulls; the white sails of a yacht flapped helplessly in the calm. This idyllic seaside scene epitomises Pembrokeshire, Land of My Fathers. I have come here in an attempt to capture the ambience of my ancestral homeland, prior to writing the family history (The Whittow Family of Pembrokeshire, John B. Whittow, 2016). This was intended to be a sort of mission, partly of enquiry, partly of meditation and largely of hedonistic delight.

Talbenny is regarded as the Whittow family church and as we wandered into its cool interior we were greeted by the parish ladies arranging flowers for a festival. They welcomed us and were delighted when they heard of my intentions for they were well aware of our name in these parts. Nonetheless, they knew of no-one called Whittow still dwelling in the county. The greystone church crouches precariously near the cliff edge on what are normally windswept shores of the Irish Sea. Here, on this windless day we were able to stroll leisurely around the graveyard trying to identify the lichen-encrusted ancestral tombs which we were told lie within the perimeter. It was here, in this 15th century church that my Great, Great, Great Grandfather, George Whittow, married Hannah Dean on the 27th of June 1779. It seems clear that Hannah was an heiress of some potential wealth because, a few years later, she inherited the estate of her father, William Dean, following his death in 1785.

Thus, lucky old George inherited the large farmhouse of Howelston, not far from Talbenny church. Such a fortuitous acquisition, though not on the scale of that of the 13th century estates at Wiston (see below), turned out to be a significant and highly propitious marker in the fortunes of the Whittow family because this George can be regarded as the patriarch of the subsequent generations. It was difficult to believe that in this quiet haven of peace the solitude must have been broken during World War II when scores of miltary aircraft roared down the runways of a large airfield a few hundred yards away in Talbenny. My father told me that long before this airfield had been constructed he brought me as a young child to Broad Haven in order to show me a prominent coastal feature known as the The Sleek Stone. I have no recollection of this visit but, more prosaically, with my present geological knowledge it seems quite clear that this is little more than a 'whaleback' rock formation where an upfolded stratum has been smoothed by the waves.

Looking north-eastwards, across the southern corner of St Brides Bay, I could just discern the tiny settlement of Walton West on a hillside overlooking the sea. This was once the home of Hugh Whittow, father of George, who farmed on this bleak hillside. The Walton West parish records show that he was buried on "May ye 13th 1777" a mere two years before the marriage of his son, as described above. His wife, Hannah, survived him for a further 25 years until she was buried at Talbenny in 1802, aged 88. Thus, my 18th century forbears were already coastal dwellers. This particular area is underlain by rocks of Millstone Grit and Coal Measures age, more akin to Glamorgan than Pembrokeshire. Indeed, coal seams appear in the cliffs at Rooks Bay, just below Walton West village. Such rocks give rise to thin, shaly and relatively infertile grey soils that are best suited to grass farming. One might conjecture, therefore, that Hugh Whittow's farm was less prosperous than those of his relatives who farmed and/or fished farther south on the coast of Pembrokeshire, at such places as Warren (Castlemartin), Angle, Marloes and Dale, all situated on more fertile soils. I was to visit those venues in due course but first I must return to the rugged cliffs of highly contorted rocks and the magnificent sandy beaches of St Brides Bay. Here the family records are very much more reliable than the sketchy ones further south.

This was the type of environment with which I was already familiar because it so closely resembled the coasts of Anglesey and the Llyn Peninsula. But when I stood on those Pembrokeshire cliffs it was not simply a case of déjà vu, there was something more – a frisson of belonging and a very definite 'sense of place'. The small church of Walton West looks almost like a replica of that at Talbenny but Samuel Lewis visited it in the mid-18th century and spoke contemptuously about its attributes: "The church is not entitled to architectural notice (and) the surrounding country is destitute of beauty" (Topographical Dictionary of Wales, S. Lewis, 1842). But in the "Buildings of Wales" Guide (in the Pevsner series) the authors would disagree with this disparaging description because not only does the church date from the 13th and 14th century but it also boasts a fine 'wheel-head cross' dating back to the 10th or 11th centuries. (The Buildings of Wales: Pembrokeshire, T. Lloyd et al. 2004). Even a late-19th century traveller spoke kindly of this ancient church because of its current restoration "...and not before it was needed, for it is on record that in the 'good old times' two boys were kept at work on rainy Sundays, sweeping the water that flowed in at the porch into a pit formed from a disused pew". (Nooks and Corners of Pembrokeshire, H. Timmins, 1895). The church's antiquity, therefore, roughly coincides with the arrival of the Wizo family from the Low Countries (see below), although they were unlikely to have visited these western shores from their Wiston stonghold, being much more likely to have been facing eastwards towards their 'enemies', the dispossessed Welsh. Timmins goes on to say, from his lofty viewpoint at Walton West: "From the brow of the hill we have three churches full in view, in diminishing perspective – Walwyn's Castle, down in the valley; Robeston farther away; and Steynton conspicuous on a distant hill". All of these settlements were associated with the Whittow family.

I needed to visit the first of these venues at Walwyn's Castle for this was where my Great, Great Grandfather, another George Whittow, lived throughout much of the 19th century. He farmed a few miles inland from St Brides Bay at a farm called 'Zyke'. The first thing that struck me was the spelling which is so reminiscent of the Dutch language and must have been a relic of the Flemish connection, even though its current name is 'Syke'. Sometimes I wonder about its derivation, for in North Wales I spent some time studying the Sychnant Pass (see above) and I know that, in English, this means 'dry valley'. Moreover, not far from my Staffordshire birthplace is a streamless valley known as 'The Sytch'. Thus, I wonder if the soils at Zyke Farm were particularly well-drained. While on the subject of placenames it is important to turn to the Dutch scholar, L. Toorians (1990), who wrote at length about Wizo Flandrensis. He tells us that "...the people of south-western Pembrokeshire spoke a language akin to, but not the same as, English because this language, like Low Dutch, and unlike Welsh, is so much like English, the area is called Little England Beyond Wales".

We wandered around the village and were first struck by the style of the church tower. It was tall and slender and had a stair-turret rising to an embattled roof, quite different to the squat bell-towers of Talbenny and Walton West. The high stature of this edifice is embodied in the Whittow Coat-of-Arms and has been explained in the following way: Owing to their coastal locations the Talbenny and Walton West churches had no need of 'viewing platforms' from which watchers could give warnings of any maritime maurauders. Walwyn's Castle, being situated just inland in a wooded valley, would need a high tower if it were to provide a similar alarm.

The quiet bosky hamlet of Walwyn's Castle has several remarkable associations and we soon learned that the 14th century church, with its Norman 'dog-tooth' ornament, was built alongside the ruins of a much older castle mound, hence its name. We listened to the local story that the earlier castle was part of the Norman lordship of the eminent de Brain family whose leader, Guy de Brain, dwelt in Laugharne Castle in neighbouring Carmarthenshire until his death in 1390. This latter castle appears to date from the 12th century which implies, therefore, that the titled de Brains of Carmarthenshire would have been associates of the Whittows, Lords of Daucleddau, since both were fighting for the same cause, to keep the Welsh subdued. But when I enquired about the derivation of the name 'Walwyn' a curious legend was recounted. It claimed that there was once an association with King Arthur and the Knights of the Round Table. I knew, of course, that several locations have similar claims but this tiny Welsh village insists that 'Walwyn' is a corruption of 'Gawin' (Gawayn, Gawayne, or in Welsh Gwalchmai), son of King Lot of Orkney, a Norse dependancy from the 9th to the 14th century. It is noteworthy that, despite the legendary nature of the story, there were certainly Viking settlements in Pembrokeshire during those centuries and that certain of my forbears married into the descendants of Vikings. The roll of rectors in the church goes back to 1311 and I discovered that a century earlier, when Walwyn's Castle was known as Castell Gawain, the land owners decided to excavate the old castle mound. This 13th century 'dig' unearthed the skeleton of a seven-foot giant and this was immediately claimed to be the remains of Gawain. It is impossible to verify such claims but we are told that the Pembrokeshire people seized upon the possible linkage and developed the legend even further by insisting that Gawain ended his days as a hermit in a stone-built cell tucked into a rocky cleft in the cliffs of Pembrokeshire's south coast. This isolated building has long been revered as St Govan's Chapel at St Govan's Head, and for centuries was a well-known place of pilgrimage. A modern guide book suggests that St Govan was in fact a Celtic missionary who dwelt in a pre-Norman cell, although the present structure dates from the 13th or 14th century (Dyfed: A Guide to Ancient and Historic Wales, 1992).

It was essential that Diane and I continued our own coastal pilgrimage by visiting this renowned ancient feature and we made our way southwards via the Bosherston Nature Reserve, with its well-known lily ponds, to the vertical limestone cliffs that give such character to this stretch of the Welsh coast. The weather was blustery but dry as we parked in the deserted cliff-top car park, greeted only by a few seabirds wheeling overhead, buffeted by the wind. Not far away along the cliffs was the much-photographed Huntsman's Leap, a spectacular fissure in the limestone. I once had a large black-and-white photograph of this excellent example of coastal erosion on the wall of my university office, so was excited to have the chance of viewing it at first hand. I had already read Steers' description of this remarkable coastline in which he explained how the detail has been created by marine erosion breaking into the subterranean cavities in the limestone. (Coastal Features of England and Wales, J. A. Steers, 1981) He goes on to say that in the case of

Huntsman's Leap a fault-line has assisted the wave erosion. But I was in for a disappointment because the red flag was flying to indicate that the Castlemartin firing range was now being utilised. Before long we heard the detonations of heavy weaponry which turned out to be from a visiting German Panzer tank regiment! It struck me as quite ironic that, forty years previously, my Neptune volunteers had mapped the coastal fortifications built to withstand such troops. Thus, I had no alternative but to clamber down a seemingly endless flight of weathered steps that led steeply seawards to high-tide level. St Govan's miniscule, spartan and very damp chapel is situated almost at breaking-wave level. I found that it emanated an air of utter desolation and exposure, sufficient to send me rather quickly back up to the cliff-top without experiencing any 'sense of place'. Yet, in the future I was to witness more of these examples of Celtic saint martyrdoms perched on storm-ravaged Atlantic shorelines when I made many sorties to the western coasts of Ireland. It was there, on the exposed ocean cliffs, probably because of the unbridled elemental forces of nature, that my feelings had been overwhelmed by the grandeur of Ireland's majestic western coastline, quite unprotected from the howling gales and from the giant waves that beat incessantly on their iron-bound shores. But I must return to the shores of my own Celtic 'homeland' in order to continue my endeavour to discover my so-called 'roots'.

As we wended our way back northwards I glanced across the tank ranges towards the settlement of Warren (in the Hundred of Castlemartin) where, in the 17th century, a distant ancestor had owned the substantial Warren Farm, important enough to be mentioned in Pevsner's Pembrokeshire Guide (*op. cit.*). At this point one must turn to the monumental work of George Owen (1552–1613), a contemporary of my forbear, John Whitto, a yeoman of Warren Farm. Owen states that: "The chiefest cornland in Pembrokeshire is the Hundred of Castlemartin as that which yieldeth the best and finest grain and most abundance, being a country of itself naturally fit for corn, having lime, sand, weed of the sea and divers other principal helps to better the soil where need is" (The Description of Pembrokeshire, G. Owen, 1603). In later centuries grain crops became less important because we read that the "...short sweet grass of the limestone pastures makes good grazing for the sheep" (The Land of Britain: The Report of the Land Utilisation of Great Britain. No. 32: Pembrokeshire. M. F. Davies, 1939). It seemed a great pity that such first-class farmland had been taken over by the Ministry of Defence during World War II and had not been reinstated for several decades after the war had ended. Nevertheless, because of the soil fertility, it is little wonder that this early bearer of my own first name became a wealthy landowner several centuries earlier than our belated visit.

We left the exposed southern coast and returned to the pretty village of Little Haven, nestling in the sheltered corner of St Brides Bay, midway between Walton West and Howelston Farm, for I wanted to explore the latter in which my Great, Great, Great Grandfather, George Whittow, had lived long enough to become yet another wealthy landowner. On researching the family history (J. B. Whittow, 2016, *op. cit.*) I had discovered that he had been able to purchase a second coastal farm, but this time on the tidal waters of a neighbouring estuary. But before setting off from our hotel at St Brides Castle, to explore this second farm at East Hook on the western arm of the Cleddau River, we joined our friends, David and Su Starkie, at a small bistro in Little Haven for a well-earned evening meal. Here, in darkest Wales, we tasted the finest Beef Stroganov ever, cooked by the Russian mother of the chef; this was one of the most surprising episodes of all our Welsh journeying. Little Haven itself, with its narrow streets and lanes is very reminiscent of a Cornish fishing village and seems destined, like many Cornish examples, to lose its solitude and become a desirable tourist venue. Eventually, I managed to revisit the sheltered spot of East Hook on the brink of a tide-washed creek of the Cleddau Rivers. It was the time of low-water which meant that the grey mudflats dominated the scene. But here, where songbirds flitted amidst the overhanging trees, I finally did experience a feeling of déjà vu, unlike our recent visit to St Govan's Head. In appearance the West Cleddau could easily be mistaken for the Helford River in Cornwall; it might also have been viewed as being similar to the location chosen by Clough Williams-Ellis in order to build his renowned Port Meirion village; or, by a considerable stretch of the imagination, it could be likened to a lesser clone of the Mawddach Estuary without the mountains. The similarities are due entirely to the haunting beauty of a thickly wooded tidal estuary. Apart from Talbenny church and Zyke farm, this quiet backwater was the type of place with which I felt an almost eerie indigenous relationship with the landscape. It is difficult to explain such feelings of 'belonging' but they certainly existed. Some would consider that this environment was not truly coastal and it is true that in the Neptune survey it lay upstream from a major road bridge and was therefore excluded. But ignoring it would be akin to excluding Frenchman's Creek from a Cornish coastal survey, in my opinion.

It seems apparent from my geneological research that at the beginning of the 18th century the Whittow family of Hook House had ascended the social ladder, from yeomanry to gentry, as epitomised in an amusing jingle surviving in the family records:

Formely
Man, to the plough;
Wife, to the cow;
Girl, to the yarn;
Boy to the barn;
And your rent will be netted.
At Present
Man, Tally Ho;
Miss, piano;
Wife, silk and satin;
Boy, Greek and Latin;
And you'll all be gazetted.

Indeed, in the 1812 County Election Returns George Whittow had styled himself as "A Gentleman". Margaret Davies in her 1939 land Use Report (*op. cit.*) states that the part of the Cleddau River area, where he now lived, had "…more large estates than in any other part of the county and considerable areas of woodland are found here, planted by the large landowners [1800–1840] for commercial as well as for decorative purposes". George would definitely have counted himself as a large landowner and would almost certainly have been aquainted with the owners of his neighbouring estates, although there is no evidence that he ever entertained the family of Sir Richard Philips (First Lord Milford) from nearby Picton Castle. Such a possibility is of interest only because of the fact that Whittow ancestral blood had passed into the very earliest Wogan lineage, builders of the first Picton Castle in 1300, shortly after the Wizo family heiress, Gwenllian, had married Gwrgan ap Bleddyn, a Welsh princeling from Brecon. It was their son, not liking his name (in Welsh meaning 'scowl'), who changed it to Wogan. Thus, I consider it important to put on record that the universal belief that the Wogans initially heralded from Ireland appears to be a falsehood.

It became imperative to visit the imposing Picton Castle which stands amidst groves of rhododendrons and azaleas that cover the demesne as it slopes gently down to the Cleddau estuary. The entrance towers remind one of the castles at Conwy and Harlech and I experienced a feeling of familiarity as we toured its lavish interior because, unlike the gaunt ruins of these castles in North Wales and that at Wiston (see below), Picton is the home of the renowned Philips family. After a freelance tour we finished in the deep vaults, dating back to Norman times, and there, much to my delight, the family tree was displayed on the wall. At its very beginning the Whittow (Wizo) ancestry was acknowledged among the castle's antecedents. Sic transit Gloria mundi. From this somewhat obscure starting-point I was now more determined than ever to trace the family's former history in this beautiful peninsular county.

In an earlier chapter I had stated that my own family came from Flanders and it now remains for me to give a brief explanation of why and how the Whittows came to settle in Pembrokeshire after they had fled from the Low Countries. The family's original Flemish name was Wizo Flandrensis and there are records to show that one of our very early ancestors was a courtier at the palace of the Holy Roman Emperor, Charlemagne. When Wizo brought his family to Wales in 1110, he was made Lord of Daucleddau by Henry I, on condition that he built a castle at Wiston (Wizo's ton) as part of the Norman frontier in South-West Wales, known as the "Landsker". This fortified boundary was intended to protect the Norman settlers, in their so-called "Englishry", from the native Welsh, who had every right to be there. For four generations the family resisted

Welsh attacks, one of which razed their castle to the ground. Documents exist to show that, under a mandate from the monarch to the Earl of Pembroke, the latter was informed that he was required to help rebuild the edifice that we see today perched on its lonely inland hill (or motte). Moreover, a modern historian tells us that Wiston Castle became more fought over than any other medieval stronghold in Pembrokeshire. (The Towns of Medieval Wales, I. Soulsby, 1982). We also learn from a different writer that Wiston's inland location was a strategic disadvantage, because access to the sea would have been essential to survive in a hostile countryside. (Political Development: Wales. G. Thomas in E. Bowen, Ed. 1957). It is certainly true that Pembroke Castle is built on a tidal creek of Milford Haven and that all the Edwardian castles in North Wales stand on tidal waters, as described in a previous chapter. Wiston's vulnerability eventually proved to be one of the reasons for the downfall of the castle, and for the killing of many male heirs of the Whittow family, after it was sacked by Llywellyn the Great in 1220. Samuel Lewis (*op. cit.*) reminds us that the castle "…never recovered its former strength, which became unnecessary, for the Welsh, after the marriage of their countryman, Gwrgan (Wogan), with the daughter (Gwenllian) of Sir Philip Fitzwizo, appears to have left the [Welsh] chieftain and his family in the undisturbed possession of it, as part of their estates". So, this bloody episode marked the ignominious end of the family title to the Lordship of Daucleddau and of the family ownership of any major landholdings in Pembrokeshire until the advent of 'Gentleman' George, a few centuries later.

When he stood on the banks of the Western Cleddau in the late-18th century, 'Gentleman' George would have found a very different scene to that at Howelston, which he still owned. No longer were his fields threaded with stone walls to protect livestock and crops from the insidous winds off the Irish Sea, for East Hook lies amidst mature oakwoods where red squirrels can still be seen. A modern writer, William Condry, advises the traveller to visit this "...tranquil world of tidal creeks...with here and there abandoned limestone quarries whose stone was taken seawards...Since then nature has moved in and created what to naturalists is a hugely enjoyable wilderness of scrub, marsh, rock and sinuous waterways" (The Natural History of Wales, W. Condry, 1981). Perhaps George Whittow may have been less interested in the natural history than in the capability of his farmland to support a succesful husbandry, comparable with that at his other farm at Howelston. But the desmesne of Hook House sits astride the Coal Measures whose poorer soils are less fertile and less capable of producing the "heaviness of the crops" found at Howelston. It is of interest, in the context of the family history, that the name 'Hook' could well be an anglisisation of the Dutch word 'Hoek', signifying a 'sharp corner' or 'bend'. If so, like 'Zyke' this is yet another example of a Flemish placename, for Hook House sits on a sharp bend of the Western Cleddau estuary.

As a country gentleman George would have taken the family to attend the nearest place of worship, which was the 14th century church of St Jerome, in the fishing village of Llangwm, a mile or so lower down the estuary. As we drove along the narrow winding roads I could imagine the family pony and trap wheeling down those leafy lanes every Sunday, the same lanes that had inspired the great modern artist, Graham Sutherland, to produce some of his best-known paintings. In his own words he claimed that "All in all I look on the hidden places where I work as a marvellous playground – my estuaries as great 'saons' where I am alone with the 'personages' I find". His collections were once on display at Picton Castle, just across the water from Hook, but alas no longer. Llangwm village proved to be somewhat special in my Pembrokeshire coastal quest, not so much for its modern face but for its former links with my Flemish forbears, because no other place in the county is more redolent of a surviving Flemish culture. Margaret Davies (*op. cit.*) noted that as late as the 1930's "The traditional dress, speech, and social outlook of the people are accepted as indicating direct descent from the Flemish immigrants from the 13th century...Their speech includes a considerable number of obsolete words and expressions not in general use in other parts of Pembrokeshire or elsewhere". The renowned naturalist, Robert Lockley, is even more explicit for he tells us "That the Llangwm women were famous for their toughness. Right into the present (20th) century they would stone strangers from [outside] their village. Llangwm women used to walk regularly, with heavy baskets of fish, to Tenby, Pembroke and other towns, being ferried across the Haven [Milford] by their husbands or themselves, even the women were capable in a boat, and were said to dominate their men" (Pembrokeshire, R. M. Lockley, 1957). These women were the original 'fishwives' no doubt. But, as a direct descendant of the first Fleming settlers, perhaps George would not have been regarded as a stranger. Although more distant relatives of the Whittow family are known to have been fisherfolk at the villages of Angle and Marloes, which face the open seas, it is the people of Llangwm, in its sheltered estuary, who are the real forerunners of those Whittows who moved into large-scale commercial fishing in the late-19th century, as will be described below.

In addition to being a prosperous farmer my Great, Great Grandfather, George, appears to have been an astute businessman because the Pembrokeshire Record Office informs us that as early as 1837 he successsfully applied for a grant to build a railway line from the local Hook collieries on his doorstep. The Pembrokeshire coalfield is very little known but its heavily faulted and folded strata run in a narrow belt from Saundersfoot, near Tenby, to the coast of St Brides Bay near Broad Haven. We know that George had bought one of the coal-mines at Hook and later a second colliery right on the shore of St Brides Bay. It was there that he installed his fifth son, William (brother of the Zyke farmer) as a director in the Limited Company of Bowen & Whittow who mined the coastal outcrop at Nolton Haven. The records show that he used steam-powered machinery, employed forty-one males and four females, in addition to thirty horses that hauled the trucks down the tramways to the beach. This was a great improvement on the workings of earlier centuries for George Owen (*op. cit.*) records that in the early 17th century "...the people carried the coal on their backs along stairs that they called landways, whereas they now sink pits...and with a windlass turned by four men they draw up the coal, a barrel-full once by a rope". One may wonder how this tiny outcrop could possibly compete with the mighty coalfields elsewhere in Wales and England. The only reason was because its very high-grade anthracite (96% carbon content) was in great demand for export to England, Ireland and even mainland Europe. I discovered that later in the 19th century the mines became too expensive to maintain, partly because they were liable to flooding, as several of them ran beneath the sea, but also because the heavily contorted coal seams proved to be highly labour-intensive to work. These crumpled rocks, formed by the convulsions of the Earth's crust some 300 million years ago, can be seen in most of the Pembrokeshire sea cliffs. Images of their geological structures were superbly captured by the famous modern artist, John Piper, who had a cliff-top cottage in North Pembrokeshire. I am the proud possessor of his "Bullslaughter Bay" which depicts the zig-zag formations and the marine-eroded caves of his neighbouring shoreline.

Today, we found almost no visual record of such unusual industrial activity on this unspoilt coast, merely a few holidaymakers enjoying the far-reaching sands and watching the windsurfers, sailors and swimmers. It is difficult to envisage the noise and clutter that must once have overwhelmed this part of the beautiful St Bride's Bay. One has to remember, however, that two centuries ago it was cheaper to fill the coal boats drawn up on Nolton beach than it was to transfer to barges on the sinuous inland reaches of the Cleddau estuary. Prior to the building of George's railway line, the coal from the Hook field had to be taken labouriously by horse and cart to the Cleddau quays. Here the relatively small amounts would have been loaded onto barges which were then worked down to Llangwm Pool for transferring to sea-going vessels which sailed with the tide down into the lengthy expanse of Milford Haven and thence to the open ocean. It is to the Haven that I must turn for this is the venue at which I had my first view of the sea at the age of five (See chapter 1).

For some unknown reasons, at various times in the latter half of the 19th century the farms at Howelston, Hook and Zyke were abandoned and three of the Whittow brothers, sons of 'Gentleman' George, went south to set up a fishery business in the town of Milford Haven. By then the family history had advanced to the time when my paternal grandmother (who lived to be over ninety) was able to recount anecdotes to me, thus giving me a clearer insight of those fateful years. It was from her that I learnt how, after eight hundred years of farming, my particular branch of the Whittow family had left their inland farms to become coastal dwellers.

Moreover, it was fortuitous that, during the preceding decades before my current 'mission', I had renewed contact with my cousin, Helen, and her husband, Bill Davies, who lived in a house overlooking the Haven. Henceforward, we often discussed the possible reasons for the family retreat from farming and had concluded that it was largely due to the agricultural depression of the late-19th century. In Southern Britain, from the mid-1880's to the early-1900's there was a period known as the 'Long Drought' and this had devastated farming in general and exacerbated the drift from the countryside to the cities. As homegrown grain became scarce it was found to be much cheaper to import food, causing many British farmers to give up farming altogether. I do know, with some certainty, that by that time "Gentleman" George had retired, with his second wife, to live comfortably in Haverford West.

Towards the end of the 19th century, as they moved down to the coast at Milford Haven, the three brothers, Thomas, another George (my Grandfather) and their younger brother, William, would have found that the town of Milford had changed somewhat since Samuel Lewis's description half a century before: "The surrounding scenery abounds with variety and beauty and in some places is highly picturesque" (Topographic Dictionary of Wales. S. Lewis, 1842). But as the deepwater estuary had become established as a major British fishing-port and new docks had been added to the old quays, so the town had begun to expand. My grandfather had set up home in a small villa in Hill Street which climbs steeply up the slope from the waterfront of the adjacent village of Hakin, a much older fishing port than Milford itself. In the hope that I could discover his home and make some sort of 'connection' we drove up Hill Street. But all was in vain because the house had been demolished many years previously. My Grandfather would have discovered that there the workforce had long been employed not just in fishing but also in boat-building, ship-repairing and sail-making and also in the export of coal and lime. I discovered an 1835 map which shows that for a short period of time Hakin was the starting point of the Mail Coach road to London when it acted as the staging-post for the packet-service from the Irish ports of Waterford and Wexford. Much has changed since those 'halcyon' days but when we visited its ancient dockside, on my 'pilgrimage', we could almost envisage the once bustling scene of a Victorian dockside, especially after reading the following doggerel of an 18th century poem, "The Fishing Lass of Hakin" by Lewis Morris (1701–1765), which epitomised the former life-style of earlier times.

"In Milford on your larboard hand
We found a town called Hakin
The snuggest place in all the land
For lads inclined to raking:
There all the girls were cleanly dressed
As witty as they are pretty
But one exceeded all the rest
And this was charming Betty".

Whether my Grandfather was aware of this verse when he took his young bride, Elizabeth (Betty) to live in Hill Street we will never know but there would have been little chance of 'raking' for there was work to be done and a fishing business to set up. This was achieved soon after Brunel's giant ship, "The Great Eastern", had departed after having been berthed on Hakin dockside for eight years undergoing repairs. At this time local newspapers proclaimed that

"The natural advantages of Milford Haven are very great and with the improvement in docks, railway and pier, it will inevitably become a formidable rival to Liverpool". This was 'boom time' and no wonder that the two younger brothers lost no time in setting up their joint enterprise on Milford's main wharf and started to purchase trawlers. At the turn of the century the number of fishing vessels using Milford docks was listed as follows: 66 trawlers, 150 smacks and 200 drifters. It is true that the bulk of these came from Brixham but all made use of the bonanza offered by the fishing grounds off the southern coasts of Wales and Ireland. I can still recall my childhood feelings in the 1930's when I first witnessed the frenzied activity on what is now officially designated as "Whittow Wharf".

Our final lingering sojourn on Whittow Wharf was with cousin Helen and her husband Bill who, by then, was in a wheel-chair, a year or so before his death. We all surveyed the modern scene of a yacht marina backed by flats, boutiques and restaurants. The sun glinted off the glistening paintwork of the bobbing hulls as the sea breeze fluttered their pennants and set their rigging twanging. These were now the 'second homes' of wealthy Londoners, not far from the end of the M4 motorway. Virtually all the signs of Milford's former commercial bustle had vanished save for a lonely Belgian trawler moored on Hakin quay. Such a visit of a fishing vessel from the Low Countries prompted Helen to appraise us of the time during the early days of World War I, when William Whittow (her Grandfather), as Mayor of Milford, was called upon to accommodate the Belgian Royal Family in his own home. My eyes tracked wistfully across the harbour. The dockside cranes, the harbour railway, the warehouses and the noxious 'smokehouses' were all a distant memory, as were the exhilarating boat trips that I had once enjoyed on Bill's motor cruiser, up the winding arms of the

Cleddau and way down the Haven to the open sea. There lay the fabled islands of Skokholm and Skomer made famous by Ronald Lockley, a former friend of Bill Davies. On talking about this well-known author and naturalist, I realised that we would have had so much in common had we had the good fortune to meet. Quite clearly, we both had a great love for all things coastal and especially the attraction of islands. Once more, a change in the weather precluded our own visit to Skomer but we just had time to visit one of my former students, Anna Sutcliffe, who now lived in a pretty cottage near the mouth of the Haven. Over a pleasant afternoon tea this sun-tanned young lady regaled us with stories about her sojourn as Warden on the latter island. Most memorable was her account of her young son at his mainland infants' school. It appears that every morning his father took him across the Sound to Marloes jetty and one day a horse swam past their boat, battling to avert being swept out to sea in the tide race. On recounting this to his teacher and classmates his veracity was questioned and a letter sent to his parents! Another of Anna's stories served to illustrate the changes that had taken place on Pembrokeshire's remarkable shores. It appears that after the bliss of island living she had been employed by one of the major oil companies to climb into the capacious dome of one of their vast silver-coloured tanks on the shores of the Haven in order to capture any birds that had inadvertently flown into the tank's interior. I was extremely impressed by the fortitude of this well-known ornithologist. Perhaps her former student field-classes on the coast had led her into this very special vocation but I lacked the temerity to enquire.

Before we left the Haven for the last time and drove to North Pembrokeshire to complete my 'geneological crusade', it became imperative to traverse part of the Pembrokeshire Coastal Path, once trodden not only by my forbears but also by my student surveyors during the Neptune survey some forty years previously. We walked out to the promontory of St Ann's Head, at the Haven's entrance, in order to view the entire expanse of this magnificent deepwater estuary that was capable of housing the entire British fleet during World War I and which Nelson described as the second-best anchorage in all the world (next to Trincomalee in Sri Lanka). Nearby, to our left we could see the inlet of Sandy Haven where Skerryback Farm lay cradled in a sheltered and wooded cove, not far from the landing-place of the Earl of Richmond in 1485, en route to the Battle of Bosworth Field where he soundly defeated King Richard III and installed himself on the throne as Henry VII. We were told this story by a distant Whittow relative who currently lives at Skerryback, long after one of my former relatives had farmed there. We used this delightful house as a base from which to explore the surrounding countryside and I shall never forget the warm hospitality and the enjoyment of seeing the Jack Russell puppies cavorting in the waterside garden. But looking further eastwards into this lengthy expanse of sea-water it was difficult not to perceive how the serene vista became increasingly disfigured by industry. What had once offered anchorage to the British Navy is now thronged with foreign oil and liquid-gas tankers wending their way to the assortment of jetties and terminals of the omnipresent refineries.

Helen and Bill's house now looks across these monstrous intrusions which dwarf the yacht club where Bill had once been Commodore and from where Helen, a very strong swimmer, used to swim right across the Haven every day. Regrettably, even as I write, I received news that dear Helen passed away in November 2017, thereby terminating the last but one of those Whittows still living in Pembrokeshire. I had known her since 1935 and

I owed almost everything to the fund of knowledge that she and Bill were so pleased to share with me. I can never forget standing with them amidst the ruined shell of Wiston Castle and trying to imagine the sort of landscape that Wizo Flandrensis must once have seen. At my advanced age it is unlikely that I shall ever return to those inspirational and nostalgic shores that are so steeped in our family history.

Diane and I tarried awhile on St Ann's jutting promontory, watching the Irish Ferry glide westwards into the deserted waters of the restless ocean. We noticed how, apart from the noise of the waves from the vessel's wake breaking on the seashore, the scene became eerily quiet once the beat of the ship's engines had died away. To seawards all was solitude, but landwards the skyline of this drowned river valley was buzzing with activity. A century ago all of these waters, both offshore and inshore, would have been bustling with a different type of activity. They would have been alive with fishing boats of every size chugging their way through the Haven's narrow entrance, hauling their precious cargoes of herrings to be kippered on Whittow Wharf. Below the cliffs the seabirds skimmed the wave-tops and set us thinking about how their ancestors would have flocked behind the trawlers as they wended their way to the quays. However, similar flocks had been decimated in 1996 when, had we stood here then, we would have witnessed a scene of utter desolation after the 72,000-ton Sea Empress oil tanker had run aground below this very spot. This cliff-edge would have been the sorrowful grandstand from which to view the slow demise of the birdlife on the polluted shores of this beautiful coastline. Scores of tiny boats would have fought to bring the living but oil-stained survivors onto the surrounding beaches which themselves remained unfit for bathers for months to come. Overall, such an episode came as a stark reminder of the frailty of the British coastline under the increasing impact of both people and technology and how the work of such conservation bodies as the National Trust will still have major roles to play in the future. It is heartening to read in recent literature that the seabird populations in Pembrokeshire are now increasing in number, a process explained by the decline in the number of oil-spills, probably resulting from the fewer oil tankers entering Milford Haven.

With this sad memory lingering in our minds we reluctantly turned away from the true Whittow heartland and set off northwards in an attempt to re-capture any vestiges of any former Whittow presences in North Pembrokeshire. There, I was hoping to discover whether I had any vestigial feelings or relationships with its coastal landscape but I also wished to re-visit places with which I had some previous knowledge. We found a pleasant hotel high on the flanks of Pembrokeshire's 'mountains' (the Preselli Hills, a mere 1,760 feet) from which we could gaze across the northern coastlands around St David's Peninsula. This is the so-called "Welshry", to the north of the Landsker, where the Welsh language is commonly spoken and the landscape is much more rugged than the region we had just left behind. When writing my book on 'Geology and Scenery in Britain' I had noted that North Pembrokeshire was underlain by slaty shales, interspersed with tough igneous rocks, quite unlike the more friable limestones and sandstones further south in the "Englishry". Thus, in the main, the northern rocks have broken down into thin, acid and stony soils that could only sustain little more than a permanent grass/sheep-farming economy except in a few coastal areas where the former Northern ice-sheets had dumped a calcareous boulder clay along the western fringes. Thus, lt would be difficult to find very many examples of a terrain and land use comparable to that of the very productive farmlands of Zyke and Hook which brought wealth into the family coffers. This northern coastland, however, more than compensates for any farming deficiences because its shores exhibit one of the finest geological exposures in coastal Britain.

Hardly a week passes without a party of geologists or physical geographers being seen scrambling along its wonderful rocky coastline. Some of Britain's most ancient rocks occur in North Pembrokeshire, with the oldest being some 1000 million years old. The latter are termed Pre-Cambrian and are devoid of fossils. In the sea-cliffs near to St David's Head, the large varieties of so-called 'igneous' rock exposures have been eroded by the waves into a spectacular array of fissures, caves, stacks and rugged cliff-faces. Igneous rocks such as these were formed from the crystallisation and solidification of both surface lava flows and subterranean molten material. What makes the St David's shoreline so interesting is that these types of rocks are usually very resistant and yet here they can be seen to have been highly folded and rent by many faults and so-called 'shatter belts', that have allowed the rocks to become more easily eroded. To seek an explanation for such complexity one must understand something of the tectonic history of the region. It was in fact a 'collision zone' where two tectonic continents collided some 300 million years ago thereby crumpling, shearing and crushing the strata. Moreover, under the colossal heat and pressure generated by this relentless impact certain rocks had changed their entire character, sometimes being completely altered by a process termed metamorphosis, hence the term 'metamorphic' rocks. Perhaps the best known of this type is the thinly cleaved rock termed slate, whilst limestone can itself be changed into marble.

I have, perforce, included this short excursion into the realms of geology because, in order to fully understand the ways in which all coastal landforms, and even their resulting soils, have been fashioned, then such knowledge of basic geological and physiographic processes is essential. To take just a few examples: How would we know that St David's Cathedral had been built from the greenish-purple fine-grained sandstones quarried from the nearby coast at Caerbwdi? Why the quarries on the peninsula's northern coast had been chosen as the source of the slates which roof the Houses of Parliament? Why, in contrast to the hedge-lined fields of South Pembrokeshire, the fields in the north are walled with thick slabs of shale and their cottages often roofed with thinner 'flagstones' instead of slates? And, finally, how would we have been able to discover that the so-called 'blue stones', that helped to build the inner circle of iconic Stonehenge, are in fact igneous rocks from the Preselli Hills?

As we drove northwards, we noticed how the scenery changed to one where isolated tor-like crags rose abruptly for several hundred feet above the coastal plateau, itself at an almost constant elevation of some 180–200 feet. From a distance they looked like islands and, indeed, that is what they once were during pre-Glacial times. Memories flooded back of those many tedious months that I had spent mapping similar features in the Llyn Peninsula which, like those in Pembrokeshire, were created by the same eroding waves during the oscillating sea-levels of earlier millennia. In almost every case these 'islands' mark the locations of the more resistant outcrops of igneous rocks. We were now entering that part of Pembrokeshire which forms the northern arm of St Brides Bay, around St David's, which a famous modern artist has described how the countryside "...possess a bud-like intricacy of form and contains streams often of indescribable beauty". This heartfelt description by Graham Sutherland is contained in a book by Richard Humphreys entitled: "The British Landscape Through the Eyes of the Great Artists" (1989). Humphreys believes that

St Brides Bay held Graham Sutherland in thrall. Although many of this artist's works were, indeed, inspired by North Pembrokeshire, his most celebrated painting, "Entrance to a Lane" (1939) was based on a typical, almost enclosed and embowered, track a few yards inland from the coast at Sandy Haven, right next to the aforementioned farm at Skerryback, once the home of a Whittow ancestor, as described above.

The northern end of St Brides Bay is renowned for Newgale Sands where miles of golden beaches become exposed at low tide. It is the only place on the Bay where a main road reaches the shore and where its accessiblity attracts a large number of day-trippers from the towns of Haverford West and Milford Haven. As a teenager I was once one of those visitors, together with Helen and her parents, and I noticed that the foreshore is actually dominated by a lengthy shingle ridge, almost like a miniature Chesil Beach. My cousin, Hugh Whittow, tells me that one of his great delights is to leave the busy streets of London, where he is the Editor of The Express newspaper, and find solace by walking his dogs into the teeth of a westerly gale on the eponymous deserted Newgale shore. He finds it something of a catharsis no doubt. Newgale is virtually a frontier village, though no signs will indicate it. We were about to enter "Dewisland", or St David's Land, the geology and landscapes of which I have already described. An observant traveller will note that from here northwards the coastal placenames change from English into Welsh as one crosses from the "Englishry" into the "Welshry". The artificial but important line of the "Landsker" reaches the sea at this point and, by and large, from this point onwards we found that, centuries ago, Norman control in Pembrokeshire had become subordinate to Welsh governance at quite an early stage in the history of the Principality.

To the east we could see Roch Castle, perched on its isolated crag of Pre-Cambrian volcanic rocks, and I knew that this was the westernmost of the Norman fortresses, some ten miles distant from Wiston Castle itself. It seemed highly unlikely, therefore, that I would find any records of Whittow settlements in Dewisland, but we would continue to follow the coast to St David's where we were surprised to make a startling discovery. But first we had to descend steeply into the deep and narrow gorge in which the ancient port of Solva crouches. Its narrow lanes and sinuous harbour entrance remind one of Boscastle in Cornwall, but the coal- and lime-carrying coasters have long since departed to be replaced by the yachts of seasonal visitors whose requirements have engendered the appearance of bistros and smart little shops.

For the next dozen miles, as far as St David's Head, the crenellated coastline reflects the differential marine erosion resulting from the juxtaposition of rocks of varying degrees of resistance, as explained above. Both Pre-Cambrian and Cambrian slates, flagstones, sandstones and a variety of igneous rocks exhibit a dazzling array of both colours and of coastal cliffs, caves and pinnacles which can only be fully appreciated from a boat. It is true that the same rocks which produce such wonderful scenery have also been quarried for their building stones, although such artificial breaks in the cliff-girt shoreline have given opportunities for the campers and caravanners, who occupy a host of local sites, to gain access to the sea. Additionally, the National Trust has opened public access to other lengthy stretches of this spectacular shoreline and, of course, everyone is free to traverse the Pembrokeshire Coast Path. The main road keeps well back from the the coast and our intention was to follow it through the 'City' of St David's and into the web of lanes that finger out to the western headlands which flank the beautiful expanse of Whitesands Bay (Porth Mawr), one of Wales's best surfing beaches. The end of our road was at Porthstinian, named from the ruins of St Justinian's Chapel. But it was not this ruin or its Holy Well that I had come to see, nor even the medieval embarkation-point for Ireland. I had come all this way to cross the Sound to Ramsey Island, for I had recently discovered that thereon lies another connection with the Whittow family.

At first sight the two-mile long Ramsey Island simply replicates the mainland scenery, where a prominent hill (646 feet) rises abrubtly from the 180-foot plateau. But this cliff-girt isle is cut off by a channel whose fearsome tide-race swirls at six knots through the partly obscured rocks known as the Bitches and Whelps. Soon after our arrival the weather had turned for the worse and as we stood on the mainland shore it was obvious that there would be no boat trips daring to beat out into the rising wind and threatening showers. I seem doomed to be frustrated in my attempts to reach these alluring Pembrokeshire islands. It was salutary, however, to see the Pembrokeshire coast in this mood for it made me realise that for many winter months, and even in the summer, this type of weather was the norm, when the few islanders might be cut off from their supplies for days on end. It was fatuous to think that the sun always shone in western Wales; this was simply the image carried away by many holiday-makers, more in hope than expectation. Surely, I should have learnt my lesson on the windswept shores of North Wales. In our disappointment I had to rely simply on what I had already learnt about Ramsey. That it is notorious for its vast numbers of rabbits (about 70,000) that were introduced by the Normans, but it is also known for its large numbers of grey seals, its choughs and for its dozen breeding pairs of lapwings (part of the Whittow Coat-of-Arms) that have, regrettably, almost disappeared on the mainland. Best of all, perhaps, from an ornithologist's viewpoint was to read of the 1930's sighting, by Ronald Lockley, of the only golden eagle in England and Wales. However, in order to envisage the misty scene that now unfolded before us on this solitary visit, one must turn to the knowledgeable words of the noted local naturalist, Mary Gillham, in her 2004 book "Memories of Welsh Islands" she described how, on her own successful visit to Ramsey, seabirds skimmed above the white water of the Bitches and Whelps tide-race; flocks of gulls, visiting gannets from Grassholm and a small bevy of kittiwakes. Today, I find it disheartening to learn that in Wales the latter species has declined by 35% in thirty years. She continues to paint this vivid picture of Ramsey, in which "...the humpy prairies of thrift in various shades of pink that spread across clifftops flecked with the blue of spring squill and white sea campion". The scene that she portrays, however, must have been similar to the one enjoyed by one of my ancestors when he went to live there in the early-19th century.

My namesake, John Whittow, born in 1795, was the fifth son of 'Gentleman' George of Howelston and Hook. He was, therefore, the Great Grandfather of John Martin Summers, the Cambridge graduate whose initials had been mysteriously added to my own surname by Tom Creighton, my Reading University Warden, whom I regard as one of my mentors (See chapter 3). When John Whittow and Frances went to farm on Ramsey in around 1835, Bishop Warren of St David's had recently completed a survey of the island (between 1779 and 1783). It stated that: "...a considerable part of the rent arises from rabbits, the land being in general of a loose and sandy nature. There are also some pasture and arable lands". However, the 1840 'Cambrian Travellers Guide' reported that "Rats have nearly overpowered the rabbits which were once very numerous". Furthermore, records show that the colonies of puffins and shearwaters had been decimated at the same time. It is good to learn that by 2001 a concerted effort by the current owners, the RSPB, had cleared Ramsey of its rats, in order to let its ground-burrowing birds return. Despite these setbacks, it appears that farming on the island has always been quite rewarding for we heard that good profits were made until the last farmer departed in 1986. Regrettably, John Whittow's sojourn on this attractive island did not last long for, in 1839, at the age of 44, he was drowned in the treacherous tide-race of Ramsey Sound. My Grandmother recounted how he was a very strong swimmer and that he regularly swam across the half-mile width of the channel. I should have ascertained whether I was named after this ill-fated forbear, although I have never been a strong swimmer, unlike my cousin Helen at Milford Haven. Thus, it is highly unlikely that my demise will eventually result from such an activity; much more likely it could have been from rock-climbing. But at my advanced age such an activity remains merely a forlorn memory.

Our 'pilgrimage' was nearly over and we had only a few more places to visit before we said goodbye to this delectable coastline. I had long wanted to commission an oil painting of Wiston Castle and who better to ask than a well-known local artist, Leon Olin, who had illustrated many books on Pembrokeshire architecture. I had been particularly impressed by his ability to capture the very essence of ancient buildings in his meticulous technique, so I was determined to seek him out in his North Pembrokeshire home. There, at Fron Haul, a picturesque white cottage set back from the coast beneath the 600-foot crag of Carn Gelli, we were greeted by Leon and his charming wife, Sylvia, also a noted artist. By now the weather had relented and we were delighted by the extensive views over the sunlit landscape as we sat drinking tea. This venue immediately captured my 'spirit of place' and sense of solitude – a far cry from the dismal weather of Ramsey Sound and its gloomy memories. The Olin's warm hospitality cast my mind back some sixty years to the time when I was befriended by a similar artist host on the slopes of Conwy Mountain at the very beginning of my adult love affair with Wales.

If the softer ambience of the leafy, burrowing lanes of South Pembrokeshire belonged to Graham Sutherland, then this current view that I so admired, with its stern, bouldery fields and stone-walled tracks, was undoubtedly John Piper country. It was here that Piper revelled in the tortured shapes of contorted coastal rocks, wind-blown trees and isolated buildings to produce some of his finest paintings, from his cliff-side cottage near Strumble Head, where he had holidayed since 1961. I am indebted to Richard Ingrams, joint author with John Piper of the book "Piper's Places" (1983), for his description of this particular inspirational 'place': "It is a tiny single-storey building, made of stone, white-washed with a pinkish tinge, and roofed with slurry, a mixture of slate and cement. Inside, the cottage is primitive but comfortable. There is only one real room which acts as a sitting- and dining-room and the right half is roofed over with a platform, reached by a step-ladder, on which the Pipers sleep…There is no electricity and no telephone. As dusk falls, Piper busies himself with trimming and lighting the Calor gas and Tilly lamps". He goes on to say: "A tour with Piper does not involve the indiscriminate visiting of every place of interest in the area but rather the selection of one or two special places which seem to sum up what a particular part of the country is all about". Such a philosophy mirrored my own intentions when I set out to write this book "The Edge of the Land". If only I could replicate the stature of Piper's own achievements! It stands to reason that I can never emulate this great man. The best that I have been able to achieve is to purchase some of his paintings, including five of his Welsh landscapes.

Our final stop was at St David's Cathedral, sited in an inland hollow, ostensibly to safeguard it from any passing maritime marauders. To me this hoary old building was yet another place that engendered a 'genius loci'. This was particularly so because, on the explicit instructions of my paternal Grandmother, I had been told that: "You must visit it to verify the Whittow connections, since it is reputed to have a family gravestone within the body of the cathedral itself". Not even my father had been able to make this discovery so it was incumbent upon myself to look for such an important linkage. A search led to us finding a well-worn gravestone that had survived the passage of countless thousands of passing feet, set in the floor of the apse behind the High Altar. It is impossible to determine if this dark green stone had been removed from the graveyard and taken into the interior, but the name WHITTO is clearly engraved on the polished surface. Regrettably, the dates have been worn away so we remain uncertain of its age. My own research has shown, however, that Wizo's eldest son, Walter, had married the daughter of David Fitzgerald, Bishop of St David's, in the late 12th century. I had further discovered that in 1172, Bishop David had been ordered to accommodate King Henry II and his retinue at a time when the rebuilding of the cathedral was draining the Episcopal funds. We learn that "…the resources of Bishop David Fitzgerald were strained to the limit by the lavish [royal] entertainment" (Dyfed: A Guide to Ancient and Historic Wales. S. Rees, 1992). It would be amusing to speculate whether the Bishop might have been pleased to see his daughter marry into the Whittow (Wizo) family in order to have possible access to some of their proven wealth. Disregarding this excursion into the realms of fantasy, that marriage might be the only possible link with the mysterious gravestone.

My Pembrokeshire coastal quest was now over and the gravity of this cathedral grave, hidden away in its dark corner, seemed to be a suitable finale. Yet, in retrospect, the location that emanated the most lingering memory has to be Whittow Wharf at Milford Haven. This was my Father's birthplace but, unfortunately, he never lived long enough to witness the naming of this notable accolade. Some of the final words must be those of Richard Whittow, a direct descendant of the ill-fated John of Ramsey: "So, should any descendant of the Pembrokeshire Whittows ever walk the Coastal Path at some future time and gaze outward to the islands, or inland to the Preselli Hills, he or she could hardly fail to experience some inner feeling, some faint glimmer of ancestral memory, unsuspected hitherto".

Arguably, Pembrokeshire possesses the finest stretch of unspoilt coastline in Southern Britain, which led to its early designation as a National Park. I have, perhaps, overemphasised the stigma of its oil and gas refineries but at least they are tucked away in the Haven, almost out of sight from the open ocean. The remaining coastline is one of remarkable beauty, matched only by the coasts of Devon and Cornwall. Both my Father and myself were denied the experience of growing-up in our true 'homeland' and there are moments when I feel that I was cheated of the chance to taste the fruits of spending my formative years living on the 'edge of the land'. On further consideration, however, perhaps the fact that I was born in the English Midlands, so far from the sea, gave me sufficient incentive to spend a great deal of my time travelling, researching, teaching and simply eulogising about the coastal fringes of the British Isles.

The only other coastal tract of South Wales with which I have any intimate knowledge is that of West Glamorgan. Ever since our oldest friends, Russell and Gaynor Thompson, returned to their homeland in the 1990's we have been able to spend many happy holidays exploring their neighbouring shores. Having been born, respectively, in Neath and Swansea they were anxious to show us these historic towns, but first, from their home in the Vale of Glamorgan, we had to drive past the widespread industrialised coast that stretches between the sand dunes of Kenfig Burrows and the Neath estuary at Briton Ferry. Little wonder that the Neptune surveyors mapped this tract as 'Beyond Redemption'. Few British shorelines, outside the coalfields, have suffered such spoliation, where the local hillside woodland has been stunted by the fumes and smoke from the seemingly endless steel works, oil refineries and petrochemical works that run for miles, squeezed between the motorway and the sea. One has to remember, however, that the car in which we were touring depended entirely on the products of such industries. The adjoining Swansea Valley, once notorious for its toxic landscape, had by then been miraculously reclaimed but its former appearance had led the poet, Edward Thomas, to speak of Swansea as that "...horrible and sublime town". I could see what he meant, for its setting on the far-spreading sweep of Swansea Bay had sufficient scenic merit, before its urbanisation, to inspire another poet, Walter Savage Landor who, with typical hyperbole, claimed that he preferred it to the Bay of Naples.

If, during the Industrial Revolution and beyond, into the 20th century, Cardiff had been the great out-port for coal and iron, then Swansea docks were once burdened with tin and copper exports. However, our hosts took us on a tour of the current seafront where rows of elegant flats and houses have created a 'most desirable' precinct. Despite acknowledging that such development had given a welcome fillip to a somewhat degraded dockland (although at a level much humbler than that of London's Canary Wharf), what I really wished to see in the city, whose streets climb steeply away from the shore, was the so-called Glyn Vivian Art Gallery. This was the building which housed the country's best collection of the works of another modern artist, Ceri Richards. Although not as well known as Sutherland and Piper, Ceri Richards, like them, found inspiration and sustenance in the coastal landscapes of South Wales. He was said to have been a brilliant draughtsman and an exceptionally 'energetic' painter (Ceri Richards. M. Gooding, 2002) and certainly talented enough to represent Great Britain at the prestigious Venice Biennale in 1962. One might well ask what this has got to do with the coast. In response I have to explain that not only was I the owner of some of his abstract paintings but it was his associations with the neighbouring peninsula of The Gower that fired my imagination. Some of Ceri Richards' finest work was inspired by this remarkable promontory and this was the real object of our westward excursion. I have recently read a remarkable little book entitled the "Black Apples of Gower" by Iain Sinclair (2015) in which the author describes how he himself roamed along the cliff-top paths of The Gower, provoked by the strange painting "Afal du Brogwyr" (Black Apples of Gower) by Ceri Richards. Another author has suggested that Richards' enigmatic picture of The Gower cliffs might possibly be interpreted as "...a partially developed vision of the paradisal island of Ys or Avalon". (Ceri Richards and Dylan Thomas: Keys to Transformation, R. Burns, 1981). Sinclair, like myself, was in thrall to this array of limestone cliffs and wave-cut platforms that had previously inspired such Welsh poets as Dylan Thomas and

Vernon Watkins, both of whom were friends of Richards. Their biographies record how they escaped from the urban streets of Swansea to find both fresh air and fresh inventiveness by exploring the caves, beaches and headlands of this extraordinary peninsula. Now it was my turn to explore this fabled shore.

Tortuous narrow lanes carried us out to the western extremity of Worms Head where we walked out along the cliff path to view the wave-eroded serpent-like ridge of tidal islands carved from tilted beds of grey limestone. Many a visitor, having clambered precariously along its rocky shoreline path, possibly to view its wonderful exposures of fossil corals, has become marooned by the incoming tide. We were not so venturesome but tarried awhile in order to enjoy the view of the cavorting seabirds and two intrepid walkers hastening to beat the incoming tide, before we plodded back to the car park at Rhossili village. So great was the tourist pressure here, where cars had been parked willy-nilly on every roadside verge, I know that the National Trust has recently paid a local landowner no less than £1 million for a field in order to enlarge their inadequate facility. No wonder that there are so many visitors because Rhossili Bay is one of the most photographed views in Wales. The contemporary poet, Owen Sheers (2015), summed up its magnetism quite succinctly when he described how early writers and artists were eventually succeeded by millions of cameras. Its magnificent sandy beach, beneath the attractive towering eminence of Rhossili Down (632 feet), stretches away to the distant sand dunes and grassy islet of Burry Holms. Little was I to know that a photograph of myself, in a contemplative mood, gazing at this inspirational view, was later to appear in a National Trust publication relating to my part in the Enterprise Neptune campaign. In this respect, I was to visit The Gower a decade later, to celebrate the 50th anniversary of this worthwhile operation (See chapter 11). Before we left this superb viewing-point we wandered into the tiny sloping churchyard of Rhossili, as is our wont, and there we discovered an interesting gravestone that commemorated Edgar Evans, a member of Scott's ill-fated Antarctic expedition. He was the first member of the party to die in that icy wilderness on the return from the South Pole. Inside the church we discovered his memorial window, much to the delight of Russell Thomson who, himself, had spent several years in the Antarctic engaged in scientific research.

Eventually, we wended our way slowly eastwards along the southern coast of The Gower, marvelling at its geological structures which have been poetically described by Iain Sinclair (*op. cit.*) as follows: "…the real, the authentic grip of locality, is in the rocks. The arms of the bay. The muscular headlands of Oxwich Point and Port Eynon Point. And the straggle of cliff paths between them. And that vision, when the tide retreats, of Carboniferous wave-cut limestone pavements: fractured, monochromatic". It is not surprising, therefore, that what one author found so inspirational was mirrored by another, for Mel Gooding, in his biography of Ceri Richards (*op. cit.*), chose those selfsame limestone pavements as illustrations for the end-papers of his monograph. It is along this coast that one can find the so-called 'bone' caves of Paviland, Culver Hole and Bacon Hole, the first of which is renowned for the 1823 discovery of a skeleton of Palaeolithic age (some 8,000 years old). It was found by the clerical geologist, Dean William Buckland, who described the red oxide-stained bones as "The Red Lady of Paviland" who had died in Biblical 'antediluvian' times. Further research established, however, that the bones, much more prosaically, belonged to a man who had lived during the Ice Age. Moreover, at Heatherslades, a post-glacial raised beach of cemented pebbles has been described by modern geologists. Its location, just above highwater level, reminded me of my own discovery at Hell's Mouth in the Llyn Peninsula (See chapter 3). Despite the fascination of these phenomena we were all too old and too wise to venture down the steep cliffs on to treacherous tide-washed rocks to view these acclaimed locations. Yet the Gower poet, Vernon Watkins, braved these hazards when he wrote with considerable apprehension and depth of feeling of how he clawed his way along the cold grey ribs of limestone, battered by the Atlantic winds and almost 'smothered' by the pounding waves. Few people are brave enough to clamber along this daunting sea cliff to visit the famous 'bone caves', although Iain Sinclair has written a lengthy description of his own intrepid venture (Ian Sinclair, 2015, *op. cit.*). Such descriptions set me thinking about the date of this remarkable cave's formation – it could not have been carved by modern waves but by those of a higher sea-level, possibly during an interglacial in the Ice Age. It seems highly unlikely that the cave dwellers would have had to be skilled rock climbers in order to reach their home; thus, one is forced to conclude that at that date a wide coastal plain existed here. Indeed, this is where these Stone Age hunters would have sought their food supply. On our return journey, after a long but most rewarding day of coastal exploration, our driver, Russell, suggested that we took time out to see a spectacular coastal landform known as Three Cliffs. I had seen pictures of this curious promontory sculptured by time and tide into a razor-back ridge of three conical pinnacles and I was looking forward to seeing them at close quarters. Apparently, Russell had ascended their sea-girt summits as a youth and was certain that I would appreciate their limestone crags and natural marine-eroded arch. We drove on and on through the intricate web of lanes: "That is the track that we are after: no, it's that one; or perhaps that one;

I don't think we are there yet; or perhaps we've passed it". By the time we'd reached The Mumbles, at the tip of Swansea Bay, amid much hilarity and many jibes, we knew that we had certainly missed the turning. Thus, I had failed to see this coastal phenomenon and felt somewhat ashamed that two experienced physical geographers had failed to read a map, but it was too late in the day to turn back.

The remoteness and solitude of this section of the Gower coast proved to be in sharp contrast to the day we went to Porthcawl, not far from the mouth of the Ogmore River. This was a feature that I had to see, largely because my Neptune surveyors in 1965 had expressed astonishment at the veritable 'townscape' of its caravan park. Since then it has expanded to become the largest caravan site in Europe. It soon became apparent that the attraction has been the three sandy beaches of Rest Bay, Sandy Bay and Trecco Bay, separated by the low limestone headlands of this former coal-exporting town. It is clearly the 'Blackpool' of the South Wales urban dwellers and, like the famous Lancashire resort, it offers a host of seaside amenities. A guide book informed us that there are paddling pools, deck chairs and wind-breaks for hire, amusement arcades, a fairground, children's playground, 'Punch & Judy', donkey rides, bingo, bowling greens, tennis courts, summer shows and a miniature railway. We were quite satisfied to bask in the sun, demolish our ice-cream cones and enjoy the sight of the world at play, before returning to the deserted shores that extend beyond Ogmore-by-Sea for several miles eastwards past Southerndown and St Donat's. Here we found a totally different environment to that of Porthcawl, because we had now reached the designated Heritage Coast of South Glamorgan which fringes the beautiful Vale of Glamorgan.

This breezy, rock-bound coast is a paradise both for geologists and for naturalists, but its stony beaches and bare wave-cut platforms, swept by the 40-foot tides of the Bristol Channel, are not conducive to 'bucket and spade' holidays. When Daniell (*op. cit.*) came this way in 1814, he remarked how "...the coast at St Donat's is low and tame, but about a league further to the westward it assumes a bolder character and continues for a few miles in a range of cliffs...remarkable for some curious excavations formed by the action of the sea, in some of which the rocks are fretted into a most perplexing variety of fantastic configurations...[so] that they look more like the work of art than a thing of nature". The multi-layered vertical cliffs of thinly-bedded blue-grey limestone are stuffed with fossils, including many corals. These were formed in tropical oceans, some 350 million years ago, in marine environments similar to those of the Great Barrier Reef of modern Australia. Such is the monochromatic linearity of the cliff-line, broken only by the occasional valley and a few vertical fault-lines, that it would be easy to think that this particular shore held little or no interest to the artist. One modern artist, however, found inspiration from the Dunraven coast and I am pleased to own two of the striking abstract impressions created by Lisa Henderson, who was born in Cardiff, and who has been able to capture the geological character of the beetling cliffs. Botanists are sometimes to be found scrambling along the base of the selfsame cliffs seeking the rather rare golden samphire that is confined to spray-washed rocks. Specimens can be found ascending the steepest faces, where they are out of the reach of rabbits and sheep, but when traced upwards they gradually give way to the more common sea pink, sea-lavender and blue-grey fescue, all of which flourish on the limestone downland. By and large this is a treeless coastline and, not surprisingly, Mary Gilham (Coastal Downs: Ogmore and Dunraven, 1993) wondered how the Victorians managed to establish and maintain woodland on the flanks of the Dunraven Valley. Today, it is merely a mass of tangled scrub, stunted thorny trees and brambles. If, with the aid of binoculars, anyone looks across the Bristol Channel to the thickly wooded shores of Somerset and North Devon, it would soon be realised that it is largely a matter of aspect. Glamorgan faces into the salt-laden south-westerly gales off the Irish Sea, whilst the opposing coast is north-facing and therefore relatively sheltered from the prevailing winds.

There are a few places in Wales where one can escape the coastal crowds and find solitude and peace. These are the havens known to naturalists, poets, writers and artists wherein they can meditate, invent or merely commune with nature. They are, in general, the 'special places', the 'dreamlands' where, even in unsettled weather, the city seems far away and the mind becomes 'blinkered' to all but the immediate environment. In such solitary coves, islets, dunes or mudflats, time seems to stand still and one finds precious moments to concentrate on the minutiae of the scene: the colour of the beach pebbles; the shapes and sizes of the sea-wrack; the make-up of the bounding rock exposure; the teeming marine fauna of tidal-pools; the bird-life; the seals; the various hues of the shoreline's saline-loving plants; or simply marvel at the steady beat of the ocean. In my extensive wanderings along the shores of Wales I have discovered a handful of such places. South Glamorgan is one; the southwest corner of the Llyn Peninsula another; Hell's Mouth in the same peninsula; the rocky wilds near Strumble Head in Pembrokeshire. They almost all have one feature in common, namely, the dearth of sandy beaches. Such beaches mean people, car parks, 'amenities', access-roads and, dare I say it, litter. Woe betide that I have given away the exact location of another of my 'special places'.

Up to this point in the narrative I appear to have spent a greater than normal amount of time in describing the coastline of Wales but there are a great variety of reasons to explain this apparent anomoly: First and foremost, it is my family homeland; it is where I have enjoyed the majority of my seaside holidays; it was where I had spent my first night under canvas; it is where I was stationed for part of my military service; my undergraduate dissertation was based on Conwy; my doctorate was centered on the Llyn Peninsula; my Neptune mapping traced much of the North Wales coastline; I had spent many hours gathering information to add to the record of the Ice Age in the Principality; finally I had often used Wales as my major outdoor 'lecture-room' in an endeavor to demonstrate to generations of undergraduates the principles of geology, physical geography and environmental management. It was on one such occasion, when standing on a high Welsh mountain, I was fortunate enough to find the visibility clear enough to capture a hazy blue image of Ireland's Wicklow Mountains far off across the Irish Sea. It is to this island that I must now turn. George Bernard Shaw dubbed it "John Bull's Other Island" but his play was written in 1907 since which time Ireland has changed out of all recognition. I was domiciled there in the 1950's and was able not only to witness some of those dramatic changes but I was also able to discover that Ireland has a character all of its own, quite distinct from the cultures of Britain itself.

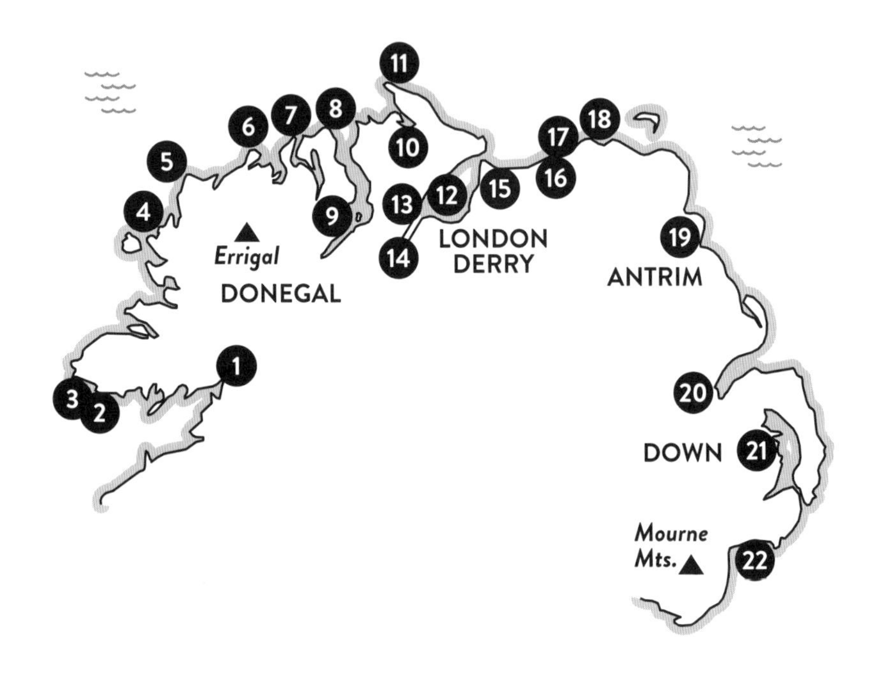

1. Donegal Town
2. The Sturrall
3. Slieve League
4. The Rosses
5. Bloody Foreland
6. Horn Head
7. Rosguill Peninsula
8. Lough Swilly
9. Inch Island
10. Inishowen
11. Malin Head
12. Lough Foyle
13. Culmore Point
14. City of Londonderry (Doire)
15. Magilligan Point
16. Portrush
17. Whitepark Bay
18. Giant's Causeway
19. Glens of Antrim
20. Belfast
21. Strangford Lough
22. Murlough

5. ULSTER

"Boswell: Is not the Giant's-Causeway worth seeing?
Johnson: Worth seeing? yes; but not worth going to see".
(Boswell's "Life of Johnson", 1778)

The Giant's Causeway, County Antrim, Ulster

White Park Bay, County Antrim, where chalk rocks are buried under layers of basalt

Striped field patterns, surviving from the ancient Irish practice known as 'run-rig'. Here they have been located on a fine succession of raised beaches, near Malin Head in County Donegal, Republic or Ireland

The vertical 1,000-foot cliffs of Slieve League, County Donegal. The site of our attempt to make the first ascent from the beach

Belfast Docks proved to be just as dreary as I remembered them when I walked slowly through the pouring rain to York Street Station to board the Londonderry train. A thought flickered through my head, as I momentarily glanced at the giant cranes of Harland & Wolf's shipyard. "Were these the selfsame cranes that helped to build the notorious liner 'Titanic' captained by the luckless Treasure Jones, born in the same town as myself?" I sincerely hoped that my own fortunes would prove to be better than his. I had already been this way, some six years previously, when on army escort duty to bring back a deserter to a military prison in south east England. I can still remember the parting words of the Regimental Sergeant Major: "And don't forget, laddie, that if you lose him you will serve his sentence in the glasshouse at Colchester". That lengthy rail journey with a handcuffed prisoner, right across the Province from the barracks of the Enniskilling Fusiliers at Omagh, had filled me with a high degree of trepidation. The current train journey, on which I was soon to embark, seemed to be only a little less daunting, but that was then and this was now.

My somewhat morose feelings were largely due to the fact that this was the second of my lectureship interviews, having failed to secure an academic post at Southampton University. And so, at the forthcoming interview, my career would be hanging in the balance. My thoughts briefly returned to the last time that I had been in such a downcast, bedraggled state, wet-through and apprehensive. It was on the rain-swept slopes of Conwy Mountain when I almost gave up on my undergraduate mapping task. The gloom, both in my head and in the sky, persisted as the Londonderry train rattled through this 'alien' countryside. I stared through the rain-streaked windows at the seemingly endless bogs and vivid green fields of County Antrim, as we stopped at every tiny station. At this stage of my life such an unfamiliar landscape was as uninspiring as any that I had ever encountered, with nothing to break the monotony of a slow journey into the 'interior'. One could not gainsay that it was truly rural and a far cry from the tainted urban scenes of The Potteries or Reading's smarter southern townscape. But after a while the rain eased off, we crossed the wide River Bann near Coleraine and I had a first glimpse of the sea. As though to signal that I was entering a totally new environment, a few shafts of sunlight brought a patchwork of brighter reflections across the surface of these sullen northern waters. The train now twisted its way along the shore beneath dark basaltic pallisades, only just above the breaking waves, an experience as exciting as that when the Cornish Express tunnels through the bright red sea-cliffs at Dawlish in far-off Devon. The view that now unfolded was quite eye-opening and confirmed the claim that Northern Ireland's scenic beauty can be found largely along its magnificent coastline. This is Ireland's own 'edge of the land' where its mundane interior meets the ocean.

Few shores of the British Isles offer such remarkable geological contrasts as that of the Antrim coast for here one can view the juxtaposition of black and white rocks. For mile after mile the coastal cliffs exhibit layer upon layer of black basalt sitting atop outcrops of dazzling bands of white chalk that extend down below beach level, just as if Beachy Head had been overwhelmed by lava flows. In later years I was to bring British undergraduates to study this almost unique marine environment where aeons of wave erosion had fretted the cliffs into such iconic landforms as the Giant's Causeway. If one follows this lengthy shore eastwards, around the massive jutting precipice of Fair Head, an equally magnificent spectacle begins to unfold. Here are the renowned Glens of Antrim where cascading streams fall hundreds of feet from the lip of the seemingly ubiquitous basaltic plateau edge. There is a striking contrast in colour between those dark walls of lava and the emerald green fields of the so-called 'ladder farms' that extend as narrow strips high up the mountain side. But I was only able to traverse this type of scenery in the future and for now I must return to my feelings on that Spring day in 1954, as my spirits slowly began to lift as the coastline hove into view from my train window.

The train soon crossed the River Roe, near Limavady, a wooded vale where the Irish melody "Danny Boy" was composed, but my eyes were firmly fixed seawards. Here was the sandy expanse of Magiligan Point, one of Ireland's finest coastal forelands and comparable both in size and shape to that of England's Dungeness. I wondered if it was relatively untrodden by tourists and could be included in my list of 'special places' that I have outlined above. Little was I to know that in the not too far distant future, long after I had left the Province, this beautiful wilderness of sand dunes would suffer the indignities of becoming infamous as the location of Ulster's largest internment camp for IRA prisoners. I was soon to learn, however, that this far-flung corner of the United Kingdom had once been a 'military coastline' because of its location as the westernmost point of our nation during World War II. Shortly after passing this sandy wilderness I began to witness the remnants of this miltary presence for, during the remainder of the journey, the low-lying coast of County Londonderry became an almost unbroken landscape of airfields, army barracks and a still active naval base. The four airfields had made good use of the very flat so-called 'slob lands' that were little more than the marshy, reclaimed estuarine mudflats of Lough Foyle. One could imagine the lonely coastal patrol aircraft departing out over the neutral Republic of Ireland, which lay on the far shore of the lough, prior to scanning the wide Atlantic waters in their search for U-Boats. The estuary eventually narrowed into a deep-water, thickly wooded channel, termed "The Narrows", and it was here that many of the surrendered U-Boats were once tethered when hostilities had ceased. Now, their erstwhile berths housed a 'mothballed' fleet of British naval craft because Londonderry was still a naval base. By the time that I had journeyed to the uttermost western limit of the United Kingdom, bright sunshine had begun to burnish the waters of Lough Foyle and the cloud shadows could be seen dappling the steep mountain sides of the nearby coast of County Donegal. This was more like it. A change of scene and a change of weather had also heralded a change in my entire demeanour. Suffice to say that the interview was successful and that the ancient walled City of Londonderry, therefore, was to be my home for the forseeable future.

The fine sandstone building of Magee College (Ulster's second university at that time) stands on a bluff overlooking the city quays on the Strand Road. I had to learn that in Ireland the term 'strand' meant 'beach' and henceforth I shall often interchange the two words when describing the Irish shorelines. I discovered that the Magee buildings dated back to the 19th century, when it was a Presbyterian teaching college, and had only just been given the status of a university, despite its very small size. Indeed, I was the first assistant lecturer to be appointed to its small but active Geography Department and I was given a free rein to develop its Physical Geography syllabus. Here, then, was a great opportunity to use the surrounding area, especially its magnificent coastlines, as an 'outdoor classroom' in which to advance the knowledge of about thirty undergaduates. The tiny student population of several hundred in 1954, had swelled to over 5,000 at the time of writing but, many years after my departure, the Department of Geography had been transferred to the new University of Ulster at Coleraine. Today, Magee has thriving courses in such subjects as Computer Science, Engineering, Business Management and a large Medical School, to say nothing of its renowned School of Irish Studies. The latter is very appropriate in a city where Irish nationalism is of paramount importance and where some 70% of its population is Catholic. However, on my arrival in 1954, I was struck by the very high rate of male unemployment and soon discovered that this great city was what we would now call a 'centre of deprivation' where, on a wet blustery day, even the paving stones seemed to seep despair. Many of its female workforce still found employment in the shirt factories but the city's flourishing wartime days, both as a prominent naval base and as the out-port for County Donegal in the Republic, had long since gone. Nevertheless, such economic drawbacks could not take away the beauty of its surrounding countryside and the challenge of its physical environment.

My Head of Department turned out to be a rumbustious ex-Irish Rugby international who was still researching the 'social aspects of settlement on the western seaboard of Ireland'. This proved to be a golden opportunity for me to accompany him and discover this wonderful Atlantic shoreline for the first time. By now, my earlier doubts had disappeared and I was determined to start a new chapter in the progression of my own knowledge in a completely new environment. Today this is referred to as a 'learning curve'.

The walled city of Londonderry can be compared with the historic Welsh towns of Conwy and Caernarfon in so far as they all share a waterside location and were imposed on the local population. But, despite its tidal situation, Londonderry has no clear view of the open sea and it reminded me, in this sense, of the town of Milford Haven. On occasion I used to sit in the tower of the university library and wistfully watch as the 'cattle boats' cast off from the quayside to carry their bovine cargoes through "The Narrows" and off to faraway Glasgow. My yearning to view the wonderful coastline of Donegal, right on my doorstep and just across the neighbouring border with the Republic, was hindered because my car was still in England. Thus, my first visit to the real seashore, was as a passenger during a visit to Inch Island in nearby Lough Swilly, where my departmental head, Dr McCourt, had a tiny cottage. I use the term 'island' but in fact Inch had long been tied to the mainland by causeways, but from its central hill I was able to look northwards along the lough to a serrated skyline of mountains and, notably, the prominent deeply-cut breach through which the tides coursed daily. I was quick to determine that the contrast between the smooth shores of Lough Foyle and the rugged shores of Lough Swilly was all a matter of their geology. The former occupies a structural downfold in Carboniferous Limestone, whilst the latter is a true fjord scoured out by glaciers through the hard rock bands of Pre-Cambrian igneous and metamorphic rocks, dominant amongst which were the so-called quartzites (hard, white metamorphosed sandstones). These had weathered into quite prominent peaks that flanked the aforementioned glacial breach and gave to the coastline its quite remarkable character. Their isolated summits, from the outset, struck me as offering future challenges to a mountaineer, so that I became impatient to explore their craggy slopes.

I learnt that the deep waters of Lough Swilly, like those of Milford Haven, were capacious enough to have hosted much of the British Atlantic Fleet during World War I at a time before the political division of Ireland. This fjord "...is best viewed, perhaps, on a fine summer's evening when the setting sun silhouettes both the stark, craggy ridge of the Knockalla Mountains, known locally as the Devil's Backbone, and the lumpy pyramids of the Urris Hills. Both of these heather-clad eminences would then be darkly mirrored in the gleaming waters of the lough which zig-zags to the open ocean". I wrote these words in my book on Ireland's scenery, some twenty years after I had first experienced this striking view but it was so unforgettable that it became engraved into my memory. Some months later, when I had the use of my own car, I was able to drive out the dozen miles or so to climb the highest peak of the Inishowen Peninsula, Slieve Snacht (2,019 feet), literally "The Mountain of Snow". In these northern latitudes this was always the first summit to be covered in winter snows, but it was its much lower peak, Barnan More, which really caught my eye, for here the so-called craggy "King and Queen of the Mintiaghs" rose like turreted castles from the peat-draped slopes. Many were the occasions, after a hard days lecturing, that I jumped into my old Morris Minor and spent a carefree hour scrambling alone on their challenging rock pinnacles until the sun went down. I had for years been a rock-climber, ever since my undergraduate days when I had chaired the Reading University Mountaineering Club and had scaled many severe rock-faces in Snowdonia. It was on one of those expeditions that I helped to rescue a fellow climber after a nasty fall, an episode that taught me to be more cautious in the future. But it was on the Welsh and Irish mountains and sea-cliffs that I learnt the skills which were to serve me well during my subsequent glacier-mapping exercises at high altitude in East Africa.

Although few Donegal peaks offered the same sheer precipices as those in Wales, I still had the urge to climb. It was gratifying, therefore, when I was invited to help found the North-West Mountaineering

Club in Londonderry. Not only did this give me a means of escape to explore Ulster's mountainous periphery but also a chance to meet non-academics outside the somewhat 'cloistered' atmosphere of the university. The club's founder was a local businessman, Joey Glover, who happily took a handful of us in his Transit van far into the wilds of Donegal. The majority of visitors to north-west Donegal keep closely to the coastline which, because of the complex intermingling of sea and mountain, is its chief glory. Uppermost amongst my many memories of those sunlit weekends has to be my first ascent of Errigal (2,466 feet). This graceful pyramid of shimmering white quartzite rises majestically above the coastal plateau and from its airy knife-edged top one can view Atlantic Ireland at its best. This is where ocean waves have etched its great variety of rocks into an intricate coastline. Out to the west the quartzite knob of Aranmore Island stands out from an older granite which forms the scores of skerries and the highly indented coastline that extends southwards from the "Bloody Foreland". The latter's bright red granitic hues are enhanced at sunset and are said to be responsible for its singular name. The view to the north is even more rewarding; the yellow sand dunes, which enclose Ballyness Bay and climb high up the slopes of Horn Head, have been formed by wind and waves after being eroded from glacial deposits. Seen under the clear, rain-washed sky that favoured my first visit to Errigal's summit, the white cottages set in their bright green fields, the tawny colours of the unimproved land with the black slashes of peat-diggings, all backed by the yellow dunes and the blue sea, created a picture worthy of any artist's brush. I was soon to learn, moreover, that this scene is typical of the picturesque seaboard of Western Ireland and that it had already been depicted on numerous canvases. After hearing tales of this fabled Atlantic coastline, I looked forward to experiencing such delights in the forthcoming years for, at that time, it was a region on which I had never set foot.

Not surprisingly, therefore, I could hardly wait to take my students to this western coast in order to teach them the principles of geomorphology. Once we had sufficient transport (some of the more mature students owned cars) we journeyed into Donegal and out onto the Rosguill Peninsula, where I was able to explain how a former island was now tied to the mainland by a narrow neck of sand and shingle termed a 'tombolo'. Despite subsequently visiting many more coastal venues on my countless number of 'field classes', it is this particular one that remains most clearly in my mind's eye because it was the first coastline that I had used as an open-air 'classroom'. Whilst I was still feeling rather self-satisfied with my exposition, I was quickly brought back to reality when we were joined by Dr McCourt who gave a masterly lecture on the history of the Irish setlement pattern known as the 'clachan'. He deftly demonstrated how the tight formation of thatched cottages that lay before us, was quite different to the haphazard scatter of cottages that is much more common in the Irish landscape. As a comparive novice, I stood and admired the way that he told us how this picturesque but tiny village settlement had grown, with no apparent planning, to form what is still referred to in Ireland as a 'town'; hence the term 'townland' which is roughly equivalent to the English parish. I soon became quite entranced by this very different cultural aspect of Ireland, which seemed to have survived in a landscape frozen in something of a timewarp. I had seen nothing like this in England or Wales, but in future years I was to find similar settlements in Highland Scotland. However, I was itching to return to my first love, that of attempting to explain how the physical landforms had been created. Not far away lay the beleaugered landscape known as The Rosses where ice-sheets had scrubbed the land of virtually all its soil before leaving thousands of large erratic boulders strewn across the scene. I had seen nothing like this in coastal Wales but Lloyd Praeger, a leading Irish naturalist, summed it up as "...a land of innumerable lakelets, a windswept heathery region, with small peaty fields grudgingly yielding crops of potatoes, oats and turnips and roads meandering through granite hillocks" (The Way that I Went, R. Lloyd Preager, 1969). I was surprised to discover that this subsistence agriculture still supported one of the densest areas of rural population in Ireland and as such it had remained almost unchanged from having been one of the notorious 'Congested Districts' which characterised parts of the western coast of Ireland during the 19th century. Once more, I found it difficult to view the physical features without linking them with the human occupance, which, when taken together, constituted a complete picture of the environment in any particular place. I vowed, during my first proper 'field' lecturing experience, that in future I would endeavour to make the students more aware, not simply about the geology and geomorphology, but the totality of the scene, in order to evoke a 'sense of place', if at all possible. I began to formulate a philosophy based on a belief that it was only when people begin to fully understand what gives a landscape its character will they begin to value it and, hopefully, care for it. By the time of the Neptune survey, more than a decade later, I had learned to practice this environmental approach with a fair degree of success.

A later student field-class was held at Ireland's northernmost tip of Malin Head, famous in the radio shipping-forecasts as a stormy sea area. Fortunately, the weather was kind to us when we arrived at this notorious spot and I was able to explain how the remarkable array of 'raised beaches' was formed. Nowhere else in Ireland can match this staircase of shingle beach-ridges. Perched at a height of 80 feet on the topmost 'fossil' beach, beneath the long-abandoned cliff-line, is the much-photographed linear village of Ballyhillin. The colourful, striped, hedgeless field-strips run seawards from each village house until they are truncated by the abandoned sea-cliff of the post-glacial raised beach which, itself, is several feet above the modern strand. Such a coastal phenomenon as this, unique in Ireland, can only be matched by the 'raised beach' staircase on the Isle of Jura in Western Scotland and a glance at a map will show that the two locations are merely sixty miles apart. I have already explained how, during the Ice Age, the thickest ice-cap was centered over western Scotland and that the greatest crustal depression and subsequent 'rebound' would have been greatest in that realm. Thus, that Scottish area and the nearest Irish seaboard would have experienced the greatest tectonic uplift when the ice-sheets had finally disappeared, thereby leaving the inherited succession of shorelines high and dry.

Following my newly acquired philosophy, outlined above, I decided that it was not only the formation of the coastal landforms that had to be clarified but the striped field pattern itself had also to be explained. That at Malin Head was one of the last survivals in Ireland of an ancient system of land-tenure known as 'rundale' in which the field strips were allocated equally among the villagers, according to the quality of the soil and land capability. In England such a medieval land-use system had died out some centuries ago (with the sole exception of an estate at Laxton in the Midlands), but in Ireland it survived longest in the hostile climate and terrain of the Atlantic coast. It was on this particular field class that I discovered that the majority of my students came from Belfast and had little if any comprehension of the type of rural landscapes that we were now witnessing. Such a discovery was another valuable part of my 'learning curve' and, later in my academic career at Reading University, I was equally astonished as to how many of my undergraduates from southern England had little knowledge of industrial landscapes. Henceforth, I reminded myself that one should not make any assumptions in the world of Environmental Education. But it is worth recounting a very amusing episode that occurred at Malin Head, to illustrate that field-classes have their lighter moments. Years later, as our party of English students 'decanted' from the minibus and advanced, line abreast, across the grassy shingle of the highest beach at Malin, we noticed that a large ram had been tethered by a lengthy rope to a stake driven into the turf. As this creature suddenly became aware of the advancing horde it panicked and ran away until it literally reached the end of its tether, whereupon it began to describe a revolving arc around the stake. The rope, at ankle height, proceeded to mow down the students like a scythe in a cornfield, much to everyone's amusement except, perhaps, for the disgruntled ram.

Not surprisingly, my visits to the coast were not merely to teach the students, because some of my fondest memories are those spent with my friends in the mountaineering club. The best of these was undoubtedly a trip through the Bluestack Mountains, an unremarkable low dome of granite, to the south-west coast of Donegal, and onwards beyond the eponymous town and the thriving fishing port of Killybegs. As we travelled the coast road westwards I became aware of a gradual transition in the scenery where the fertility of the land manifestly declined, trees almost disappeared, all to be replaced by bare rock and bogland. (Ireland, T. W. Freeman, 1950). Put more prosaically, we had left the richer fertile soils of the Carboniferous Limestone and returned to the barren Pre-Cambrian rocks of Atlantic Ireland.

A small group of us were intending to make the first ascent of the daunting sea-cliffs of Slieve League, some of the most spectacular in western Europe. Only in a few places are the cliffs actually vertical, as at the "Eagle's Nest", but the summit cairn (1,972 feet) stands on the very edge of the main cliffs which stretch for nearly two miles. Between the "Eagle's Nest" and the summit, the coastal path traverses a narrow knife-edged ridge, appropriately termed the "One Man's Path", which separates the precipitous sea-cliff and the back-wall of a glacially eroded corrie on the landward side. We are told that on the flanks of the corrie-lake one can find the finest collection of Alpine plants in the whole of Ireland, sheltered from the ocean's blast. Moreover, it has been suggested that the vertical sea-cliffs of the Eagle's Nest are probably the remnants of another corrie because Slieve League once had its own small ice-cap. If this is true then it demonstrates the magnitude of the wave erosion on this storm-lashed Atlantic coast and the degree to which the shoreline has been driven landwards.

We assembled on the beach and gazed up at the 1,000 feet of folded strata of Pre-Cambrian metamorphic rocks, trying to work out the most likely route of our proposed ascent. The first hundred feet looked promising, for the coastal vegetation had been stripped away, presumably by gigantic storm waves, thereby exposing ribs of bare rock. School-teacher, Denys Helliwell, took the lead and I was second on the rope, but after ascending most of the lower face we met an impasse and bands of very loose vegetated rock. After descending we looked elswhere and discovered another daunting challenge at The Sturrall, a jagged ridge reaching seawards from the cliffs for a few hundred yards. At an elevation of about 200 feet above the waves, the horizontal, saw-toothed traverse had never been attempted but it offered us a sporting challenge. After I had roped up, I gingerly set off, followed by Boyd Jack, a sixth-form student at a Londonderry grammar-school, along its vertiginous, loose quartzite pinnacles, and it soon became quite clear why this prominent future sea-stack had remained unconquered. The seemingly impregnable crystalline white rock had been scoured and broken up by the salt-laden winds and was held in place only by the stunted maritime vegetation. We spent the first hundred yards engaged in what rock-climbers term 'gardening', in order to establish firm footholds. But the more plants that we removed the more rapid was the speed at which quite substantial blocks of quartzite somersaulted into the yawning waves below. By now we were inching along on our backsides and once again we were forced to retreat having decided that discretion was the better part of valour. It had grown increasingly likely that one or both of us would soon plummet into the sea, and there were no air-sea rescue helicopters in those days. If nothing more I had learnt a lesson in the importance of the process of weathering in the formation of rocky coastlines. Inadvertently, we had also carried out a degree of coastal erosion that would normally take decades if left to natural forces.

A few years after I had left Northern Ireland I received a most distressing letter from the mountaineering club secretary, informing me that our greatly admired chairman, Joey Glover, had been assassinated by the IRA, in an act of mistaken identity. During my three-year contract in Londonderry, the political unrest had become increasingly more manifest. In the first year I had taken lodgings a mere mile from the Border and each night on my return from the university I was stopped and searched by the Ulster 'B Special' police. Amongst their ranks were some of my own Geography students who laughingly prodded a sten-gun through my car window. The next morning, in class, between their yawns, they discussed how they had taken pot-shots at anything that moved in the fields, including donkeys and cows. Such an unpleasant inconvenience caused me to take new lodgings in the city, much nearer to the university. This too proved to be somewhat of a disaster because the IRA detonated a massive bomb just at the end of the garden when they destroyed the BBC television transmission tower and blew me out of bed. I had not experienced a detonation of such magnitude since my army days in the artillery. In fact, the loss of transmission hardly affected the city dwellers because they could pick up signals from the Belfast transmitter. The viewers over most of Donegal, however, were not so lucky because they lost their TV pictures for several weeks. One result of the rising tensions, before the so-called "Troubles" witnessed gunfire in Londonderry's streets (including the infamous 'Bloody Sunday'), was the curtailment of our climbing trips along the coast of beautiful Donegal. Although we looked eastwards into Counties Antrim and Down the scenery and the challenges were not the same, except in the Mountains of Mourne which were too far away for day trips. However, by then I had been invited by a colleague, Nicholas Stephens, a Geography lecturer in Queen's University, Belfast, to accompany him on his research activities on the coast of Strangford Lough. This shallow-water inlet in County Down is characterised by its convoluted coastline of drowned drumlins and extends for forty miles inland as one of the largest marine inlets in the British Isles. Nick Stephens was carrying out the same sort of survey that I had once been engaged in, across the Irish Sea in North Wales, namely, the mapping of raised shorelines. Strangford's gentler, low-lying coast of thick glacial drift was in sharp contrast to the inhospitable, but more attractive, rocky shorelines of Donegal, and it had remained sufficiently undeveloped by intrusive settlement for our 1965 Neptune surveyors to map most of it as 'pristine', a decade in the future. Strangford's coastlands possess a much greater degree of well-managed farmland, on better yielding soils and less harsh terrain than those of the Atlantic seaboard of Donegal. At Strangford one is constantly aware of lush, livestock-grazed pastures stretching right down to the sheltered shoreline, with barely a rock outcrop to be found, except at the tidal-scoured mouth of the lough which is less than 800 yards across. So important is its flora, its avian fauna and unspoilt scenery that this virtually enclosed arm of the sea has long been designated as an AONB. In this respect it had joined three other stretches of Ulster's coast that have all been given the same accolade. These comprise: First, the remainder of the County Down coast that extends from Strangford, past the flowery sand-dune shores of Murlough and the romantic footslopes of the Mourne Mountains, all the way to Carlingford Lough on the Border with the Republic; secondly, the Antrim Coast and the adjoining Glens; thirdly, the sandy foreland of Magilligan's Point in County Londonderry (both of which have been described above). A glance at any conservation map will illustrate the fact that some three-quarters of Ulster's coastline have been given some degree of protected status, a considerably greater percentage than in England or Wales. Not surprisingly, the National Trust was quick to acquire a great deal of this wonderful sea-lough, at various stages, under the Strangford Lough Wildlife Scheme (initiated in 1966). By means of Neptune funds and generous gifts, more than 21 sites have passed into Trust ownership since that date. It is, however, worth pointing out that the Ulster planning authority's control, over those same decades, has been considerably less strict than those of England and Wales. This laxity of coastal planning restrictions has resulted in a mass of relatively recent sporadic development along this shore, thereby threatening an increase in the environmental impact on this internationally important location.

As the third and final year of my appointment drew to a close, I became increasingly involved not only in writing-up my doctoral dissertation but also in seeking an academic appointment elsewhere. Thus, I spent more and more of my time at my desk, rarely venturing across the Border. Nationalist unrest was beginning to show unpleasant signs of escalating in Ulster's towns and cities, manifesting itself when my car, with its English number plate, was stoned as I drove through the notorious suburb of Bogside in Londonderry. It was my own fault because I had been warned not to venture into that zone, which was later to become a 'no-go area' for British troops. Matters seemed to have reached a head when the IRA hijacked a goods train en route to Londonderry and, after throwing the driver and fireman off the train, opened the throttle and sent it driverless into the city terminus where it seriously damaged the station. The situation became so bad that I had to abandon my coastal visits across the border to Donegal and confine my trips to Culmore Point, a couple of miles down-river and at the mouth of The Narrows. This small shingle foreland, below the tiny village of Culmore, was not only a picturesque viewpoint but it also became an escape from the bustle of the city and a place to meditate and plan my future. In due course I took my brushes and canvas in order to capture this attractive image of tidal waters and to take away a memento of my sojourn in Northern Ireland. The oil painting that I produced now hangs on my study wall and I glance at it as I write these words. Never before or since have I painted a picture that unveils my subconscious thoughts as much as this particular view at Culmore. I will attempt to give the reader some impression of the constituent features that make up the finished canvas: The waves in the tiny bay are beginning to grow in intensity; the grey-black clouds are being driven northwards, portending an approaching storm; the sun has disappeared; a solitary boat is drawn up on the shore; not a single person is in sight; a dead tree overhangs the shore; the white cottages of the small village still look peaceful in their empty fields but the distant mountains of Donegal are starting to fade into the distance as if they are bidding farewell. Such a forlorn image must have revealed my concern for the impending political unrest that would shortly escalate into the so-called "Troubles", culminating in horrendous episodes of slaughter at such places as Enniskillen, Omagh and Carlingford Lough to say nothing of "Bloody Sunday" in Londonderry itself. What is so surprising is the fact that I set out to paint a simple view of rural Ireland but one which became sublimated by my inner feelings.

Within a few weeks I had packed my suitcase into the car and had left the Province of Ulster, both to get married and to commence a new academic career in far-off East Africa. But I was never going to forget the happy years that I had spent roaming its mountains and spectacular coastlines. Moreover, it is important to remember that, in my three-year tenure, I had also taken every opportunity to enjoy the western shores of the Republic of Ireland. Initially, I had conducted field-classes from Mageee University College southwards into the Republic and these had proved so rewarding that, in future years, I was able to repeat the excursions at the same venues with students from the University of Reading. All of the memories evoked by such trips, together with our own family holidays, will be described in the following chapter that describes my impressions of the beguiling coasts of Western Ireland.

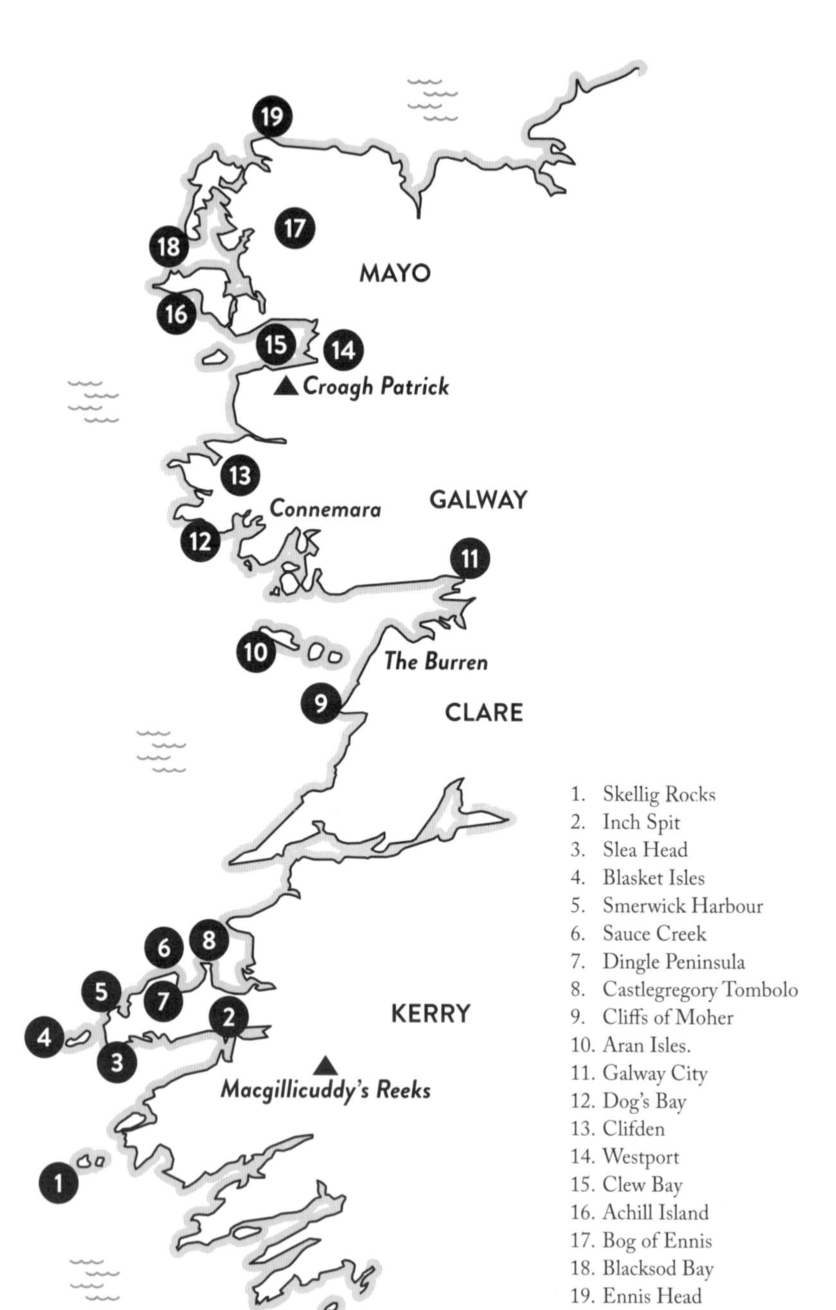
19
17
18
MAYO
16
15
14
Croagh Patrick
13
GALWAY
Connemara
12
11
10
The Burren
9
CLARE
6
8
5
7
KERRY
2
4
3
Macgillicuddy's Reeks
1
1. Skellig Rocks
2. Inch Spit
3. Slea Head
4. Blasket Isles
5. Smerwick Harbour
6. Sauce Creek
7. Dingle Peninsula
8. Castlegregory Tombolo
9. Cliffs of Moher
10. Aran Isles.
11. Galway City
12. Dog's Bay
13. Clifden
14. Westport
15. Clew Bay
16. Achill Island
17. Bog of Ennis
18. Blacksod Bay
19. Ennis Head

6. WESTERN IRELAND

"Cut off from its neighbours by the sea,
with the immensity of the Atlantic washing half its shores,
its cultures, like its physical structure and evolution
have had an 'Ultima Thule' quality that has hardly deserted [it]
at the present day"
(The Face of Ireland, Michael Floyd, 1937)

A 'run-rig' field pattern on the peat-covered coast of Achill Island, County Mayo, Republic of Ireland. Each narrow strip would be owned by a different individual

The 2,000-foot cliffs of Achill Head on Croaghaun Mountain, Achill Island

The northern face of Croaghaun Mountain, showing a glacial corrie at sea-level. Note how the glacial moraine is protecting the corrie lake from the sea

The conical shaped peak of Slievemore (2,204 feet), Achill Island. Note how the small corrie (the only one on the mountain) contrasts with the deep corries in the previous picture.

A group of university students looking into Sauce Creek, Mt. Brandon, County Kerry

A typical scene in Connacht in the West of Ireland. This view of Connemara, looking towards its convoluted coastline, would hardly have changed since the time that the author J. M. Synge visited here a century ago – *See plate section for colour version*

The French fishing-boat, the Kornog, in Clew Bay, County Mayo. This vessel was the one on which we carried out sea-floor mapping in 1960. Croagh Patrick Mountain in the distance.

The vertical Cliffs of Moher, County Clare

Anyone glancing at a map of Ireland will begin to understand what Floyd was thinking when he wrote those percipient lines, for, in physographic terms, the Emerald Isle is one of contrasting halves. The dividing line runs for a distance of approximately 300 miles (as the crow flies) from the southernmost point of Cape Clear to the northernmost point at Malin Head. To the east of this imaginary boundary the eastern half of Ireland is a well-endowed countryside of prosperous farmland and fine woodland, whilst the lands to the west are largely scarified, bare and far less wooded. The contrast in landscapes is partly due to their geological differences, somewhat a result of their respective histories, but mainly an outcome of their leeward and windward situations; the eastern half has been sheltered from the full force of the 'blitzkrieg' of Atlantic weather from time immemorial; the western half has suffered from both the vagaries of heavier rainfall and the battering of the ocean waves over the same length of time. Therefore, as far as their respective coastlines are concerned there is a remarkable disparity: The eastern coastline is characterised by some 1,500 miles of generally unbroken, regular linearity with no more than four islands and a handful of estuaries and sea loughs; that to the west displays more than 3,000 miles of irregular, convoluted and ragged shorelines with many burrowing sea loughs and at least one hundred significant islands. This western configuration is largely a reflection of the much greater power of the natural forces of erosion that have battered these exposed western coasts, in which wind, wave and glacier-ice have thrust their elemental might against the final bastion of the continent of Europe. It is to the west coast that I will now turn and endeavour to describe, with a great number of superlatives, my memories of this majestic seaboard. I discovered that not only its landscapes but also its cultures are quite different from those of Eastern Ireland and that its slower tempo of life induces a dreamlike nostalgia so typical of the Celtic West, whether it be Wales, Scotland or Cornwall.

The feeling that time stands still along these peripheral shores (as I had already discovered in Donegal) has been captured in the words of that great Irish writer, Sean O'Faolain, who wrote "...as the traveller goes farther and farther west, he puts back his watch – but here one puts it back not by hours but by centuries. Away down on the wild and jagged coast of Kerry, or over on the tattered fragments of Connemara, it is the Middle Ages" (The Story of Ireland, Sean O'Faolain, 1937). It is true that, economically, Ireland has now moved on apace, many things have changed, but the west coast that I visited half a century ago still projected the weather-beaten face that so many people find so attractive and appealing.

I first went to County Mayo with a party of Magee University students in the Easter vacation in 1955. Its atmosphere immediately overwhelmed me for it displayed all the cultural aspects that Sean O'Faolain had described. 'Serious' tourism had barely arrived and the landscape appeared to be in a time warp. It is not surprising that the eminent Irish artist, Paul Henry, had painted many of his remarkable landscapes in this region for this was the type of scenery that appealed to the visitors. Little wonder that his evocative images have been used to illustrate books on Western Ireland, because his towering white cumulo-nimbus clouds (threatening an imminent downpour typical of these parts) serve to dwarf the crouching white cottages, the black peat-cuttings and the ultramarine ocean beyond. Many of his pictures were painted on the most delectable island of Achill and this was where one of my first Irish field-classes had been based. Taking a youthful group of students brought back memories of my own teenage visit to a camp on the coast of Penmaenmawr some decades before. In so far as both groups were entirely urban dwellers and were seeing a 'new' coastline for the first time, it is little wonder that each party had seemed somewhat overawed by the experience. It would be nice to think that, because I found this island environment so stimulating, my teaching became more enthusiastic or even inspirational. Although such thoughts may appear to be 'wishful thinking', my philosophy has always been to give students as much 'exposure' as possible to the real world outside the lecture room. How else could one discover the true nature of the environment in which we live?

Achill Island has a diversity of coastal scenery that can rarely be matched elsewhere in Ireland and the immense scale of its sea cliffs reminded me of Slieve League in Donegal. Lloyd Praeger, the doyen of Irish naturalists, was so impressed by its scenery that he spoke of the "...unchanging features of Achill...the broad undulations of the treeless, roadless moorland, the tall hills, its illimitable silver sea, the savage coastline, the booming waves, the singing wind, the smell of peat smoke and seaweed and wild thyme" (R. Lloyd Praeger, *op. cit.*). It is true that much of this romantic atmosphere remains, presenting the type of scenery that makes many an urban dweller long for an escape to the Gaelic-speaking fringe of Atlantic Ireland. Inevitably, Achill Island is changing as the Irish Tourist Board spreads its fame throughout the world. The 'roadless moorland' now has miles of excellent tarmac to carry the sightseer around the 'Atlantic Drive' of its southern peninsula. The 'savage coastline' has now been invaded by the ubiquitous caravan, whilst the villages have sprouted hotels, restaurants and gift shops, like many other 'Celtic' shorelines. But the 'silver sea', the 'booming waves', the 'tall hills' and the climatic elements remain, so that, off the beaten track, Achill remains as hauntingly beautiful as ever. I attempted to convey such sentiments in my book "Geology and Scenery in Ireland", twenty years after my first visit. In the intervening years I had been back to this Atlantic coast on several occasions, not only to collect more information but also with my family in order to enjoy its ambience, simply as a tourist.

Achill is a large island with a coastline about eighty miles in length, although purists claim that because of its road bridge, strictly, it is not insular. As in the cases of Anglesey and Skye such arguments are spurious because, manifestly, all are islands in their own right. We had come here in 1955 to learn the secrets of its cultural survivals and also to examine the ways in which the 'booming waves' had etched its Atlantic coastline, already deeply sculpted by glacial erosion. From our base at the well-known Amethyst hotel in the village of Keel, we had the square mile of Keel Lough on our doorstep and I was able to demonstrate how it had been formed after the blocking of its coastal stream by a massive storm beach of shingle that had separated the lough from the glittering expanse of Trawmore Sand and the open sea. The bay's south-westerly aspect, facing the full 'fetch' of ocean waves and bounded by tall enclosing headlands, reminded me of Hell's Mouth in the Llyn Peninsula. Even its name Trawmore (Large mouth) has similarities, but there the comparisons cease; Hell's Mouth is backed by high cliffs of glacial material, as described earlier, whilst Trawmore's hinterland consists of a plain of marram-fixed dunes, boggy pools and acres of samphire, sea asters, rushes, sedges and bent grass all of which are tolerant of sea spray. So exposed are these shores that the oldest of the thatched dwellings had been built with their doorways facing east away from the Atlantic storms. During our Easter visit, however, the island was blasted by gale-force easterlies from Europe and we found the older folk sitting crouched around their peat fires wrapped in blankets. We were told that this type of weather was an aberration and that Achill was famed for its mildness, as exemplified by its vegetation. On its roadsides the hedges comprise a mixture of bramble and fuchsia but peat-cuttings were still to be seen on the surrounding boglands. We went in search of the very rare Mediterranean heath on the island's northern coast but without success, having to remain satisfied by J. H. Tuke's 1847 comments of how "...a young man gathered me a branch of the Mediterranean heath, whose blossoms redeemed by their beauty the barrenness around. The heath brought back for a moment the rememberance of its lovely home by the blue waters of the Riviera". (A Visit to Connaught in the Autumn of 1847).

One of the main reasons for our visit was to allow Dr McCourt to introduce the students to a relict land use, termed 'rundale', a further example of that near Malin Head. I had already noted that Paul Henry had remarked how in Achill the "...fields were no bigger than a large table cloth, and a man might own a field or two beside his door and another bit of land, about the size of a small suburban front garden, a mile or so away". The survival of such a primitive land-use in Western Ireland has drawn many scholars to marvel at the few remaining examples that both Tuke and Praeger would have recognised in their 19th century visits. In addition to hearing about this subsistence farming, fertilised mainly by copious amounts of seaweed from the nearby shoreline, we also learnt about the ancient practice known as 'booleying' and we were fascinated to discover that this practice had survived in Achill within living memory. We trudged the muddy roads to a decrepit thatched cottage in which an ancient crone sat in the 'chimney corner'. Since she spoke only Irish we were indebted to an interpreter who passed on our questions. It transpired that the old woman was renowned throughout the nation as the last person to practice 'booleying', which was a type of Alpine 'transhumance'. I certainly experienced a haunting 'frisson' when listening to the cracked but lilting voice of a person approaching her hundredth birthday. Such antiquity reminded me of the time that I had looked into the eyes of the giant tortoise on the tiny island of St Helena which had lived from the time of Napoleon's imprisonment there. But heaven forbid that I imply how the old lady resembled a giant tortoise, despite her wrinkled visage!

I believe that it is important to quote in full a description of the almost forgotten ways of Irish peasant life, written in the mid-19th century by Sir William Wilde (father of Oscar) who, like the old woman sitting in front of us, had been an actual eye-witness of the practices she was about to recount: "During the spring the entire population of several of the villages we allude to in Achill, close their winter dwellings, tie their infant children on their backs, carry them with their loys [spades] – and some carry potatoes, with a few pots and cooking utensils – drive their cattle before them, and migrate into the hills, where they find fresh pastures for their flocks; and there they build rude huts and summer houses of sods and wattles, called booleys, and then cultvate and sow with corn a few fertile spots in the neighbouring valleys. They thus remain for about two months in the spring and early summer, till the corn is sown: their stock of provisions being exhausted, and the pasture consumed by the cattle, they return to the shore, and eke out a miserable, precarious existence by fishing". These were the words of an eminent Dubin surgeon but few Geographers could have expressed this long-lost practice so succinctly. I commiserated with the old lady about the privations that she must have suffered in her youth but her lined face broke into a smile as she recalled her 'frolics' with the teenage boys. She continued by telling us about the way in which the booley huts were constructed: a simple circle of rough stones was roofed with pieces of driftwood from the shore which were then roped together to form a low-angle cone; upon this insubstantial construction a layer of turf and heather was added. Only when this tiny hovel became converted into a permanent home would the dwellers add a layer of rye thatch. These must have been the type of structures seen by a Londoner, Edward Newman, who, in 1838, described Achill as "…more like a foreign land than any I have visited; the natives reside in huts, which a good deal resemble those of the Esquimaux Indians". Some seventy years later a report to the Congested Districts Board in 1906 revealed that little had changed in many of the permanently occupied homes on Achill. It describes how in the one tiny windowless room, around a central fire, there emerged "…a dozen geese, several hens, a cow and a calf, a horse and a colt, two or more toddling youngsters, one or two youths or maidens, and the father and mother".

Before we bade farewell to this amazing 'Oidheche Sheanchais' (Irish Story teller), she made us promise to visit the abandoned village of Slievemore some 200 feet up the slope of the prominent eponymous mountain, because of its association with the mid-19th century Great Irish Famine, that had occurred only a few years before her birth. We clambered up the heathery slopes to reach this remarkable linear 'street' of about one hundred houses where Dr McCourt talked about its history. Although it has many similarities to the better-known deserted village of St Kilda, since both look forlornly down to the neighbouring shore, that at Slievemore appears to have been forsaken considerably earlier than the Scottish example. It has been suggested that it was fully occupied in 1838 when the Ordnance Survey mapped the island at which time it was reckoned to have accommodated one tenth of Achill's population. By 1846, however, the entire popuation of Ireland had been halved by the Great Famine. Much has been written about this catastrophe, caused by failures of the potato crop, and we were shown remnants of the so-called 'lazy beds' in which the sole means of sustenance had once been grown. These tiny overgrown patches of ridged ground provided a sad testimony to the tragic events of some 170 years ago and, whilst we ate our packed lunches, seated amongst the roofless village houses, I could see that several students had been quite moved by the recollections of the historic experience. Such a response bore out my contention that certain events cannot be learnt simply from a text book, although the mood of our surroundings was neatly recaptured in later years by an Irish writer in his description of this 'ghost village': "The grey walls, the grey stones on the barren hill, the empty street seem suffused with this atmosphere, and even the sunlight shines grey as it glances off the rocks and stones" (Connaught, Sean Jennett, 1970).

The dominating cone of Slievemore (2,204 feet) sits centrally in the Island and a viewpoint high on its steep slopes gave me a splendid opportunity to introduce the students to a summary of Achill's geology and scenery. This lofty perch also provided a chance to look westwards to the type of landscape that has always held me in its thrall, that of craggy mountainous peaks cliffed by the sea. Here at Achill Head were facsimiles of Penmaenmawr, Holyhead Mountain, Yr Eifl and even Slieve League but painted on a much larger canvas. I couldn't wait to explore the jutting headland of ancient metamorphic rocks that thrusts out into the ocean like an oversized enlargement of Worms Head on the Gower. Unlike the latter, however, the marine cliffs of Croaghaun (2,192 feet) have been quarried by individual mountain glaciers that have etched out the armchair-like depressions known as corries, similar to those that we have already encountered on Slieve League in Donegal.

We journeyed out to Achill's western tip until we reached the roadhead at the lonely and miniscule Keem Bay, nestling between steep coastal cliffs. Here, geochemical activity has affected the mineral content of the rocks during periods of metamorphism and, at the junction of the schists and quartzites, has created small pockets (cluses) of amethysts. Needless to say, the students were keener to search for these semi-precious stones than to listen to my expositon on geology and on both wave- and glacial-erosion processes. Sir Arnold Bax, the British composer, referred to the Keem Bay 'treasures' when he too was bewitched by Achill and spoke of the "…amethyst caves and the green Atlantic". Although Bax lived in London he was born in Connacht, and had paid frequent visits to his homeland; he could easily be speaking of Achill when he wrote poetically of Western Ireland:

"There the dream-grey eyes of the humble
Will pour mist on my pain,
And the sea's old sleepy rustle,
The soft sigh of the rain,
And the blessed scent of the turf-smoke
Will give me content again".

More prosaically, we were all, both students and staff, fascinated by the doughty islanders who we saw launching their flimsy-looking, canvas-covered boats, known as 'curraghs', out into the heavy swell of the open ocean (no 'old sleepy rustle' on this occasion) for Keem Bay was once famous for its shark-fishing industry. But this was not for the Great White man-eaters but for the massive Basking Sharks that cruise around these shores. This species of shark, the second largest fish in the world, had been taken for centuries, both for its valuable oil and for its less valuable flesh. We were very lucky to witness the operation in action during which the denizens were first netted and then harpooned. The year of our visit coincided with the industry's record catch (1,708 fish) but I have read that the fishing had declined over the succeeding decades (a mere 29 fish in 1971) and I have since read that today this primitive type of fishing has probably disappeared. We also learnt during our visit that most Achill fishermen peferred not to take the risk of shark-fishing but trawled instead for the more saleable white fish, although the worthwhile collection of inshore shellfish has recently been boosted by the burgeoning tourist trade. When I returned to Achill with a party of undergraduates from Reading University, more than a decade later, we discovcred that tourism was beginning to provide the greatest source of income for the islanders. Sadly, I have recently heard from a former native of these parts, that this industry is beginning to cause something of a decline in the former attractiveness of the Achill ambience. But in the early-1960's the beguiling, almost dreamlike, solitude had still not disappeared and my English students spoke of their captivation with the island's scenic atmosphere and its surviving cultural heritage. Their enthusiasm proved to be of such an extent that a handful returned to write their dissertations on the Achill life-styles. Indeed, one of of my young ladies married an islandman.

From my own viewpoint I was itching to ascend to the summit of Croaghaun mountain because I had been told that the outstanding feature of the western end of the island is its north-west facing sea-cliff which plunges almost vertically from the summit cairn. This magnificent precipice, steeper than that of Slieve League in Donegal and higher than the famous Cliffs of Moher in County Clare (see below), is regarded by some as the finest sea-cliff in Western Europe, if one disregards those in the Faeroes and in Norway. Its panoply can only be viewed in full from the sea or, with great difficulty, from the jagged spine of Achill Head which, like the One Man's Path on Slieve League, possibly represents the remnant of a former dividing ridge between two corries (termed an 'arete') now invaded on both sides by the ocean. We had been told that Croaghaun's northern clifflines are also etched by corries, indicative of a former local ice-cap. But in order to view these phenomena we had to clamber from sea-level to almost 2,000 feet over the plateau-like summit. I was pleased that the students thought such exertions were worthwhile because only then were they able to marvel at a rarely visited collection of glacial phenomena unequalled anywhere in the British Isles. The embowered corrie lake of Lough Bunnafreeva West is perched behind its moraine on the very edge of the stupendous Croaghaun sea-cliff and, since cliff recession is slowly undermining the moraine, the lake-level is gradually falling, as can be seen from the abandoned shoreline. Further to the east, at lower elevations, three other corries occur, each with its jewel-like lake impounded by its crescentic moraine. That of Lough Nakeeroge East is the most interesting for its moraine is being actively eroded by the modern waves and it seems only a matter of time before the sea drains the corrie lake and breaks through into the corrie itself, the rock-floor of which must lie below sea-level. Only on the Island of Hoy, in the Scottish Orkney Isles, have I seen a corrie at modern sea-level. Personally, I was delighted to have this unique opportunity to view the type of coastline that I find most inspirational, that of mountains descending to rocky shorelines.

Despite its height and proximity to the shore, the equally high Slievemore has no major sea-cliff and only a single corrie. When the students asked me to explain the contrast I was able to demonstrate that whilst Croaghaun is exposed to the full force of Atlantic erosion, the less bulky Slievemore is relatively sheltered on the north coast, facing away from the direct attack of waves of maximum fetch. Moreover, instead of a wide summit plateau, its conical form would have presented a much smaller gathering-ground for any large snow fields to form during the Ice Age. Once more I was able to use the coastline as an open-air classroom whilst thoroughly enjoying my own experience of exploring a new maritime environment. The afternoon weather proved to be sunny and warm and after our exertions on the mountain tops, I was sure that a visit to the strand at Keel would provide a welcome break for everyone. Whilst the students frolicked in the sea I knew that I had to walk to the south-east corner of Trawmore Sand to get a closer look at the prominent Menawn Cliffs at the end of the bay. Here the full might of the ocean waves has carved the quartzite rocks into a series of arches and stacks, so that the so-called Cathedral Rocks have become one of the best-known scenic attractions in Achill. As I write I am able to relive this experience by looking at a watercolour of this very scene, that I bought many years later. I knew that the fine straw-coloured sand, upon which my teenagers were cavorting, had been eroded from the quartzites of the Menawn cliffs, but at this stage of the day I realised that such information would have been of no interest whatsoever to their young minds. I concluded that there was a limit to what they could assimilate in such a strenuous day, despite their exhuberance. Enough is enough!

Very soon the field-class was over and the students left to make their various ways home. I loaded my car and set off alone to explore the northern landscapes of Mayo. The Irish poet, George William Russell (AE), after visiting the wilderness known as the Great Bog of Erris in North Mayo, described "… a lonely road through bogland to the lake at Carrowmore". Such a description whetted my appetite to see for myself this countryside that had also inspired another literary figure, J. M. Synge, to write one of Ireland's best-known plays "The Playboy of the Western World". Throughout my thirty-mile journey across this wasteland I began to realise that I had never experienced a more desolate landscape – a seemingly endless expanse of heather-covered peat-bog that extended westwards to the appropriately named Blacksod Bay. Here was a coastline in which the thick layer of peat could be seen to extend below sea-level and where the bleached pine stumps, still in the position of growth, were draped in seaweed below a six-foot high tidal notch cut into the peat itself. From such phenomena anyone could ascertain that such a high degree of coast erosion was indicative of a rising sea-level and that the region must once have been heavily forested. I was reminded of the drowned 'forest beds' of Cardigan Bay where, in the so-called inundated Cantref-y-Gwaelod, the sea had advanced for scores of miles since the retreat of the ice-sheets. North Mayo is a region of heavy rainfall and of low population density and as I drove through heavy showers across this desolate coastal terrain of scatterd patches of green amongst the endles bogs and their slashes of black peat-cuttings, I experienced a feeling of loneliness, solitude and even despair, as if the scene itself had transferred its sombre mood into my own persona. Even the mighty 800-foot north-facing cliffs failed to inspire me, especially by comparison with the majestic precipitous shores of Achill. I could see no sign of tourism and yet here was a strikingly attractive coastline that was almost 'Terra lncognita' and, unlike Achill, appeared to be well away from the tourist trail. I thought to myself "God help the surviving Armada seamen who crawled ashore from their wrecked galleons on to this rockbound shore, several centuries ago".

Another Magee field-class took us much further south on these western Irish shores, this time to the County of Kerry. There the extensive exposures of resistant red sandstone had been fashioned by the Atlantic waves into a series of monumental peninsulas and intervening deeply penetrating bays cut into the less resistant Carboniferous Limestone. I had been on holiday in England which entailed taking the Irish car-ferry from Holyhead to Dublin on a night crossing. By the time I had reached the remote Dingle Penisula, in the far south-west, the day was almost over but as I drove the last few miles westwards beyond the town of Dingle and on to the unmade road which skirted the beetling cliffs of Slea Head, a most unforgettable scene unfolded. The settting sun was dipping behind the black silhouettes of the Blasket Isles and had transformed the white-washed cottages in the tiny village of Dunquin, into glowing jewels. I rate this view amongst the most memorable in my list of coastal vistas. In retrospect, I have noted that I am constantly describing sunsets along western seaboards but very rarely, if ever, sunrises on eastern shores. But such an omission will be rectified in a later chapter.

At the guest-house door I was greeted by Mr Kavanagh himself, a heavily-built, middle-aged and unshaven character dressed in muddied corduroy trousers and very large boots. His greeting was affable enough but I couldn't help thinking that he had every appearance of the 'stage Irishman', depicted in the plays of Synge. He looked as if he had just returned from the peat-diggings and had propped his 'loy' (spade) at the back door. He showed me to my tiny, cold and draughty room with its threadbare carpet. In his lilting Irish brogue, he informed me that tea would be ready soon, although this turned out to be an evening meal based on stacks of potatoes. The students were already ensconced in the small 'hotel' known as 'Kruger' Kavanagh's Guest House, but what I found so astonishing was the presence of several members of the university rugby club at the invitation of Dr McCourt, who was their coach. My next discovery was that the guest house had no bar but that inconvenience was quickly overcome when the rugger 'hearties' drove some miles away to purchase a barrel of beer. Having been shaken on the twisting and potholed tracks the amber liquid exploded in a deluge of froth, once it had been tapped, soaking the lounge carpet. I quickly gathered that, like most undergraduate bodies all over the British Isles, alcohol would remain an important priority. My mind went back to the time of my first arrival in Londonderry where, within a few weeks, I had been taken across the Border into Donegal to an all-night 'drinking-den' where I was induced to drink a glass of 'potheen' (pronounced 'potcheen') an illicit firewater distilled from potatoes. Even a sip had a kick like a mule but at least I was advised that I could quickly become drunk (or even dead) if I over-indulged. In this respect I later discovered an amusing anecdote in a book by Tony Gray, a feature-writer with the Irish Times, where he described a meeting with an Irish policeman or Garda: "If there is so little illicit distilling these days why not make it legal? I asked him. Well, he explained, it's a bit of a curiosity and the tourists are mad to try it. You'd kill the trade altogether by making it legal…As long as it's against the law, you'll always get some fellow prepared to keep it going" (The Irish Answer: An Anatomy of Ireland, Tony Gray, 1966).

The next morning, after a fairly noisy night, we were due to set off to view the ancient settlements of nearby Slea Head, if we could tempt the students out of their beds. The brisk breeze from the Atlantic soon blew away the cobwebs and we were introduced to the 'largest collection of pre-historic dwellings to be found in Ireland'. We roved around these remarkable stone structures, including primitive rock shelters, standing stones and souterrains (underground tunnels). But by far the most memorable were the remains of no less than 400 beehive dwellings built from slabs of local red sandstone which splits easily along its bedding-planes We were told how these skilfully constructed homes, despite their cramped interiors, had been occupied sporadically until medieval times and such information reminded us how serious were the population pressures on these western promontories, even up to a century ago. But it has long been known that it was in this stormy environment, on the fringe of Europe, that western Christianity survived 'by the skin of its teeth' during the Dark Ages. From our lofty viewpoint we could see the splintery pyramids of the two Skellig Rocks, far away on the horizon, where monks had constructed their 6th century monastery on the topmost pinnacle of the Great Skellig. Closer too were the long chain of the Blasket Isles, four miles long and a mere half mile wide, where a 1,000-foot knife-edge ridge has been carved by the waves into six islands. Only the Great Blasket was inhabited and that tiny settlement had been abandoned a couple of years before our arrival, and yet our host, Mr Kavanagh, told us that, during the last century, it had been a 'Mecca' of Irish culture.

Such information was worthy of further exploration, until we learnt that we would all have to travel by curragh at great expense and potential hazard if we wished to experience the atmosphere of this fabled island. Thus, I had to be content with reading the travails of that great romantic writer, Sean O'Faolain, when he wrote about his visit to the Great Blasket some twenty years previously, also in a curragh and in a mood of extreme trepidation: "I knelt in the prow and faced the dark bulk of the Great Island. It was not a bad sea … The darkness of the Middle Ages now fell on us … I sat by the hearth with the island's famous shanachie, Tomas O'Criomhthainn, and – perhaps I was evilly disposed – I thought that he was a pompous old man, and I contradicted all his proverbs… I enjoyed tussling with old Tomas and he enjoyed tussling with me, and I noted that the company enjoyed it even more so. It is probably a novelty to hear a shanachie contradicted" (An Irish Journey, Sean O'Faolain and Paul Henry, 1941). When I was an undergraduate my love of islands had led me to collect virtually every book on this subject. Indeed, I was once asked, by the commissioning editor of Penguin Books, to write a book on world islands that I had visited on my travels. Alas, the publishers had to be content instead with my three books on the British Isles. But amongst my own collection, in addition to that of Tomas's "Islandmen", I had also read "Twenty Years A-Growing" by Tomas O'Sullivan, "The Western Island" by Robin Flower and "Peig" by Peig Sayers. The latter's wizened image had been sketched by Robert Lockley's wife when she and her husband had left their own island home in Pembrokeshire to visit the Blaskets. I would love to have known what their own impressions had been of the equally desolate conditions of island living. Robin Flower's description of his first meeting with the formidable, pipe-smoking Peig revealed her extraordinary personality and reminded me of my own meeting with the old lady on Achill Island who had beguiled us with her tales. Flower went on to describe how Peig illuminated the conversation with her lively and humerous memories of the past. But enough of this Gaelic indulgence. My job was to teach the students something of Kerry's landform processes and the evolution of its scenery.

As usual, I started by looking at the local coastlines and the ways in which the detailed cliff-forms have been governed by the geological structures. To the north of Dunquin, for example, the waves had made major breaches in the red sandstone 'hogsback' cliffs between Ballydavid Head and Sybil Point, thereby allowing the sea to invade the Ballyferriter lowland to create the shallow bay of Smerwick Harbour. The absence of the high raised shorelines, that we had witnessed in Donegal, together with the few exposures of post-glacial beaches had suggested to Nick Stephens that the region was tectonically stable because it had not experienced the same degree of post-glacial isostatic adjustment as that of Northern Ireland. (N. Stephens, 1970). The contrast could be explained by the different thicknesses of their respective ice-caps. That in North West Ireland, near to the centre of the Scottish ice dome, was many times thicker than that in Kerry and Cork which was little more than a limited mountain glaciation.

It has been shown that the highest summits of the Dingle Peninsula had never been overridden by ice-sheets during the Ice Age, because the massive northern Irish ice-sheet had failed to link up with the smaller Kerry-Cork ice cap. Consequently, one can discover on the unglaciated terrain several examples of landforms fashioned largely by severe frost-action which had shattered the hard rocks and churned their overlying soils. Such features are termed 'periglacial' or frost-formed landforms, foremost amongst which is the splintery eminence of Minnaunmore Rock which interjects its serrated skyline near to Clogher Head. There seems little doubt that this ridge of ancient volcanic rocks is a good example of a tor, not unlike those that I had seen in Pembrokeshire, carved from similar rock-types. The Blaskets, also, exhibit many tor-like rock outcrops, because they too were never over-ridden by glaciers. That is not to say, however, that the magificent peak of Mount Brandon (3,127 feet) failed to have its own suite of deeply carved corries. And it was to its summit that we had to ascend, not only to view the surrounding coastlines but also to see a rare Irish example of a specific feature of glacial erosion. Brandon Mountain extends for a distance of six miles, from north to south and, where its northern slopes have been cliffed by the sea at Brandon Head, the precipices of Sauce Creek and Beenaman cliffs can be seen to rival those of Slieve League and Achill Island as some of Ireland's highest sea-cliffs.

We laboured to the summit, an ever-extending straggle of students quite unfamiliar with this type of exertion, and finally, at the cairn, I drew them together in order to inculcate their minds with some 'pearls of wisdom' on glacial landforms. Little did I realise that they were much more interested in the whereabouts of the student who had been designated to carry up the bottles of Guinness. Finally, this somewhat overweight young man arrived puffing and panting under the burden of his heavy rucksack. The much fitter rugby players, who had remained with our party, had obviously pulled a fast one by evading this chore. At last it became possible to lead them all along the rock-strewn summit-ridge towards the even more dramatically shaped separate eminence of Brandon Peak (2,764 feet). Here, we stood in awe as we peered down the rarely viewed deep gash which descends, almost vertically, from the intervening col, across the cliff-face and down to the base of the mountain. This feature must once have been filled by a large, heavily crevassed glacier, tumbling steeply in a series of ice-falls. Today the imposing scene is termed a 'glacial stairway' in which a descending succession of small lakes, perched on their rock-steps, are linked by a cascading stream all the way down to Lough Cruttia. The water-features are termed 'paternoster lakes' from their likeness to a string of rosary beads (very appropriate in a Catholic country), and the surrounding ice-smoothed and polished rock slabs, bright pink because of their total lack of vegetation, appeared so fresh that it seemed as if the glacier had disappeared only yesterday, instead of 10,000 years ago. Little did I know at the time, that within a year or two I would be working in a very similar environment but this time far from the coast in Equatorial Africa. Moreover, this was to be at 15,000 feet on the rapidly decaying glaciers of the Rwenzori range of Uganda, not just above sea-level in Ireland.

The Mount Brandon landforms were certainly worthy of the lengthy slog and the students all agreed that they were something rather special, or was it simply the bottles of Guinness talking? Lloyd Praeger spoke of Mount Brandon as the finest peak in Ireland and even a layman would possibly rhapsodise about the magnificent views that could be seen from the summit, just so long as the weather was kind. Prominent in the northern vista would be the largest beach formation in Kerry, that of the Castlegregory Peninsula. This four-mile long sandy promontory of marram-fixed dunes, is a further example of a 'tombolo' in which tidal currents have linked together some of the limestone Magharee Islands (The Seven Hogs) and joined them to the mainland. In so doing a shallow lagoon, Lough Gill, has been impounded behind the landward end of the tombolo. On turning in the opposite direction, to view the the southern shores of the Dingle peninsula we could discern other lengthy sand-spits, foremost of which is that at Inch, some miles to the east of Dingle town. This spit is matched by that of the Cromane foreland on the opposite shore of the estuary of the River Laune. Together they have almost closed-off the estuary to form the shallow Castlemaine Harbour, a name which belies the vislon of a haven for shipping, for it is nothing more than a maze of shallow water, sandbanks, mud flats and saltmarshes. But I was able to explain how the two spits have different morphologies; whilst Inch is a true coastal spit formed by wave action on the shingle and dune-derived sand, that at Cromane is not a true spit but an old glacial morainic mound now tied to the mainland by a peat-bog and a tombolo of beach sand. We did not have to look far for the source of the glacial morainic material, for a few miles to the south, the high mountain-wall of Macgillicuddy's Reeks had been rent by the deep glacial valley in which Lough Carragh is cradled. There was no time to climb Ireland's highest mountain (Carrauntoohil, 3,414 feet), much to my own disappointment but to the students' great relief, I am certain. No doubt, I should have ascertained by then, that not everyone has the same desire to climb high mountains or even tramp almost endlessly along seashores. I could claim, however, that being able to look down from high summits to the surrounding shores was as good as, if not better than, viewing from a plane or using aerial photographs.

I was to return to Kerry on several other occasions: once to supervise Richard Bryant, one of my postgraduate students, who was mapping the western extent of the former ice-cap, the features of which we had been examining a decade earlier; and on a few occasions, either to gather material for my Penguin Book on "Geology and Scenery in Ireland", or simply to holiday with the family and complete a few oil paintings of these breathtaking coastlands. It will have been realised at this point of the narrative, that these were the types of landscapes that I find most inspiring: sea-girt mountains, closely-grazed turf and gnarled vegetation, endless vistas beneath ever-changing skies, all bathed in the ethereal luminous light of the western ocean. It must be remembered, however, that I was a visitor from England, looking at these coasts with rose-tinted spectacles. An Irishman might have very different views, as epitomised by J. M. Synge who, on a visit to Dunquin at the beginning of the 20th century, witnessed groups of people on their way to Mass: "…the men in homespun and the women wearing blue cloaks or, more often, black shawls twisted over their heads. This procession along the olive bogs, between the mountains and the sea, on this grey day of autumn, seemed to wring me with a pang of emotion one meets everywhere in Ireland – an emotion that is local and patriotic, and partly a share of the desolation that is mixed everywhere with the supreme beauty of the world" (Synge's Works: In Wicklow, West Kerry and Connemara. J. M. Synge, 1919). Talking of the locals attending Mass reminded me of the time at 'Kruger' Kavanagh's guest house when, on a Sunday morning, he blithely informed us that there would be no lunch, because all the staff had gone to church. "It will be fine" he said "if you go down to the shore and knock some limpets off the rocks. You won't starve because we eat them all the time". This was certainly a breath of homespun Ireland.

Three years after leaving my post in Londonderry my life had moved on apace; by then I was married, had spent three years in East Africa and was waiting to take up my new academic post in California. It came as something of a surprise, therefore, when a letter arrived bearing a French postmark. It turned out that it was an invitation, from Professor Andre Guilcher in the University of the Sorbonne in Paris, asking me if I would like to join him in a coastal mapping enterprise in western Ireland. I had been introduced to this like-minded Physical Geographer by Professor Steers a few months earlier when we all three had attended the International Geographical Union Symposium in Denmark. Thus, Guilcher had been one of those windswept scientists on the dune coast of the island of Rømø, that I have described in the Prologue. But his planned Irish research project was to be on a very different type of coastline, that of Clew Bay in County Mayo, within sight of Achill Island. It transpired that he proposed to determine the morphology of the sea-floor by the use of a marine survey. He and his fisherman crew were intending to dredge the sea-floor and take samples of the materials, be they mud, sand, gravel or boulders. My job, it seemed, was to stand in the wheelhouse to monitor the depth-sounder and record the exact location of the samples. This would be my first research programme on the sea instead of on the land and would see me exchanging geological hammers, compass clinometers and aneroid barometers for maritime charts, oilskins, a sharp pencil and a pair of good sea legs. It was really not very convenient because of my impending departure for America but who could spurn such a unique opportunity?

Clew Bay itself had been carved by marine erosion along a narrow corridor of Carboniferous Limestone between two major highland promontories of ancient Pre-Cambrian rocks. But what made it of such great interest to geomorphologists was that it was Ireland's best example of a drumlin coastline partly submerged by the sea. Strangford Lough exhibits a similar shoreline but nowhere near on the scale of that of Clew Bay. Moreover, Strangford Lough is virtually land-locked and sheltered from major wave erosion whilst the drumlins of Clew Bay have been open to the full force of Atlantic erosion since they were uncovered after the recession of the ice-sheets. Thus, the archipelago of some eighty whale-backed islands exhibit varying degrees of morphology, according to whether they are fully exposed to the wave attack or sheltered in the innermost tracts of the Bay. The eroded glacial material from the steep west-facing drumlin cliffs, usually of boulder clay, has been redeposited by both wave- and tidal-forces to form shingle spits, tombolos and forelands. Some of these shingle spits have succeeded in linking several of the most seaward of the drumlin islands, thereby protecting some of the inner islands from erosion. It was the intention of our mission to map the submarine position of the totally destroyed drumlins and to be able to discover the exact limits of their original westward extent. Many of the larger islands are now grazed by cattle and a few of them have retained a handful of buildings but, in common with many other parts of Ireland's Atlantic seaboard, most of the cottages are derelict and thistles now thrive in the former pastures.

Having sold my car, prior to leaving for America, I was forced to travel to County Mayo via the Holyhead-Dublin ferry and take a train to Westport. Professor Guilcher met me at the station of this small coastal town and drove me out to Old Head quay near to Louisburgh, overlooking the drumlin 'swarm'. After a pleasant meal with his wife and daughter, who would remain at the hotel, I was appraised of the research project in detail, before we all strolled to the end of the sea wall to admire the sort of rain-washed Atlantic skyline that has long beguiled visiting tourists. The next morning the Breton fishing vessel hove into view, picking its way slowly through the tortuous channels. It turned out to be a small, stumpy, shallow-bottomed trawler, named the "Kornog", manned by a skipper, an engineer and two deck-hands, all weather-beaten, bearded and unable to speak any English. "This is going to be somewhat tricky" I thought to myself, because any instructions sent to the wheelhouse, unless translated en route, would have to be interpreted by means of my very basic French.

The next few days we strove to carry out our seemingly endless tasks, twisting and turning through the narrow waterways; Guilcher and the deck-hands up at the prow hauling dripping canisters on board, and me alongside the gruff and taciturn skipper, who smoked foul-smelling Gauloises, both of us trying to maintain our balance on the pitching vessel. But at least he had the helm (wheel) to steady himself whilst I clung to the nearest object. I shall never forget the incessant clanging of the ship's bell whenever we heaved and tossed. The food was very basic, consisting mainly of fish and I was delighted to discover that I wasn't sea sick, unlike Andre Guilcher who parted company with his sardine breakfast every morning. After a few days the weather began to worsen, coinciding with our venturing further out into the relentless ocean in order to map those drumlin remnants now totally submerged. The increased storminess led to difficulties of trawling which meant that we gathered fewer and fewer samples and, in any case, I was due to leave for the UK to give time to pack for California. Unfortunately, the tide was ebbing and the skipper was unable to get me anywhere near to our Old Head moorings. Thus, he took me ashore in the ship's boat and left me on one of the larger islands, where the lighthouse indicated the presence of people. I waved goodbye from the beach and sought out the lighthouse keeper who kindly agreed to row me to the mainland in his tiny dinghy. The nearest point on the mainland, however, was a few miles from the railway station at Westport and the evening was drawing on. Carrying my suitcase, I tramped along a narrow seashore track until I reached a lane where in due course I hitched a lift in a farm vehicle. The friendly farmer, enquiring why I was wandering alone in this forsaken spot, roared with laughter when I explained my circumstances. "Hard luck" he said, "you've missed the last train to Dublin and the next day's train isn't until noon, so you'll have to stay the night in Westport".

As we arrived in the town, at twilight, I was astonished to find the normally quiet streets of Westport were swarming with very inebriated hordes of people, almost like a football crowd. My newly found friend informed me that I'd chosen a bad time to look for accommodation because the following day, Sunday, was the annual pilgrimage to the oratory on the summit of Croagh Patrick (2,510 feet). The setting sun lit up the gleaming white stones of the track which zig-zagged up the steep slopes of this quartzite pyramid and which were kept freshy scuffed by the thousands of feet (and sometimes knees) of the countless numbers of pilgrims. A visit to an uproarious bar confirmed the lack of beds and I wandered disconsolatley to the station, intending to spend the night in the waiting-room. A kindly lady, hearing of my problem, offered me a room in her guest house, due to a cancellation, and I was grateful to take up her offer. The room proved to be cold, draughty and the damp bed-sheets were covered with seagull droppings, after having been brought in from a lengthy sojourn on the washing-line. They were considerably worse than my shipboard blankets which, themselves, had stank of fish, diesel oil and Gauloises, but the guest house at least gave me somewhere to rest, fully dressed on top of a decent bed. It was considerably better than a hard waiting-room bench and it was free of the swaying motion of a shipboard berth. I was aware of strange comings and goings along the corridor that left me thinking that most of these visits could have been to the lavatory to relieve the intoxicated guests who had staggered in during the early hours, singing hearty Irish ballads.

After a very restless night and an excellent breakfast, I had time on my hands to explore the town and watch the pilgrims toiling up the mountain path. Westport, huddled amidst its drumlin hillocks, is hidden away from the sea, despite its name. Although planned to be a major port for northern Connacht, the empty warehouses at its quay testified to the failure of such an enterprise, due partly to silting of the channels. Nevertheless, the planned town of 1780, with its interesting polygonal market place, its beautiful stream in a tree-lined Mall was reminiscent of an Amsterdam canal, while its fine Georgian mansion of Westport House, added to the charm which is often missing from some Irish towns. Moreover, its setting beneath towering mountains led the novelist, W. M. Thackeray, to describe this locality as possessing the "...most beautiful scenery in all the world".

Another writer arrived in Westport, many years after my visit, hoping to climb Croagh Patrick and find solitude. Alas, he found himself in similar circumstances to myself for it proved to be a day of pilgrmage. The writer was the acclaimed Cambridge don, Robert Macfarlane, who, like myself, writes about his travels to exotic corners of the British Isles. He reports that he had not expected the number of pilgrims, nor had he expected to find the amount of litter on St Patrick's summit: "...chocolate-bar wrappers stuffed into rock crevices, rotting banana skins lying outside the door to the new oratory. It was an uneasy mix of the sacred and the profane" (The Wild Places, Robert Macfarlane, 2007).

As I sat on Westport railway station waiting for my train departure I had time to think about what had been achieved during my brief but exhilarating stint of 'offshore geomorphology'. It was certainly very different from all the coastal research that I had carried out in Wales and from the many hours of lecturing on Irish landforms to classes of Irish students. We had ascertained that the outermost coast of Clew Bay had retreated about ten miles since the beginning of the post-glacial submergence and that the current rate of wave erosion on the west-facing drumlin cliffs was more than 1 foot per year. More significantly, from a commercial viewpoint, we had demonstrated that some of the channels in this complex archipelago were silting up at an increasing rate. Overall, I had learnt, at first hand, about the dynamics of ever-shifting shorelines in this part of the British Isles, a lesson with which I would become much more familiar when I came to live near to the coast of Norfolk.

I thought that Clew Bay's coastline was the most complex that I had ever seen, until I visited Connemara whose shoreline is the most convoluted anywhere in Ireland. Connemara is part of County Galway which itself is part of the province of Connacht and every Irishman is familiar with Cromwell's damning phrase "To Hell or Connacht" when he confined many native Irish to the desolate western seaboard during his brutal regime. He summed up his own perception when he remarked that there were not enough trees to hang a man nor soil to bury a man. Yet here lies a paradox for, in modern times, everyone, be they Irish or British, sings the praises of Connemara's beauty. Sir Arnold Bax, for example, having read W. B. Yeats's "The Wanderings of Oisin" quickly became entranced and thought of Connacht as his 'Tir-nan-Nog', when he rhapsodised how It's "...atmosphere is hovering between the world we know too well and some happy otherworld that we begin to glimpse when we are growing up and never reach. I can't explain it, but it is so, and every person is enslaved by the magic of it". But, this romantic landscape of bogland, bare rock, drystone walls, blood-red fuchsias, white cottages and grazing donkeys, embowered by a glittering ocean, is one that tourists find beguiling, but it has its darker side. Our old friend Sean O'Faolain summed up this environment when he wrote that: "No man can look on the lovely face of Connemara without feeling the tragedy of mortal impermanence, the harshness, indeed the unfairness of the struggle between man and nature which wears him out and outlasts him" (Sean O'Faolain and Paul Henry, *op. cit.*). He was echoing the words of the famous Irish poet and nationalist, Patrick Pearse, a native of Connemara, who, on the night before his execution by a British army firing squad, wrote of "The beauty of the world hath made me sad. This beauty that will pass, and fade, and be no more". So, what is it that grips the soul and causes artists, poets and writers to become so emotional when they portray its wild beauty? I was unable to explain such passion but I too was to find Connemara a quite remarkable experience. Its landscape soon became so deeply fixed in my mind that its reputation had drawn me back to Ireland's west coast for a family holiday.

When I first drove out westwards through the bustling streets of Galway city and the prosperous hotels of Salthill, I soon entered the uncompromising wilderness of Galway granite, where almost all the settlements and improved land hug the treeless coast. O'Faolain noted this dichtomy in the landscape and pointed out that the lack of any signs of prehistoric culture inland suggested that this had always been the case. Nevertheless, local tradition has it that in earlier centuries one could walk on the tops of the trees from Letterfrack, in west Connemara, all the way to Galway city. It is true that, as on the coasts of the Great Bog of Ennis (noted above) tree stumps can be seen beneath the peat but there is a current lack of arboreal vegetation anywhere along the shores of Connemara. This is hardly surprising because a combination of salt-laden winds and a shortage of wood for building has seen virtually everything but stunted shrubs destroyed. Here, the winding coast road is bordered by ice-polished granite whose large crystals of pink feldspar give the rocks their distinctive colouring, although the granite boulders have often been dulled by profuse lichen growth, especially where they have been used for drystone walls. Such growth is indicative of the constantly high humidity of these parts but it brings splashes of brighter colours into the olive drabness of the bogland. A profusion of granite boulders scattered over the landscape is one of the most notable features near to Spiddal, and it was here that J. M. Synge noticed how "...the fields looked so small and rocky that the very thought of tillage in them seemed like the freak of an eccentric". Nonetheless, I found that a remarkably large population is supported on this barren coastal margin which was once part of the notorious 'Congested Districts' where "...cottages swarmed by the roadside and in the boreens". The ubiquitous stoniness is the result of glacial erosion because Connemara had its own little ice-cap, centered amidst the picturesque "Twelve Pins", a mosaic of prominent quartzite pyramids rising steeply above the bogs. The glaciers had moved radially outwards beyond the present shores, even reaching across Galway Bay as far as the Aran Isles. And it was these glaciers that had not only scoured away most of the soils but had also quarried out structural weaknesses in the granite which allowed the rising post-glacial sea to penetrate deeply inland.

West of Costelloe one enters a dreamlike landscape consisting of more than one hundred square miles of island-studded ocean; a labyrinth of land and sea unparalleled elsewhere in Ireland. Little wonder that the name of the village of Camus ('Crooked shoreline') reflects this tortuous coastline along which centuries of peat-digging have also revealed the polished and mamillated bedrock. The legendary subsistence economy of potatoes and oats was still prevalent during my first visit, whilst the home industries of knitting and tweed-making were seen to support the meagre income derived from fishing. But fishing on a large commercial scale, like that at Killybegs in Donegal, has never really succeeded here, for the Atlantic swell is continuous and the submerged rocks and sandbanks in the serpentine channels remain severe hazards.

Many of the islands are now linked by bridges to the mainland, having been constructed mainly during the so-called scheme of 'Relief Road' building during the famine years of the 19th century. As I drove over miles of winding roads I found it difficult to envisage, through the eyes of a visitor, the poverty that must once have prevailed on what I perceived only as a magnificent coastline of rocky headlands and coral beaches, secreted in hidden bays. I had to turn, once again, to J. M. Synge, who had followed those same roads half a century before me: "We drove many miles, with Costello and Carraroe behind us, along a bog-road built up on a turf embankment, with broad grassy sods at either side, perhaps to make a possible way for the barefooted people, then two spaces of rough broken stones where the wheel-ruts are usually worn, and in the centre a track of gritty earth for the horses". He continues: "As we drove quickly by we could see that every man and woman was working with a hang-dog dejection that would be enough to make any casual passer mistake them for a band of convicts" (J. M. Synge, *op. cit.*). Not until we holidayed on a remote Scottish island in the 1970's were we able to witness a similar type of back-breaking toil in a similar environment (see the following chapter).

On returning to Connemara with Diane a few years later, to gather more material for my forthcoming Penguin Book, we found that much had changed for the better. There were more cars on the improved roads, many new houses had appeared, especially along the coast, new hotels had opened and people looked more prosperous. Since joining the European Union Ireland has flourished even more; those stony roads are newly surfaced, the cottages freshly painted and I have recently learnt that Patrick Pearse's cottage, in the very middle of the Connemara bogland, is now a celebrated Visitor Centre. It seems that the coastal dwellers, in particular, have built up a flourishing international tourist trade which, considering the perfect combination of high mountains (The Twelve Pins), great seascapes and rain-washed visibilty, have tended to push much of Connacht's tragic history into the background.

We were forced to spend an unplanned stop in Clifden, in the far west of Connemara, after our car suffered a temporary breakdown. This tiny market town, on a hidden arm of the ocean, appeared almost as a paradoxical oasis in the desolation of a waterlogged country, bcause its spired churches, set amidst woodland, seemed so out of character. Its tiny harbour, at the head of a narrow and difficult estuary to navigate, is generally used only by small boats from the neighbouring islands, instead of any large fishing vessels. Next day, when we set off once more, we were told that we should take the coast road to Ballconneely because then we would pass the memorial to the first non-stop Atlantic flight by Alcock and Whitten-Brown, since this is where they crash-landed in Derrygimlagh Bog in June 1919. Of far greater significance to me, however, was being able to visit the so-called 'Coral Strand' at Mannin Bay and one has to admit that the beach looks like a tropical coral strand at first glance. However, the title is a complete misnomer, for this 'coral' is no more than a curious calcareous seaweed that has abstracted its lime from the seawater. Waves have broken the 'coral' into tiny branch-like slivers which crunch beneath ones' feet above the high-tide line, but around the low-tide level it is possible to see this extraordinary wrack, termed 'Lithothamnion', growing in situ. Not surprisingly, this lime-rich seaweed has long been 'harvested' by the locals to serve as a fertiliser for their deprived fields.

Nearer to the delightful coastal village of Roundstone it is possible to discover a real coral beach at Dog's Bay whose Irish name “Port na Feao'oise” (Shore of the Plover) is surely a great deal more attractive than the canine version, despite its unpronouncability. We parked the car and walked towards the sea to be greeted by an extraordinary riot of colour. A short tombolo of blown sand has tied the small granitic island of Goirtin to the shore and has allowed the build-up of a crescentic creamy-white beach. This was no seaweed but a collection of broken marine shells with barely a sand grain in sight. From this beach geologists have recorded no less than 124 species and varieties of 'foraminifera', tiny microscopic creatures which formerly lived in deeper waters offshore. The absence of quartz-sand grains at this locality has been explained by the difficulties of longshore wave-movement within this tiny embayment. It wasn't only the turquoise shades of the inshore waters but the remarkable profusion of plants that have given to this coastal strip such a kaleidoscope of colour. Moreover, as the plants stretch inland up onto the lowest slopes of Errisbeg Mountain, overlooking the bay, they become mixed with a profusion of rare and exotic heathers, such as St Dabeoc's Heath which, together with dwarf gorse, create a striking image of purple and gold in late summer. Is it any wonder that this part of Connemara's southern coast has become so popular with artists? My brother-in-law, Ken Beresford, a talented artist from the Royal College of Art, produced what I believe is one of his finest canvases at this very picturesque site.

Several years later I was invited to review a book on Connemara for a scientific journal, and I found an immediate rapport with its author, Tim Robinson, whose description of the region's natural phenomena brought the landscape alive. Here was yet another 'Oidheche Sheanchais'(Storyteller) on Ireland's Atlantic shoreline but, unlike our Achill raconteur or Peig of The Blaskets, Tim writes in a metaphysical yet scientific style as befits a 'romantic materialist', as he terms himself. His methods are those of a beachcomber/

Llandudno Bay from the Great Orme looking eastwards to the Little Orme

Conwy Mountain, North Wales, the location of my First Degree research camp site

Braich-y-Pwll headland, near Aberdaron, Llyn Peninsula, North Wales with Bardsey Island beyond. This coastline was one of my 'special places'

Wiston Castle ruins, Pembrokeshire. The ancestral home of the Whittow family for some two centuries (c. 1100 to c. 1300). (From a painting by Leon Olin)

Whittow Wharf, Milford Haven, showing modern development (1990's)

A typical scene in Connacht in the West of Ireland. This view of Connemara, looking towards its convoluted coastline, would hardly have changed since the time that the author J. M. Synge visited here a century ago

The Straits of Iona, looking east to the Ross of Mull

Nunnery ruins on Iona

Cadgwith Cove, Cornwall

Mullion Cove, Cornwall

Blakeney Point marshes looking seawards to the fringing dunes

Boardwalks to protect the dunes from trampling at Blakeney Point

The Hebridean Princess off the Cuillins of Skye

The coal-strewn beach at Easington Colliery, Durham before National Trust ownership

The same beach after National Trust reclamation

chronicler, setting out to discover, analyse and catalogue the minutiae not only of Connemara's shorelines but also those of the Aran Isles and The Burren (which was to be our next venue) in his 1996 book "Setting Foot on the Shores of Connemara: and Other Writings". He is a sort of cartographer who maps by means of spatial and multi-dimensional constructs which reflect his training as a former Cambridge mathematician. When turning his attention to Ireland's most fragmented coastline (which must have taxed the 19th century Ordnance Survey field surveyors to their utmost limits) he describes its 'fractional dimensionalities' into what he terms a 'Connemara Fractal'. He proceeds to conceive of a strange map consisting of one line so convoluted that it visited every point of the territory and he likened the texture of Connemara to 'fractal geometry' which he believes was to Celtic Art what Euclid was to Classical Art. Such a comparison is based on his contention that the repetitive interweaving patterns of simple linear elements explains the fascinating beauty of Connemara's shores. Despite his somewhat tortuous mathematical explanation I began to understand the linkage between the tangled form of Connemara's ragged shoreline and the Gaelic stonemasons' intricate patterns which, over hundreds of years, they had laboriously chiselled into thousands of antique Celtic crosses. Such Celtic art was not solely the preserve of the sculptors, however, for on the fabled Aran Isles a wonderful skill of folk-knitting has thrived for centuries. I was told that the intricate patterns of the Aran sweaters, worn largely by the fishermen, were each unique and of a distinctive design in order to identify the individual when his drowned body was brought ashore. Much publicity was given to the island's fishing industry in the iconic film "Man of Aran" made by Robert Flaherty in 1934, where it was shown how the doughty islanders went out in their flimsy curraghs to fish for sharks. Unfortunately, the film was lambasted by the critics and by the Aran folk themselves because of the dozens of errors in the filming. Nonetheless, it gave the islanders such international fame that they now survive almost entirely on tourism and the export of their beautiful sweaters. Like several other of these remote western islands, Aran was a place where Christianity survived during the Dark Ages, as "…the greatest spiritual storehouse the world has ever known: more saints, hermits and holy pilgrims lived and died there than in any other place" (Aran: Islands of Legend, P. A. O'Siochain, 1952). It was this tranquil spiritual quality that has led to the saying that "In Aran one can find solitude without loneliness".

Once we had left behind the waterlogged landscape of Connemara we moved on to another ocean-fretted coastline but this time there was hardly a drop of water to be seen, except from the sky! And it was here that we found 'solitude but with considerable loneliness' because this was The Burren, renowned throughout the British Isles as the finest 'karstland' to be found within their bounds. The term 'karst' refers to a terrain created by limestone solution and characterised by a virtual absence of surface drainage which has led to a scene of waterless depressions, fissures, collapse-structures and an extensive underground drainage system. But the Burren is also a fairly uncommon example of what is termed 'glacio-karst' where over-riding ice-sheets are thought to have swept away almost all of its original soil and rounded off all the plateau hilltops. Because this process means that modern settlement is sporadic on the bare, greyish limestone it comes as something of a surprise to read that in pre-historic times The Burren was heavily populated and farmed. My former Irish colleague, Professor Frank Mitchell, poses the question "Where have the forest and the soil gone?" He suggests that too much farming activity is his preferred explanation. He continues: “There is pollen evidence of Neolithic presence in the region, and it was certainly heavily settled when the Neolithic was giving way to the Early Bronze Age about 4000 years ago, because there are numerous megalithic tombs scattered across the Burren uplands”. It appears that when the ice-sheets had receded, a mantle of glacial debris was left on the limestone surface upon which a primeval soil developed and a fragile plant cover became established. Mitchell explains that over-exploitation by farming practices meant that “…once the plant cover was disturbed or burnt – a very common practice with prehistoric peoples – and the decayed vegetable debris of which it was composed was exposed to the air, then the soil material began to oxidise and disappear” (The Way that I Followed, Frank Mitchell, 1990). Atlantic winds and rain, over the succeeding centuries, have almost finished off what humankind had started. Such an environmental impact almost mirrors that which prevails on the British coasts of today where, in many places, the human footprint is destroying, or at least seriously impacting on, the landscape that Nature has so bountifully provided on almost all the British shores. (The Burren. David Cabot & Roger Goodwillie, 2018).

As we left the coast road to view this remarkable scenery of bare limestone pavements and tiny almost grassless fields, enclosed by miles of drystone walls, we wondered why the farmers had laboured to build these painstaking enclosures, when there were hardly any livestock to be seen. The answer seemed to lie in the fact that many of these stone boundaries were built in those pre-historic times to which Mitchell refers. Nonetheless, despite its emptiness, it is an entrancing landscape, especially along the coastal hills and plateaux where, by slowly turning one’s head, it is possible to look from a waterless and desolate terrain across mile upon mile of restless ocean in such a close juxtaposition. I was reminded of other empty shores of my memory, but they were the arid and barren sub-tropical sandy desert fringes of Africa and western Australia, that were equally devoid of coastal dwellers.

We sat on a low stone wall, overwhelmed by the solitude and the far-reaching barren, stony landscape, yet only a few steps from the coast road. It set me wondering how the few farms that we could discern were able to find a supply of water, but I rapidly realised that the copious rainfall of this western shore would be captured by every possible means. My mind went back to a time almost forty years previously when I had wanted to know why there were dewponds on the equally waterless chalk downs above Beachy Head. Yet, even here in this Irish wilderness, there was a hint of green against the greystone vistas and this, we found, was provided by the scattered ash trees that had somehow managed to survive in pockets of remnant soils. But we had no time to delve deeper into the solution 'grikes' where botanists such as Lloyd Praeger, had discovered an amazing array of rare plant survivals in the deep fissures. Some, such as the spring gentian and mountain avens, are rare Alpines, and Lloyd Praeger tells us that "With these there are others which are very rare in the British area, like the hoary rock rose and pyramidal bugel; [some] are conspicuous by their immense profusion, like the bloody cranesbill and madder, hartstongue and scale fern. The result of the luxuriance and abundance of these is that over miles the grey limestone is converted into a veritable rock-garden in spring, brilliant with blossom" (Lloyd Praeger, *op. cit.*). Regretably, we were in The Burren in the autumn, so were robbed of this pleasure. But we were soon to awaken from a sort of reverie and move further southwards along the rockbound coast of County Clare.

Many people had told us that we must make a determined effort to see the Cliffs of Moher which, in all sorts of weather conditions, but especially in a westerly gale, remain one of the scenic highlights of Ireland. Indeed, local lore has it that these famous cliffs are to west Clare what the Giant's Causeway is to north Antrim. Even forewarned, after driving across miles of featureless meadowland, we were surprised when the road suddenly stopped on the very brink of an awesome precipice. This line of sea-cliffs, built from horizontal layers of gritstone and flagstone, stretches for five miles at heights of more than 600 feet. The sea-cliffs of Achill, Slieve League and Mount Brandon may be higher, but nowhere else in Ireland are the sea-cliffs so vertical or so overhanging as those of the Cliffs of Moher.

Anyone who suffers from vertigo would be well-advised to stay away from the cliff-edge because a few upended flagstones were the only protective barriers when we visited. If one does venture to look down on the constantly beating waves and the surrounding lines of white foam encircling the cliff-foot, they will realise that a stone dropped from this viewpoint would fall directly into the sea. It was possibly the discovery of this uncommon attribute that could have been in the minds of the directors of the box-office hit, "Ryan's Daughter", produced by David Lean in 1970, because the film's opening sequence depicts the female star's parasol falling from the cliff-top vertically into the sea. One has heard the terms 'poetic licence' and 'artistic licence' but this shot must be classed as 'cinematic licence' because the film was supposed to be set near Dunquin in County Kerry many miles away. As described above, I had taken a party of British undergraduates to that wonderful piece of coastline shortly after the award-winning film had been released and the locals were still full of excitement because many of them had been employed as 'extras'. On taking the students to see the old schoolhouse, perched on the edge of the coast road, and built especially for the film, I asked them to tell me the type of stone that had been utilised; was it igneous, metamorphic or sedimentary? After looking at the geology map they responded with a variety of answers, only to be dumbfounded when I told them that it was constructed entirely from fibreglass! But to return to the Cliffs of Moher, which we found uniquely photogenic, so that it came as no surprise when a picture of this very coastal phenomenon was chosen by the editorial board of Penguin Books to grace the front cover of my "Geology and Scenery in Ireland" when it was published in 1975. I always wondered if the editorial members had ever seen the film in question. From my own viewpoint, such a striking photograph might also be regarded as quite symbolic, epitomising a sort of personal 'Ultima Thule', or as an appropriate farewell to my peregrinations along the unforgettable seaboard of Western Ireland.

I cannot possibly leave these enchanting coastlines without mentioning the paintings and etchings of an eminent Royal Academician, Norman Ackroyd, who knew, and treasured, these shores as much as myself. Not since Turner has an artist been able to capture the very essence of coastal weather because Ackroyd tells it like it is – in both calm and storm – not only in Western Ireland but also in the far-flung Hebrides. I have recently been delighted to listen to a BBC Radio 4 broadcast when he was interviewed, on the occasion of his 80th birthday, by no less than Robert Mcfarlane, an author with whom I have the greatest empathy. Ackroyd spoke of his "Thinking Hands" which simply took over his entire persona when he faced the vagaries of the Atlantic weather from the bows of a pitching and tossing boat. It was with considerable nostalgia that the broadcast took me back to those same coastal waters. This was a welcome meeting of the minds – the artist and the writer – both of whom display a deep understanding of the ambience of these remote and inspiring coastlands.

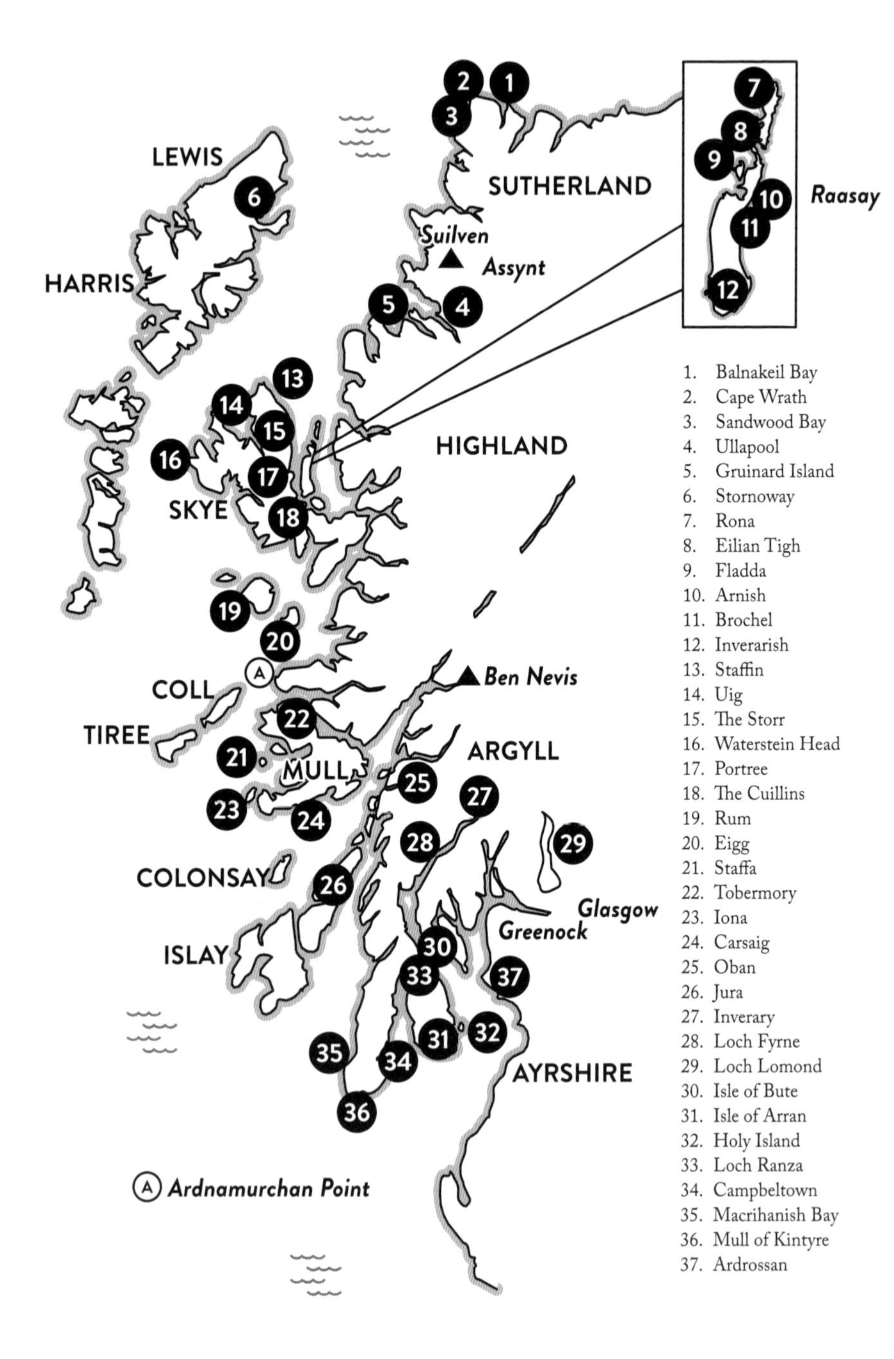
LEWIS
HARRIS
SUTHERLAND
Suilven
Assynt
Raasay
HIGHLAND
SKYE
COLL
TIREE
MULL
Ben Nevis
ARGYLL
COLONSAY
ISLAY
Glasgow
Greenock
AYRSHIRE
Ardnamurchan Point
1. Balnakeil Bay
2. Cape Wrath
3. Sandwood Bay
4. Ullapool
5. Gruinard Island
6. Stornoway
7. Rona
8. Eilian Tigh
9. Fladda
10. Arnish
11. Brochel
12. Inverarish
13. Staffin
14. Uig
15. The Storr
16. Waterstein Head
17. Portree
18. The Cuillins
19. Rum
20. Eigg
21. Staffa
22. Tobermory
23. Iona
24. Carsaig
25. Oban
26. Jura
27. Inverary
28. Loch Fyrne
29. Loch Lomond
30. Isle of Bute
31. Isle of Arran
32. Holy Island
33. Loch Ranza
34. Campbeltown
35. Macrihanish Bay
36. Mull of Kintyre
37. Ardrossan

7. WESTERN SCOTLAND

"There is pleasure in the pathless woods,
There is rapture on the lonely shore,
There is society, where none intrudes
By the deep sea and music in its roar"
(Childe Harold. Lord Byron 1788–1824)

The narrow path leading down to the causeway of Fladda looking from the Isle of Raasay. Note the rectangular fish-trap, uncovered at low-tide, and the north coast of Skye on the horizon

The sea cliffs, carved from Torridonian Sandstone, at Man Cave on the coast of Fladda

The view looking northwards from the summit of Eagle Mountain on Raasay. This landscape of bare ice-scoured Lewisian Gneiss shows the northern peninsula of Raasay, the humpback island of Eilean Tigh and the island of Rona, beyond the strait of Kyle Rona. At the time of our visit in 1972 all were totally uninhabited

Portree in Skye

The basaltic cliffs of eastern Skye with the pinnacle of the Old Man of Storr

The white sand beach of Mellon Udrigole looking to the high mountains of Assynt in Western Scotland

Fingal's Cave on the renowned Isle of Staffa, Hebrides

The western shore of Mull, looking towards its highest mountain, Ben More (3,218 feet)

The Straits of Iona, looking east to the Ross of Mull – *See plate section for colour version.*

Nunnery ruins on Iona – *See plate section for colour version.*

I thought that I had run out of supelatives when describing the coasts of Ireland but now I come to relate my travels along the shores of Western Scotland I fear that I shall have to search even deeper to do justice to their magnificent landscapes. Such wonderment is particularly true when I attempt to describe the Hebrides, for there, similar to Ireland, lie lonely isles of craggy shores, steepling cliffs, heather-clad braes and blazing sunsets, all encompassed by swirling seas. For myself, Scotland has a magnetism that I have found in few other places; its atmosphere and its people have an allure that is difficult to resist. Moreover, I have discovered that I own some fifty books on Scottish scenery, all of which I have read with enthusiasm. It is not surprising, therefore, that soon after my own book on Ireland had been published I set to work writing yet another volume to add to this lengthy Scottish list. Much of the material within this chapter relates to the many travels that I made, almost always with Diane at my side, in order to complete "Geology and Scenery in Scotland" for Penguin Books, a work that I have long regarded as a particular labour of love.

Although not exactly Terra Incognita, I had certainly not travelled as much in Scotland as I had in Wales or even Ireland. Yet a brief field-class north of the Border as an undergraduate had certainly unlocked some of Scotland's magic. This excursion had been to eastern Scotland, based on the Cairngorms, thereby leaving the enchantment of its western coast as a pleasure in store, soon to be rectified in 1956. That Easter, not long after meeting Diane, her parents took us to stay in a hotel in Oban from where we cruised around the Isle of Mull and made our first memorable visit to Iona. This sacred isle left such an impression that we called our daughter Fiona when she was born in 1960. I became firmly hooked on the breathtaking scenery of the Western Isles and we both vowed to return although, because of our several years spent abroad, this proved to be some time in the future. Perhaps my obsession with the western coastlands and islands of the so-called Celtic Fringe could be explained by my inbred but unknown feelings of the seaboard life of my Pembrokeshire ancestors but, at the time, I gave little thought to such explanations. On returning from America we were both still enamoured of the Hebrides and visited them on a couple of occasions. Those immortal lines of Sir Walter Scott: "And we in dreams behold the Hebrides", remained as apposite in 1969 as they had to that callow undergraduate two decades earlier.

Thus, it followed that, whilst enjoying another Scottish holiday in that fateful year, a remarkably fortuitous encounter led to us purchasing a property in Scotland. We were staying in a hotel in Portree at the end of a lengthy visit to the Isle of Skye and the Outer Hebrides, during an unusually rainless and hot spell of weather, when who should walk into the hotel but a departmental colleague, Piers Blaikie and his wife Sally. It appeared that they had been sailing their own yacht around thc Inner Hebrides when they had anchored off a small uninhabited island on which the three remaining habitable cottages were for sale. They led us from the hotel to the end of Portree's small quay and pointed eastwards to the distant Isle of Raasay. "That tiny smudge of green below the sunlit cliffs of Raasay is actually an island called Eilean Fladda and the three empty cottages looked in pretty good order". Back in the hotel bar perhaps the subsequent round of whisky played an important part in the discussion that followed but we decided there and then to make a 'sealed bid' for the freehold (under Scottish law) of all three cottages, purely on the word of Piers and Sally. No better example could be found of the recklessness of youth, for all of us were on fairly modest salaries at the time.

After returning to Reading, and after making a more serious re-assessment of our finances, we decided that it would be necessary to set up a syndicate for a number of reasons: first we had to raise sufficient capital; secondly, we had to have an adequate number of owners to cover four separate bids (viz. one for all three cottages and one bid for each individual property); and finally, it was important to have enough people to help with the renovation and maintenance of these isolated dwellings. To cover all the possible combinations, we asked two other departmental couples, David and Su Starkie and Erlet and John Cater, if they wished to complete the syndicate, an invitation to which they eagerly agreed. The outcome came as a great surprise for, even though we failed to buy all three, we soon became the joint-owners of two cottages on the tiny island of Fladda (Norse: Flat Island) off the north-west coast of Raasay. The enthusiasm tended to obscure the absurdity of the situation, that of the eight owners only two of them had actually set eyes on our newly acquired properties. What is it about islands that captures one's romantic imagination? I had pondered this very question in the prologue of this current work and concluded that as urban dwellers many of us have a desire to escape to the coast and possibly to an island. Moreover, the four families in question had been in complete unison in deciding to invest in properties several hundred miles away from Southeast England. Such a decision was taken in the full knowledge that these were not normal holiday cottages that one could visit fleetingly for a quick weekend. Fladda had to be seen as a serious long-term ownership and one worthy enough to undertake the lengthy two-day journey north. It soon became clear that the lure of the Hebrides was as strong as ever and not only 'in our dreams'.

Naturally, we couldn't wait to inspect our purchase so, in Septmber 1970, we borrowed the departmental minibus and, after gathering an assortment of household essentials, food supplies and Calor gas, we drove up to North-West Scotland, a journey of almost 700 miles. Diane, Fiona and I were accompanied by Liz Scoates, a former postgraduate student of mine who had just been appointed to Fiona's new prep-school. Piers and Sally joined us at Helensburgh on the Clyde estuary and we finally arrived on the Isle of Skye after crossing on the car ferry from the Kyle of Lochalsh. We were informed that if we wanted to reach Raasay then we would have to phone the ferryman who lived in the tiny island 'capital' of Inverarish, the home of the majority of Raasay's population. He agreed to meet us at the rudimentary slipway at Sconser, on Skye, where, beneath the pink-screes of the striking granite cone of Glamaig (2,537 feet), we watched the white-painted ferry-boat (a small converted lifeboat) leave the opposite shore and chug slowly across the Sound of Raasay and into the sheltered waters of Loch Sligachan. The skipper, Alistair Nicholson, turned out to be Raasay's leading citizen and entrepreneur. Not only did he run the ferry but also the island's only guest house, in addition to being the County Councillor. He was a stocky, weather-beaten man of few words and an authoritarian temperament, who hurried us aboard with all our chattels "because the weather is against us". This demeanour proved to be an unfair reflection of his true character for, in future, we found him to be a friendly and solicitous character who, with his charming wife, proved to be an enormous help in our venture despite his opening remark "Why on earth would anyone want to come all this way to live in such a desolate and remote place?".

We had arranged for another islander, Peter Gillies, to load our gear into a pick-up truck and this short and spare, gently-spoken gentleman proved to be the harbourmaster, roadmender and Raasay's solitary policeman. Anyone looking at a map of Raasay will note that it is a long but narrow feature, running for fifteen miles from north to south and less than four miles across at its widest point. He drove us for ten miles on the island's only proper road, across increasingly desolate moorland with occasional plots of improved land where sheep were grazing. Memories of Ireland's remote western fringes crossed my mind as we journeyed north, crammed into this mud-spattered vehicle, and, as in parts of Western Ireland, we never saw another soul at the roadside. The road terminated at the lonely ruin of Brochel Castle, once the home of the chieftain of the McLeod clan some centuries before. We unloaded our gear, with the help of Peter Gillies, who then pointed up a steep hill, wished us luck, with a bemused twinkle in his eye, and drove away. Our adventure was just about to begin. From this point on, a stony track twisted its way for some three miles over bare rocky hills and boggy valleys, with scarcely a view of the shoreline let alone our island which kept itself tantalisingly hidden until the last few hundred yards. By now, true to Alistair Nicholson's claim that "The weather is against us", rain had set in, not heavy or torrential but with a true Hebridean steadiness. Our bedraggled party, staggering under our assorted loads, carried on along the switchback course of the uneven track, slowly abandoning certain pieces of equipment periodically along its length: the portable toilet went first; next some of the tinned food packs; then a rucksack of cleaning equipment. But we kept our sleeping bags, our alcohol and our large canister of Calor gas (which was my particular burden), because, after all, we had to get the priorities right. On returning for these articles the next morning we found that some Good Samaritan had gathered them all together and left them in a heap, two miles nearer to Fladda. We were later to discover that our saviour lived at the only surviving croft at the north end of Raasay. We must have unknowingly passed this remote settlement because it was set back behind a small sheltered copse at a place called Arnish. Intent on reaching our goal we had trudged past the abandoned tiny settlement of Torran, with its empty schoolroom and semi-derelict church, at which point the track degenerated into a mere path which wended its way up and down through pretty birch woods before finally petering out at the narrow channel which separated us from Fladda itself.

The island looked so close but might well have been miles away since the tide was high and the rudimentary causeway submerged beneath several feet of water. Thus, cold, tired and hungry, we were forced to sit on the rocks for an hour or two until the tide had receded sufficiently to allow us to cross, slipping and stumblimg on the seaweed-draped boulders which masqueraded as a causeway but which had badly deteriorated since the island had been abandoned several years ago. A steep climb up a cliff, some 140 feet high, following a line of so-called steps, finally brought us to a grassy platform on which the three cottages stood. Their whitewashed walls were stained by the weather and the peat smoke of yesteryear, but otherwise appeared starkly white against the ruined grey remains of a dozen former dwellings, which crouched amidst the nettles in the shelter of a few rocky outcrops. A solitary Norway Spruce grew in the 'garden' of the nearest cottage but the wire fence had long since collapsed and been trodden into the grass and the bracken ferns by the sheep which were currently grazing by the back door of the nearest cottage. Needless to say, not having seen a visitor for several months, they scattered in all directions as we fumbled for the key to open the faded and wind-battered door.

With considerable trepidation we entered the scullery and then the living room, expecting to find a scene of dereliction and decay, since these crofts had been empty for a lengthy period. Instead we entered something of a timewarp, for the room was exactly as it had been left by the former inhabitants, just as if they had simply walked away and left their personal belongings to indicate a complete break with the past. The room was still furnished, up to a fashion, with a Victorian chaise-longue, a large but decrepit leather armchair in the chimney corner, a mixture of rustic chairs around a substantial dining table on which lay an open Gaelic Bible and a well-worn flat cap. Several sepia and black-and-white family photographs were found in the cupboard drawers and we felt slightly embarrassed as if we were intruding into a family funeral. And in one sense that is what it was, because after centuries of occupation these hardy islanders had been forced to ask to be re-housed in Inverarish, thirteen miles to the south. They had taken all that they could carry, in a repetition of many Hebridean islands' abandonment over the decades. We later learned the familiar story about the younger people leaving to seek their fortunes elsewhere and never returning to the family croft. Fladda's island school (the only remnant of which was a concrete base) served as a further sad reminder of a once larger population (as many as fifty inhabitants in former decades), had long since closed and the children forced to walk a couple of miles back to the schoolroom that we had passed on our initial arrival. Once the men had grown too old to row the fishing boats the islanders' subsistence economy had been doomed and the three remaining familes forced to leave the island. Such a harrowing departure was yet another example of the former overcrowding of these western shores due to the infamous Highland Clearances of the late 18th and early 19th centuries.

I had always dreamed of island living as something approaching an Arcadian lifestyle and for the next decade it proved to be one of the most wonderful experiences of our lives, even though the first few years were rather Spartan, with no phones, no electricity, no piped water-supply and no means of bathing. In fact, we would be living in the sort of environment that I had been witnessing in the fastnesses of Western Ireland. But one has to remember that for centuries those Irish dwellers on the wave-battered coasts of Donegal, Mayo and Kerry had no choice but to survive there through the long winter months. We, on the other hand could choose to visit only in the summer, although Piers and Sally often wintered there, alone with the sheep and free from visiting yachtsmen.

Few people enjoy digging their gardens and one might hazard a guess that on Fladda one could escape from such chores. Peat digging, however, is a totally different matter and soon it became a labour of love. To drive a spade into a black face of peat and watch a glutinous wedge of primeval organic soil detach itself from its parent material must surely rank as one of the most satisfying exercises devised by humankind. Not surprisingly, we found that all the peat near to the cottages had long since been stripped away so we were forced to trek to the nether fringes of the island for our supplies. Thus, despite the pleasures of digging, it proved quite laborious to carry many loads of peat across trackless undulating terrain but this is how the islanders had had to survive. They would, of course, have had ponies and we found a primitive peat sledge in the old barn, but no matter how we tried to devise a way of using it, the final answer was always 'Shanks's Pony'. The warmth and acrid sweet smell of a turf fire, particularly on a stormy night, made the effort worthwhile, especially with a dram of whisky in one's hand and the sibilant hiss of the Tilley-lamp drowning the noise of the gale. In enjoying one such comfortable ambience there arose a very disconcerting episode when, long after sunset and during a howling storm, we were startled to hear a knock at the door. Since the tide was high we knew that this interruption must be caused by benighted yachtsmen and so it proved. Two cold and wet weekend sailors had been forced to anchor their open boat in our harbour and asked if they could spend the night in the shed on our tiny beach. After we had re-opened the whisky bottle and they had dried themselves before our fire, we got talking about our respective family circumstances. It transpired that they lived on the north-east coast of Scotland but spent most weekends sailing their yacht around the Hebrides. On hearing that I was on a mission gathering material for a forthcoming book on Scotland, one of our two visitors gave me his business card and invited us to call when we reached the County of Sutherland in the far north east. It was only after they had departed at midnight, to sleep in our second cottage, that I glanced at the card and, to our surprise, it read "Robin Sutherland, Dunrobin Castle, Brora, Sutherland". Could this be the Duke himself? We will never know, because some weeks later we drove past Dunrobin Castle as dawn was breaking on a Sunday morning, much too early to renew acquaintances.

On every visit each owner worked diligently on both cottages simply maintaining and, whenever possible, improving the amenities. Water supply was the main problem and we later learnt that this had been an even greater drawback when the island population was much larger. There was a single well in front of the better of the two cottages but often this ran dry in the summer, despite the legendary wetness of the Hebrides. Apparently, the nearest alternative source of supply was on Raasay itself, where a perennial stream crossed the path several hundred yards back aong the track. Imagine struggling with two buckets up the rudimentary steps ascending from the beach simply to have enough water for cooking. We only went once to that well. When it came to bathing, it was simply a sprinkle from a bucket outside the back door or skinny-dipping in the cool sea. After a few years we laboured long and hard to build a rainwater reservoir in an adjacent ruin and one of our visiting guests, Bill Fieldhouse, built a windmill to pump water to an upstairs tank to enable us to have showers, while still depending on supplies from water-butts for all the cooking. Unfortunately, despite leaving instructions on how to dismantle the windmill when leaving the island, one of the owners, who will remain nameless, left it running. The winter gales shattered the blades and sent the wreckage cartwheeling into the sea.

Every island needs a boat and Piers quickly resolved this problem in the first year by bringing a small sailing-dinghy to Fladda. Diane and I are no yachtsmen but we happily rowed it round the south harbour before dragging it back above the tide level. All was to change when we took some other friends, Peter and Kay Boulton, on one of our summer visits. Peter, being ex-Royal Navy, was an experienced small-boat sailor and he soon hoisted the sails and made our dinghy ready for venturing further out to sea. At last we could explore our island coastline and sail out to the offshore skerries where we were told excellent scallops could be found. Things are very different when one is afloat, not only from the changing perspective of the coastline, when one is on the outside looking in, but also in ones increasing awareness of the ocean's moods. I am reminded of the apposite remarks of the travel writer Edmund Vale: "To a sailor, any sea you might name would conjure up an embodiment of tide-rips, overfalls, soundings, prevalent wind-drift, fog banks, landfalls and departures" (The Seas and Shores of England. Edmund Vale, 1936). Fortunately, I had learnt about many of such maritime elements in my brief sojourn aboard a French research-vessel in Ireland's Clew Bay, as described above.

In terms of sea-fishing, we were all landlubbers and, although we had the fishing rights, we were pretty unsuccesful. It is true that we caught a few mackerel by line, but most times we caught nothing but seaweed. There was one great occasion, however, when, on a hot sunny evening, we heard a great clamour from the seabirds in the channel. Quickly looking through our fieldglasses we discovered that there was an enormous shoal of whitebait, trapped on a falling tide by the rocky causeway. Bill Fieldhouse and I launched the boat and rowed out into the channel but immediately realised that it is very difficult to catch these tiny fish without a net. Diane soon came to our rescue by delivering a pair of net curtains from the kitchen and these together with a soup ladle yielded a wonderful silvery harvest. The evening meal consisted of barbecued whitebait soaked in lemon juice and washed down with Guinness until we were all comfortably full. Thereafter, we lounged on the grass behind the cottage and enjoyed the tranquility of a lengthy Hebridean evening, quite oblivious of events that were unfolding in the south harbour. Not until we heard shouts and laughter did we venture back to the cliff top to behold a very large green-painted square-rigger anchored out in the deeper water.

Dozens of passengers had rowed ashore on the other side of the channel and were wandering off up the slopes of Beinn na-lolaire (Eagle Mountain). We toyed with the idea of inviting them onto the island but finally concluded that there were far too many to offer proper hospitality, and by the following morning they had gone. Bill had spent a lifetime working for the BBC 'monitoring service' and weeks later on his return to his office he was dismayed to find that the visiting ship was no less than a BBC Natural History unit making a film on the Scottish Islands. Thus, in terms of our TV appearances 'Sic transit gloria mundi'. Moreover, we never even saw the film for some unknown reason.

Over the years we were visited by a variety of sailing boats, some of whose crew came ashore onto Fladda. One unknown Scottish Nationalist painted their symbol onto the black shed on the beach, as a warning to the Sassenachs, much to the embarrassment of our visiting shepherds, especially since they actually owned the shed. The shed was also the scene of a much more amusing episode for, early one morning, we found an envelope pinned to its door enclosing a ten-shilling note and a message to say that a visiting yachtsman had gathered some mussels from our beach and hoped that the money would be appreciated. As 'poor islanders' we had a good laugh and hastily pocketed the money. More seriously, one morning a French yachtsman came ashore in some distress. It transpired that he had crossed the causeway at mid-tide and torn the keel off his boat. Moreover, his wife had fallen down the hatch and had injured her back. On requesting "Please may I use your phone?" we had to walk back three miles to Arnish on Raasay and use the public phone box to summon help for both his wife and his boat. On asking him about his nautical charts, in order to explain the hazards of our causeway, he admitted that he was sailing around Scotland by means of a road atlas!

Fladda is singularly lacking in sandy beaches but at its northern tip, termed An Roin (The Seal), there are imposing shingle beaches thrown up by storms that may have emanated in distant Arctic latitudes. The highest one, some thirty feet above sea-level, is clearly a 'raised beach' of great antiquity, analogous with those at Malin Head in Northern Ireland. It was here, amidst the attractive clumps of thrift and the ugly piles of flotsam, we once discovered the skeleton of a basking shark, reminding us of the many schools of these harmless monsters that we had spied when crossing The Minch, en route to the Isle of Lewis and Harris. During the Scottish high summer, we often lingered on this northern headland to witness the breathtaking sunsets across The Minch. Their reflections spread a cloth of gold on the sea, way beyond the lonely Shiant Isles to where the mountains of the outer isles became black silhouettes against the flaming skies. From An Roin we would wander back to the cottage to enjoy an 'al fresco' meal as the twilight deepened, kept company by the nibbling sheep. It was on such evenings that we marvelled at the total silence of this idyllic place, where the perfect peace was disturbed only by the warbling call of the curlew and the piping trill of the oyster catchers as they made their final forays on the shore. No matter how memorable were the highlights of our former overseas experiences, such as our first sight of East Africa's 'Big Game'; my excitement at climbing to 15,000 feet on the Rwenzori equatorial glaciers; experiencing the wonderful coastal settings of Cape Town and San Francisco; or being overwhelmed at the sheer scale of Yosemite's cliffs; few experiences have brought me greater satisfaction than those carefree, sunlit days on Fladda where the air is like wine and the solitude is almost palpable.

When we went across the causeway to explore Raasay itself it soon became evident that even the hardiest crofters had a quite different perception of island-life than we had ourselves. One is forced to concede that any romantic view of these remote islands has to be tempered by the islander's belief that their world is ruled largely by natural forces that can never be entirely tamed. Moreover, once we had made a belated visit to our nearest neighbour, the eminent Gaelic Scholar, Calum Macleod, in his croft at Arnish, we learnt a few historical 'home truths'. After Calum and his busy wife Lexie had kindly entertained us to tea, using milk fresh from one of their few cows, he proudly showed us the prizes that he had won for his Gaelic poetry and it was only later that he began to describe some of the major events in the history of Raasay. Several books have been written on the Highland Clearances and it would be impossible to recount the details in full. Suffice to say that Calum showed no signs of bitterness that his forebears had been forcibly evicted from the good farmlands at the south end of the island and moved to the stony fastnesses of the north. Surprisingly, he laid great emphasis on the foibles of the great clan chieftain, the Macleod of Raasay, who, having recovered from backing Bonny Prince Charlie's failed campaign in 1745, lavishly entertained Boswell and Johnson in his mansion at Inverarish, during their memorable journey to the Hebrides in 1773. To summarise Calum's views I am quoting in full the ensuing fate of the island from the end of the 18th century until the mid 1850's: "…the Macleod's threw themselves into a financially unsustainable frenzy of high living. First, their tacksmen left and by the 1830's Raasay, like many other Highland estates, suffered clearance. Estate management before the Macleods left in 1843 resulted in the suffering and poverty of later decades. The new owner, George Rainy, showed an understanding of the estate and its people, which subsequent owners did not. By the 1870's Raasay was a sporting estate and the living conditions of the crofter population deteriorated markedly". These were not the words of an English incomer but of a scholar, Norma Macleod, whose father was born on Raasay (Raasay: The Island and its People, Norma Macleod, 2002). This wonderful raconteur, Calum, sitting by his peat fire, that never went out, continued by telling us how his ancestors helped to build the infamous 'deer wall' that spans the narrowest part of the island from coast to coast. Here was not only a physical means of retaining the deer for the shooting parties of Victorian times but also a palpable symbol of exclusion of the crofters from the prosperous southern pastures which comprise four-fifths of the island.

Listening to his stories in his gentle lilting voice was equivalent to envisaging a picture of Raasay a century ago. We could now understand how Fladda had been so crowded in those earlier years. Like Fladda, it appeared that, at the same time, the northern four miles of Raasay were once 'crowded' with two or three villages but were now totally uninhabited and rarely visited except annually by the shepherds. Together with Peter and Kay Boulton we were determined to visit this deserted landscape and also get a closer view of South Rona, an equally deserted island. Mindful of the fact that the causeway would become covered long before high tide, we all set off on a gruelling slog through a trackless terrain of bog and rock. As we hacked our way through tangled and head-high bracken fern, I was reminded of the way I had once helped my porters to slash a new path through the forested slopes of Rwenzori, some decades earlier, in order to carry out high-altitude glaciological research. We passed many heaps of overgrown stones, that had once been the homes of island families, features that filled us with a feeling of sadness, similar to that experienced by J. M. Synge in Connemara. But Synge had felt wretched about witnessing a living image of despair: we were walking over the vestiges of a dislodged community.

During our trek we disturbed nothing more than the occasional greenshank and the pair of golden eagles that had built their eerie high on the cliffs facing Fladda. On reaching the northernmost tip of Raasay, now a place of absolute solitude, we thought about the barefoot children that must once have been forced to cross this barren terrain en route to their school at Torran, some five or six miles away. We gazed across the narrow but savagely tide-ripped channel of Kyle Rona to South Rona which had been completely cleared and which had lain empty (except for the lighthouse keepers) until the Royal Navy had established a top-secret submarine base at its northern extremity. We learnt that it was a testing-ground for deep-running torpedoes in what I knew was one of the deepest chasms in the British continental shelf and that the testing ground meant closing the shipping route in the Inner Sound that separates Raasay from the Scottish mainland of Applecross. Such closure meant that, for some years, the mail steamers and ferries could no longer call at Raasay pier or even Portree on Skye en route from Kyle of Lochalsh to the Outer Hebrides; one now has to drive many miles north to Ullapool in order to cross to Stornoway. Only once did we see naval ratings land on Fladda but we were occasionally monitored by helicopters. Their intrusion not only broke the pervading calm of the island but also served to remind us that we could never leave the real world behind. Such an airborne clamour had already broken the tranquility when the Concorde airliner was completing its trials across the peaceful Hebrides. In recent years Raasay has had to get used to a different intrusion into its insular and relaxed way-of-life, for we hear that small cruise ships are calling at the pier.

Standing forlorn in the channel of Kyle Rona was the small tidal island of Eilean Tigh (the House Island) with its solitary ruined cottage almost buried amidst the weeds and bracken. The ferryman, Alistair Nicholson, had told us earlier that this was the croft on which he had been born prior to his entire family moving away to enjoy a more civilised life in southern Raasay. This explained his remarks at our first meeting "Why on earth do you want to purchase property in this northern wilderness and travel hundreds of miles from the south of England?". As we sat eating our lunch we tried to imagine how the Nicholson family had managed to eke out a living on this rock-bound, postage-stamp sized island in such a starkly beautiful but seasonally hostile wilderness. I recalled reading one of my books by the famous Scottish naturalist, Frank Fraser Darling, who described visiting Eilean Tigh in the 1930's, accompanying the doctor from Skye when he made his annual visit to tend to the needs of its single family. His nostalgic description outlines the way in which two excited children and their frenzied dog ran down to meet the boat. Alistair Nicholson confirmed that he was one of those children but he himself had no nostalgia for his isolated chidhood. As casual visitors and incomers we again felt a sadness when we reflected on the reasons for this abandonment but reasoned that were it not for the desertion of northern Raasay we would never have had the unforgettable experience of island-life in a wilderness, that I am attempting to describe. We thought of it as idyllic but it was clear that Alistair thought very differently and when we looked at desolate Eilean Tigh we began to understand his feelings.

Over the years we got to know our nearest 'neighbour', Calum Macleod, quite well and found him to be one of the most remarkable characters that we had ever met. Like most men of Raasay, Calum had more than one job for, in addition to being a crofter, he had been the lighthouse keeper on South Rona and a postman, but it was as a road-builder that he will be best remembered. He was a wiry, well-muscled man of medium height and with a shy smile which creased his weather-beaten face beneath the battered flat cap that he always wore. We only once saw him without his cap and were almost startled when it revealed a sharp demarcation line between his leathery-brown face and a shining white bald head. Whenever we crossed over to Raasay we found him working on the track from his croft at Arnish all the way to the tarmac roadhead at Brochel. He laboured single-handedly, with a wheelbarrow, sledge hammer, pick and a shovel, although he admitted that the Government had allowed him to dynamite the most stubborn of the rocky outcrops that baulked his efforts. He was determined to build a road fit for vehicles across the unyielding terrain, and it became clear over the years that this was a 'cause célèbre'. Although there had been plans some forty years previously to build a road from Brochel to Fladda to serve the hundred or so people who lived on this forlorn peninsula to the north of Brochel, nothing had materialised. Thus, in 1964 he set out alone to construct almost two miles of serviceble single-track road because he decided that nobody else would build it. When we first met him in 1970 he had been working at this incredible venture for six years and it would be another ten before it was finished. The history of "Calum's Road" has been superbly described by Roger Hutchinson, an award-winning author, (Calum's Road, Roger Hutchinson, 2006), who believed it to be a wonder of the modern world. Moreover, he went on to think of applying to UNESCO to have Calum's road recognised as a World Heritage Site. What an accolade that would be.

After several years of prevarication, the Scottish Development Department agreed a grant of £101,612 to tarmac the road that he had built but it took until 1982 before the surfacing was completed, just in time for Calum to take his wife for her hospital appointments for, by then, Lexie was crippled with arthritis. When we first met Calum he was in his sixties and as strong as an ox; we saw him, one evening, row some miles out to the western skerries to tend his lobster pots and on another occasion carry a telegraph pole single-handedly. But on one fateful January day in 1988 he was found sitting in his wheelbarrow, guarded by his faithful sheep dog, having passed away from a suspected heart attack. At the Brochel end of his road a solitary stone memorial has been erected bearing inscriptions in both Gaelic and English:

CALUM'S ROAD
This former footpath to Arnish – a distance of 1 and 3/4 miles
was widened to a single-track road with passing places
and prepared for surfacing by
MALCOLM MACLEOD B. E. M (1911–1988) SOUTH ARNISH
He accomplished this work single-handedly
over a period of ten years

To my mind an even more fitting epitaph, and one much more explanatory than the cold stone cairn, is that of a quotation from Roger Hutchinson's biography: "However essentially practical he may have been, Calum Macleod carried the weight of his people's history on his shoulders and in his mind. Council bureaucrats and engineers, however imaginative and however willing to be sympathetic, saw nothing but a bumpy, dusty track to nowhere. Calum saw children playing and old ladies enjoying the autumn of their lives in Arnish, Umachan, Torran and Fladda". So far as we 'incomers' on Fladda were concerned, it was the young ladies, young men and children who benefitted most because with the new MacBraynes car-ferry and Calum's Road we could now drive as far as his croft at Arnish, visit Raasay's only shop at the south end of the island, and make occasional forays across to Skye. It is quite ironic that the island "children and old ladies" who once lived on this remote corner of Raasay will never benefit from Calum's enterprise because they have long gone. Instead it is incomers, like ourselves, who have recently renovated the church and schoolroom at Torran and will never suffer the privations of the former occupants.

Prior to this new 'amenity' we had been forced to tramp from the roadhead at Brochel, hire a fishing boat from Portree or take Alistair Nicholson's small motor-launch from Inverarish when we needed to bring essential provisions and building materials to our isolated island. Therein lay two amusing anecdotes. On one occasion, due to shortage of bread, we had walked some four miles to the roadhead and driven ten miles south to the Inverarish shop where we found it to be sold out of bread. On enquiring from the owner, the reason for this shortage and pointing out that the MacBraynes steamer now called each day and could deliver fresh supplies, he replied "But I have only bought bread on three days a week for as long as I can remember. If I bought it every day it would only confuse the islanders". Such is the price of isolation. The other story concerns one of our regular holidays at Alistair Nicholson's new hotel (which replaced his guest house). One sunny evening, when we were due to drive north to the end of the road, and after the ferry service had finished for the day, Alistair took us aside and said "Pack your bags and bring the car and trailor (loaded with building materials) down to the pier. I intend to run an evening cruise up the west coast of Raasay and we can take your goods at the same time". As skipper of the MacBraynes ferry, he guided the car and trailor onto the ferry and, together with a number of assorted tourists, we cruised up to Fladda. On arrival he manoeuvered this large vessel close inshore and we reversed the car as far as possible through the ferry doors and then manhandled the trailor ashore. Every visitor happily carried paint pots, bags of cement, timber and corrugated iron sheets on to Fladda, saving us hours of hard labour. After they had re-embarked we all watched the ferry sail away, with the now empty car and trailor aboard and a lone piper playing a soulful lament as they disappeared around the headland. The skirl of the pipes slowly died away as the ship's bow-waves left a few wavelets breaking on the rocks, before it all returned to the silence of tranquility. Fond memories are made of such things, and I have to admit that there were a few tears in the eyes of our small party as we turned away from our vantage point on the cliff-top.

Many years later, when we left our beloved Fladda for the last time, because by then we had found that the exertion of a lengthy car journey, followed by the burden of carrying heavy goods, was becoming too onerous, we decided to spend a few days at Alistair's hotel. We felt that as a fitting gesture to the friendly islanders we would attend the Sunday service at the Free Presbyterian Church on the hill overlooking the bay at Inverarish. It certainly proved to be an enlightening experience, for the service was entirely in Gaelic and the hymn singing unaccompanied by music. Moreover, the singing, led by a precenter, was conducted sitting down and the prayers were intoned standing up. Because of our presence the preacher had the courtesy of bellowing his 'hellfire' sermon in

English, or maybe it was to show the Fladda incomers the error of their ways, for I feel sure that he had heard on the 'grapevine' that we had often worked on the Sabbath. Nevertheless, all the villagers smiled and wished us well as they left the church. There can be few places of worship that can boast of a finer view than this tiny Raasay outpost. Out beyond the channel and the derelict mansion of Raasay House, where Boswell and Johnson had once been wined and dined, the towering peaks of the Black Cuillins and the Red Cuillins rise dramaticaflly from the coastline of Skye, sometimes shrouded in mist but often with their intricate details etched sharply against the rain-washed blue sky. We have never been back but this was the sort of image that has remained indelibly printed in my mind.

Forty years after we had forsaken Fladda, we were fortunate to meet up again with one of its two remaining owners, Piers and Sally Blaikie, who still holidayed regularly on the island. The stories that they recounted made us conclude that we had seen Fladda in its heyday for there had been so many changes since our departure, and not all for the better. On the positive side was the opening of Calum's Road and the renovation of the old school-house and empty church at nearby Torran by incomers from southern England., as mentione above. Moreover, the salmon fish-farm had disappeared from the south harbour, thereby allowing the marine life to re-generate. On the negative side, apart from the grievous death of Calum Macleod, the sheep had been removed from the island, a loss that had removed Nature's 'mowing machines' and allowed the bracken fern to re-colonise most of its area. Apparently, the Forestry Commission still owned the planting-rights and had covered much of Fladda with both coniferous and deciduous saplings. Not only had this venture totally changed the character of the island scene but had also obliterated all the former sheep tracks. We were told that the sudden appearance of woodland had encouraged a herd of Red Deer to swim across from Raasay and proliferate on Fladda. The result has been complete devastation of the young trees (except for the birch which they find inedible) and the introduction of ticks into the shoulder high bracken. Indeed, one of the other owners has contracted Lyme Disease.

Just as we were due to say farewell to Raasay, we were delighted when, as something of a parting token of our friendship, Alistair Nicholson invited us as his guests, on a 'farewell cruise' around the entire island of Raasay. In hindsight I have to say that this proved to be amongst the most moving and nostalgic of all my coastal journeys, especially when we sailed along Fladda's west coast and viewed Uamh nan Daoine (Man Cave) for the last time. This 100-foot deep chasm reminded me of the equally spectacular clefts of south Pembrokeshire but this cave stood on our very own island and was therefore special. Then we were able to view another, more historic, cave on the nearby Raasay sea-cliffs of Loch a' Sguirr because this cave had been found to hold extremely rare pre-historic bones and tools that have been dated to 7600 BC, a time when Mesolithic hunters and gatherers had settled this coastline very soon after the disappearance of the glaciers. Next it was the narrow, swirling, tide-rent channel of Kyle Rona and a pause to cast our eyes, once again, over the deserted Isle of Rona. Alistair told us that this was not always so, because its desolate bare terrain suddenly became overpopulated with families evicted from the better lands of southern Raasay during the 19th century. He went on to say, with a wry smile on his face, that in 1919, four of those evicted families, tired of scraping a living on the naked rocks of Rona, seized land back in their former homesteads in southern Raasay, thus becoming known as the 'Rona Raiders'. The men had been arrested but eventually released, following a public outcry, and they had returned home accompanied by a piper. At that time, Raasay's poet, Sorley Maclean (1911–1996) was only a child but this whole injustice inspired him to write bitterly in Gaelic about these clearances. A translation reads:

"The fields empty under sheep
from the Raised Beach of Eyre to Meall Damh
... The children, women and big men
of Raasay among the rocks of Rona
Children, women and big men on whom
Rainy brought destruction"

We looked, once more, on the tiny deserted island of Eilean Tigh, where Alistair had been born, although he declined to comment. Turning southwards we saw, for the first time, the empty eastern coast of Raasay, once crowded with townships each one of which housed some forty or fifty souls. We marvelled at the precipitous mountain cliffs, which stood back from the coastline itself but overlooked a series of landslips dating from earlier geological times. Here the type of rocks appeared to be out of place in western Scotland. because I knew that the 1000-foot rock face of horizontal light-coloured strata is an example of what is termed a fault-line escarpment. The cliff face of shales and calcareous sandstones of Jurassic age had collapsed along faults because their underlying layers are composed of insubstantial clay beds. It is just as if a section of the Cotswold escarpment of southern England had been bodily transferred to the Hebrides. The hummocky landscape between the cliffs and the shore is capped by relatively lime-rich soils, giving rise to fertile pastures which led to the earlier survival of the settlements on this isolated coast. Today their deserted slopes are clothed with thick forestry plantations, largely of spruce, amongst which we saw Red Deer roaming. Before the widespread felling during World War II many of the slopes of southern Raasay were clothed with deciduous woodland of elm, oak, beech, ash and chestnut, many of which had been planted by the incoming Victorian landowners. The trees were not the only floral species that were introduced here because, in a notorious academic scandal of the 1930's, a well-known botanist was shamed after leading his undergraduates on field-classes in order to 'discover' rare Alpine plants that he had previously planted. Sorley Maclean was "…fond of the 'old woods' of Raasay" and wrote how:

"Heartbreak is about the mountains
And in the woods for all their beauty
though the restless sportive blood
rages triumphantly in the young".

But, as we had discovered in our short time on Fladda, there were only a few young people remaining on the main Isle of Raasay because many had left to find their fortunes elsewhere. It had become an island of old men, most of whom were forced to shoulder the burden of filling two or three occupations.

And, finally, our 'cruise' vessel turned the southernmost point at Eyre and brought us back to 'civilisation' at the pier. No one could have asked for a more poignant or a more memorable ending to those wonderful summers during which I had fulfilled my lifelong yearning to be an islander. Was such a desire based on an atavistic memory locked into my DNA, carrying me back to an ancestral home on an island on the North Sea shores of the Low Countries? Or was it nothing more than a juvenile upbringing when a youngster's reading was often based on Arthur Ransome's

"Swallows and Amazons" literature? Today, a young person's reading is much more likely to be based on the "Lord of the Rings" or the escapades of "Harry Potter", although one has to admit that all these types of literature were based on worlds of fantasy.

Forcing myself back into the world of reality, I still had to travel many miles to complete the research needed for "Geology and Scenery in Scotland". Having gathered sufficient material from the Scottish Lowlands, whose east and west coast contrasts bore a similar dichotomy to the Irish coasts, though nowhere near as wild as those of Ireland, I now had to turn northwards to the renowned Highlands of Scotland. Although I was forced to perambulate the entire Scottish coastline I have to admit that, following my pleasure at experiencing the delights of the rugged scenery of Western Ireland, as I entered the realms of north-west Scotland my expectations ran extremely high. First, we drove along the tattered coast of Wester Ross before entering the almost surreal landscapes of Assynt. Here lies one of Britain's most primeval shores, for not only is it composed of its oldest rocks, termed Lewisian Gneiss and Torridonian Sandstone, but it also boasts some of its most spectacular and least visited mountains. It must be remembered that we were travelling in those parts half-a-century ago and the roads at that time were usually single-track and the settlements as scattered as those of westernmost Ireland. One was forced to detour miles to round the deeply penetrating sea lochs, unless there was a tiny ferry at such places as Strome. But these deviations had the great advantage of taking us 'off the beaten track' to visit the hidden beaches and magnificent far-reaching seascapes of this remote coastline. It is in these tiny bays that one becomes acutely aware of the kaleidoscope of colours that grace the tidelines. Unlike the muddy waters of many of England's estuaries, the sea lochs of Western Scotland are fed by crystal clear rivers, often devoid of sediment. Where they meet the Atlantic rollers, surging across bare rock, they combine to produce a marine transparency that gives the inshore waters their vibrant colours: purple where the sea flows over patches of seaweed, a beautiful jade across the patches of sand and aquamarine above the submerged rocks. These are the coastlines that have appealed to countless artists, ranging from William McTaggart in the 19th century to the so-called 'Scottish Colourists' of S. J. Peploe and E. C. B. Cadell in the 20th century. It was reproductions of their canvases and sketch books that will have brought pleasure to thousands through the medium of postcards and book illustrations and also helped to bring about the more recent 'invasion' of cars and coaches into the solitude of this once neglected coastline. As we will see in the Isle of Skye, tourism sometimes becomes overwhelming. And the weather is not always like that depicted on the postcards and posters. I possess a large watercolour of a dour mist-shrouded Hebridean shoreline by E. W. Haslehust (1866–1949) whose palette of moss green, pale lilac and sombre grey epitomises the numberless days of cloud and rain that is more typical of these shores.

Nowhere else in the British Isles can one discover such monolithic mountains as those of Assynt, where the peaks rise steeply from their surrounding fjords and lochs like towering skyscrapers. In shape they mimic the sugar-loaf peaks of Rio Janeiro but the Scottish examples are not made of granite but tough sedimentary Torridonian Sandstone. Who will ever forget the mighty tower of Suilven (2,399 feet) standing alone like a gigantic lighthouse above an alien 'sea' of Lewisian gneiss? Or the pyramids of Canisp (2,779 feet) or Cul Mor (2,786 feet) with its 'icing sugar' cap of glittering white Cambrian quartzite? It has been claimed by some mountaineers that this group must be ranked amongst Scotland's most shapely summits despite their relatively modest altitude.

Such claims raise the question: How does one rank the attractiveness of a mountain? So far, in this narrative I have waxed long about different peaks that are situated along our shorelines, often marvelling at their sheer immensity as they rise from the ocean. I believe that such grandeur can be explained by the striking angular contrast between the vertical mountain face and the horizontal expanse of the sea. This is both a geometric and an elemental form beloved by artists and photographers. It is, indeed, the "Edge of the land" writ large. On the one hand it is the junction at which the landsman is forced to halt and admire the prospect of the seascape from his lofty viewpoint or, on the other hand, where the sailor pauses to admire the frowning cliff-line from his lowly viewpoint, whilst taking care that a shifting breeze does not suddenly turn the scenic experience into a watery hazard. It could equally be argued that an 'attractive' mountain may lie inland with no need of the sea to enhance its stature. Some mountaineers judge mountains simply on their elevation, such as the intrepid climbers who collect "Munros" (Scottish peaks over 3,000 feet in height). Others think only in terms of the jagged outlines of their summits, exemplified by the Cuillins of Skye or the pyramid of Tryfaen in Snowdonia. It has to be said, however, that most artists and photographers prefer to have water in the scene because of its ability to mirror the mountain itself. One only has to think of the English Lake District, the Killarney Mountains in Ireland or The Trossachs of Scotland. A writer's adjectives may range from: Awesome, Sublime, Formidable, Breath-taking, Picturesque or merely Pretty; everyone can choose their own superlative. I know with certainty where my own mountain preferences are located, whether it be England, Wales, Ireland or Scotland, and what would be the choice of my own superlatives, but in a book with this title I suppose that I am biased.

It was now time to move on and follow, at a leisurely pace, unfamiliar roads on which there were fewer and fewer people and only infrequent motor vehicles to be seen. It is in places such as this that one has to think seriously about petrol, food and a bed for the night. We were entering very unfamiliar territory, not exactly a true wilderness, because there were habitations but, in the context of the British Isles, this was its 'empty quarter'. I am always fascinated, when I watch the evening news on one of the TV channels, to reflect on the map (shown behind the newscaster) which depicts the lights of a night-time overview of our islands. North-west Scotland is startlingly black, virtually devoid of any lighting, and matched in its intensity only by central Wales.

On and on we drove, armed with notebook and camera, to record the barren grandeur of Scotland's north-west seaboard. Nowhere in overcrowded Britain can match this type of coastal wilderness, an emptiness that I have seen only in Ireland's Burren and the westernmost peninsulas of Donegal. A combination of acid rock types, with their poor soils, relentless rainfall, peat bogs and the scarification caused by former ice-sheets, has left this remote corner of Britain almost devoid of the imprint of civilisation. I was told that its landscapes are reminiscent of the coasts of Labrador and it is no coincidence that many of the Scottish crofters, evicted from their homesteads, emigrated to the far side of the Atlantic where they would have felt a 'sense of place', a sort of familiarity with their new environment. Such a replication of landscapes would come as no surprise to geologists because they know that, before the 'Opening of the

Atlantic', due to the monumental fracturing of tectonic plates many millions of years ago, North-west Scotland and North-east America were conjoined. Thus, we were driving across ancient rock-types that were commonplace in Newfoundland and the eastern coasts of Canada.

The weather seemed to be bountiful, as cloud shadows raced across the heather and gorse-covered peninsulas and where shafts of sunlight sporadically dappled the surface of the multitude of sea-lochs. I could imagine coming here when towering cumulonimbus clouds brought hefty showers to freshen up the visibility and highlight the white cottages alongside the tiny bays of white sand. Such views would certainly match the romantic visions once depicted in Paul Henry's canvases of Western Ireland, many of which helped to bring the tourists flocking. I think that one will begin to understand why similar Scottish images have already encouraged English urban dwellers to drive hundreds of miles to be equally captivated by such idyllic scenes. However, it was not only the scenery that drew people to these trackless coastal fastnesses because, for some like ourselves, their very remoteness is an attraction in itself. One would enter a very different and unfamiliar world in this westernmost part of Sutherland because it is one of the very few lengthy stretches of the Scottish coastline beyond the reach of the motorist which makes it a true Ultima Thule. Only intrepid walkers such as Nicholas Crane and Robert Macfarlane would be able to enjoy the beguiling beauty and solitude of Sandwood Bay, which, were it more accessible in this day and age, would be overwhelmed by caravans, car parks and snack bars.

When we ourselves reached the north-west corner of Britain, under sunlit skies, we came as close to the bastion of Cape Wrath as we were ever likely to get at the roadhead village of Balnakeil. It came as something of a surprise to find that tourism had beaten us to it. For here, on an attractive estuary, a 'craft village' had been established in 1964 by Sutherland County Council in order to attract craftsmen to produce textiles, pottery, jewellery and paintings of a 'folksy' design. One should refrain from adopting a pejorative attitude, however, for this was a sincere attempt to create employment and provide other, much-needed, facilities. At the end of a lengthy drive, we were certainly happy to stock up with both food and petrol. The wish did cross my mind, however, "Please do not let this British outpost become a John o' Groats or a Land's End". Away from the 'honeypot' of the village it was possible to walk along the unspoilt sands of Balnakeil Bay to the solitude of Faraid Head. We sat there watching the gannets nose-diving into the ultramarine inshore waters of the Pentland Firth, savouring a chance to relax in an atmosphere of absolute peace and quiet that is so often sought for but rarely found, when we were suddenly dive-bombed by 'bonxies', the aggessive great skuas whose territory we had invaded. Such an attack by the local wildlife was, perhaps, quite understandable but moments later our enjoyment of this Arcadian wilderness was shattered by the roar of low-flying RAF jet aircraft and the detonation of their bombs as they used a nearby island for target practice. Jerked roughly from my daydream visions of a placid seascape, I was catapulted back into a nightmare of recollections: explosions, reminiscent of the almost forgotten days of my house's bomb damage in the Blitz; the thud of the IRA explosion in Londonderry; the ear-splitting blast of the guns on the Royal Artillery firing ranges in Wales. After recovering my senses, I posed a rhetorical question: "What is it about some of our most beautiful coastlines that seems to attract the noisy intrusion of the military?" I thought about the gunnery ranges of Tonfanau in mid-Wales, against which Cledwyn Hughes fumed; the tank-testing coastal tracts of my Pembrokeshire homeland, that thwarted my own explorations; the rocket-testing range of South Uist in the Outer Hebrides, which periodically breaks up the silence of its shelly, dune-fringed beaches of precious 'machair'; the forbidden isle of Gruinard, near to Ullapool, closed to the public since it was purposely contaminated with toxic anthrax during World War II germ warfare experiments; the ravaging of Suffolk's shingle peninsula of Orford Ness over many decades in the name of military science. We are officially informed that all of these (and many more) coastal sites have been occupied in the 'national interest' and in some ways one can understand why they had to be situated in isolated locations away from public danger. Thus, as in the case of most of our nuclear power stations, such developments and activities have been driven to the coastal periphery of our crowded island. Understandable, perhaps, but nonetheless an invasion that is anathema to those, like myself, who treasure our coastline which is already under threat from other types of development, as described in earlier chapters. Everyone must have heard of the hackneyed phrase "They don't make land anymore, for when it's developed it's gone for ever". This is equally true of our coastline which, when taken together with the threat of rising sea-levels due to climate change, is predicted to diminish in length as time progresses. Thus, we should treasure every mile: since my Neptune survey in 1965 it is statistically possible that we have lost up to 320 miles due to development or neglect. This conjecture is based on my Millenium report's findings that coastland was disappearing at a faster rate than had previously been thought. To take into account this projected degree of loss

I concluded that it had become imperative for the National Trust to carry out a further coastal survey in a format similar to that of 1965. (See chapter 11).

At this juncture another rhetorical question crossed my mind: "Why had I, on a remote and beautiful Scottish headland, suddenly been plunged into such a gloomy diatribe against past, present and future impacts on our precious coastline?". After a momentary reflection, I decided that it was only because I had absconded from the distractions of a workaday urban environment, where constant noise was part of one's everyday life, and that I was temporarily occupying what I will call a 'dreamscape' of pure escapism in which I could think more clearly. My time on Fladda had certainly been an insular 'dreamscape' and perhaps George Orwell had also found it necessary to escape to the sanctuary of the secluded Hebridean island of Jura before he was able to compose the 'doomwatch' thoughts and predictions of his "1984" masterpiece. But it was now time to cast such misgivings aside and head southwards to an island on which Orwell would have failed to find the sanctuary that he sought. This was the Isle of Skye, which we had visited on many earlier occasions.

Few of Britain's islands have received such a degree of attention by writers, poets and artists as that of Skye. It seems to have had a magnetism stretching back through the centuries and I own at least a dozen books relating to the so-called "Misty Isle", which chronicle its geology, its scenery and its natural history in addition to the many volumes written on its historic associations. I have said elsewhere that, since the building of a bridge to the mainland, it is strictly not an island. But once the Channel Tunnel had been opened Britain itself was no longer strictly insular. I have been told that some romantic souls continued to use the car-ferry to Skye even after the bridge had become operational. At a considerably smaller scale, because of its tidal causeway, a pedant could even question the status of our beloved Fladda. This is the belief of the purists, but let them argue with a Hebridean Scot or a Little Englander and they will soon meet their match.

Fabled by its associations with Bonny Prince Charlie and the "Skye Boat Song", the attraction of this mountainous island has increased exponentially over the decades and with it the impact of tourism. Since the building of the bridge the inadequate island roads have become choked with traffic and the tourist accommodation overwhelmed to such an extent that the Local Authority has proposed draconian legislation to curb the 'invasion', notwithstanding the greatly increased revenue and employment prospects. There has even been talk of imposing a 'tourist tax', a threat utterly opposed by the hoteliers. We had been lucky to have made our early visits in the 1960's and 1970's, long before the building of the bridge and at a time when we could relax on the coral beaches of Claigan with no other person in sight. On our first visit we had been able to drive along the coast road from Portree northwards to Staffin without meeting another vehicle, despite the fact that this stretch of coastline is one of the most spectacular in Scotland. I am told that today there are queues of coaches and caravans wishing to view its scenic grandeur. The landscape owes everything to its geology because the massive cliffs of basaltic lava, that stand back from the coast itself, have collapsed, like those on Raasay, into a number of extensive landslips owing to the frailty of their underlying strata. One of the lowest slips has dammed up a string of lakes known as the Storr Lochs, thereby giving rise to a scene of vertical cliffs mirrored in placid water, so appealing to artists and photographers alike. The Storr itself, like the equally spectacular Quiraing further north, is a towering pallisade of eroded basalt that has weathered into grotesque pinnacles. The most famous is the 160-foot spire of the Old Man of Storr which stands proud of the rockface, like a gigantic sea-stack, but it is already tilting, in the manner of Pisa's famous tower. Its instability is due to the hundreds of feet of 'incompetent' Jurassic limestones and clays which had been buried by the outburst of volcanic activity more than 50 million years ago, but it has to be realised that the cliffs themselves have subsequently been over-steepened by ice-sheets moving along the scarp-face. Where the underlying Jurassic rocks have been cliffed by the ocean they offer a prospect of horizontal multi-coloured bands, giving rise to the soubriquet of "Kilt Rock" down which a waterfall leaps straight into the sea. Each morning on Fladda we had been able to walk up onto a hill and view this unforgettable panorama, highlighted by the rising sun which projected the shadow of the "Old Man" on to the black face of The Storr which rises to a height of 2,605 feet. One day the "Old Man" will collapse, in the manner of a true coastal sea-stack, not from wave erosion but from the instability of its foundations.

From almost any viewpoint on the southern coast of Skye the magnificent Black Cuillins dominate the skyline, a scene rhapsodised by Sir Walter Scott and recaptured by Turner's brush. But to really appreciate their overwhelming majesty one must land on the shores of Loch Scavaig and follow the cascading stream up and over the ice-smoothed ridge behind the beach. Here you would be following in the footsteps of many eminent travellers, who had been this way over the centuries, and who had gazed in awe across the dark waters of Loch Coruisk at the amphitheatre of jagged peaks, almost all of which rise to heights of over 3,000 feet. Thomas Pennant, the indefatigable Welsh traveller, came to Skye in 1772 but failed to visit Loch Coruisk, although he saw the Cuillins from the summit of Beinn na Caillich (2,403 feet). Dr Samuel Johnson sailed to Skye the following year but was fairly contemptuous in his descriptions of Scottish scenery, much preferring to be lavishly entertained at Talisker and Dunvegan Castle. Some forty years later that well-travelled artist, William Daniell, having just painted a picture of the Old Man of Storr, climbed from the seashore of Loch Scavaig into the brooding hollow of Loch Coruisk. Here, he produced what must be regarded as one of the most awesome impressions of mountain scenery in the history of landscape art, notwithstanding his artistic licence. The view he described as: "So steep and sudden is the acclivity that, at one glance, you see the whole face of the mountains from the foot to the summit; a continued plane of solid rock, rising upwards on all hands for more than a mile, and presenting a barrier over which there is no egress ... it appeared as if all living things had abandoned this spot to the spirit of solitude. I held my breath to listen for a sound, but all was hushed". Modern visitors have concurred and stated that even on a day of blazing heat the place has remained sombre and cold. One has to remember, however, that in the Hebrides there are often, almost surreal, moments of utter calm, an experience we regularly enjoyed on Fladda both at dawn and dusk, and even here in the heart of The Cuillins. But Hebridean weather always has the last word, as both Daniell and myself discovered. Heavy rain and snow-storms driving in across the Minches can quickly turn the jagged Cuillin ridges into something quite frightful.

It is on record that, as a Cambridge music scholar, Ralph Vaughan Williams holidayed on Skye and climbed the graceful spire of Sgurr nan Gillean (3,167 feet) but I doubt that he would have visited lonely Loch Coruisk. As a composer of pastoral music, he would have found no inspiration in the harsh landscape so vividly described by Daniell; there would have been no sign of a 'Lark Ascending' in such a sterile scenic void. However, it remains of interest to record that, after Vaughan Williams had witnessed an island service conducted by a Gaelic preacher, similar to the one in which we had participated on Raasay, his future compositions were said to have been influenced by what he had heard. He noted how the preacher had altered the rhythm and intonation of his delivery into a form more akin to a song and such an experience is said to have guided the structure of some of his future folksongs.

Geologically speaking, Skye is probably the most complex of the Hebrides. The Geologists' Association Guide states that "...the broad features of the Tertiary igneous geology are shown in a more spectacular way on this island [Skye] than in any other area". It took me several days to circumnavigate its intricate shoreline and then translate its complexity into the sort of prose that a layman could understand. How, for example, was I to explain the differences in shape, colour and genesis between the Red Cuillins and the Black Cuillins? Quite clearly the former, with their cascading screes descending right down to the coast road, are made of pink granite, the formation of which I have already described. The Black Cuillins, however, are quite another matter. Together, with their accompanying shapely peak of Blaven, their dark-coloured rocks rise abruptly from the surrounding moorlands like primordial cathedral towers. "In essence, the [Black] Cuillins are an arcuate mass of ultrabasic peridotite which has subsequently been invaded by a large number of olivine-rich gabbro sheets. The whole plutonic complex has been intruded into the earlier basaltic lava plains". These are the very words that I wrote in 1977 but, in perusing them forty years later, I have realised that further explanations are necessary because I am no longer writing a book on Geology and Scenery but simply some memories of my coastal associations.

Skye, like Mull (described below) is part of what is termed the 'Tertiary Volcanic Province of North-West Britain and North-East Ireland' when, some 50 to 60 million years ago, after the rupturing of the Atlantic plates, this region would have resembled that of modern-day Iceland. Huge masses of molten material, of differing chemical compositions, surged upwards from deep within the Earth's crust. In so doing they forced the overlying thick layers of older basaltic lava into domes which, in succeeding years, have had their summits entirely stripped away by erosion, except where basalt still forms a residual cap on the top of Gars Bheinn (2,934) the southernmost peak of the Cuillins. Just to complicate matters, the activity did not cease until the uprising Black Cuillin dome began to crack allowing a final series of intrusive igneous rocks to slice upwards through the mass following these narrow vertical fissures in the covering rocks. These final intrusions are known as 'dykes', because their resistance to weathering has left them standing like stone walls in the landscape as their surrounding rocks have been partly worn away. The most famous example is the so-called "Inaccessible Pinnacle" which stands on the summit of Sgurr Dearg (3,206 feet). This formidable 220-foot rock spire can only be ascended by a skilled rock-climber and I shall never forget the look of immense joy and relief on the face of Nick Crane when he achieved his lifelong ambition to scale its daunting 'needle', a feat which seems to have escaped Robert Macfarlane. It was in Nick Crane's spin-off book from the acclaimed TV programme "Coast" that he describes the view from its miniscule summit: "Far below, the blue sea clung to the Cuillins' taffeta skirts. And far away on the monstrous deep once sailed by men in skin boats, I could see the Outer Hebrides, floating in line astern along the horizon. It was a view that had been carved by ice and then inundated by water" (Coast: our Island Story, Nick Crane, 2010).

We journeyed on northwards along the Skye coast, away from the beguiling hills of the Cuillins, skirting the penetrating finger of Loch Harport and into the 'lava landscapes' of the almost trackless peninsula of Duirinish. Here the twin flat-topped, basalt-layered hills, appropriately known as "Macleod's Tables", dominate the skyline and, beyond their remarkable mesa-like shapes, a tourist would be well advised to wander off the beaten track for a few miles to view the precipitous sea-cliffs of Waterstein Head (966 feet), almost matching the Irish Cliffs of Moher in terms of their verticality. Here, across the attractive Moonen Bay, with its hanging waterfall, is the lighthouse of Neist Point, that creates a prominent 'full stop' at Skye's westernmost extremity. Not far from here we decided to take time off, as the sun reappeared, and luxuriate on the white coral beaches of Clagain on the neighbouring peninsula of Vaternish. Such an episode of pure relaxation, where the solitude remained unbroken for hours, gave me precious time, as at Cape Wrath, to recapitulate and conclude that I must beware that my manuscript must not wander off into the realms of a simple tourist guide. Thus, when clouds began to gather in the Atlantic skies, we reluctantly dragged ourselves away from this heavenly haven of peace and drove on around the massive indentation of Loch Snizort to the most populated of Skye's peninsulas, that of Trotternish. As I have already hinted this northern 'wing' is also the most visited by tourists, many of whom are en route to the Outer Hebrides via the ferry port of Uig. Trotternish is a geologist's paradise for, in addition to its overwhelming volcanic landforms, it has layer upon layer of sedimentary rocks that seem out of place in North-west Scotland. I have already remarked upon the unlikely exposures of Jurassic sedimentary rocks in eastern Raasay, but here, stretching for about twenty miles from north of Portree, Skye's north-east coastline has been sculpted from sedimentary rocks of a similar age. Consequently, the landscape is one of fertile pastures and quite prosperous crofts, quite different from those of Rona and northern Raasay, a 'stone's throw' across the channel. One only has to visit the two areas to understand the extent to which geology had so profoundly affected the lifestyles of both sets of islanders. It is largely a matter of the derived soils. In Trotternish the acid-free, easily-tilled topsoil supports a reasonable farming economy that creates vistas of yellow hayfields, sleek herds of cattle, large flocks of sheep and well-managed fields of arable crops, around the smartly-painted houses. A mere four miles away, across the Sound of Raasay, I have described how the acid soils on the ice-scoured rocks of Pre-Cambrian age have resulted in a wilderness of bracken, a mere scattering of sheep, abandoned potato-rigs and greystone ruins on Raasay's northern tip. Moreover, if we had only known, when we stood on Fladda's empty northern tip of An Roinn, and gazed across the water to those thriving Skye townships, that some thirty years later, there on the coast of Trotternish, a momentous geological discovery would be made. On the tiny peninsula of Rudha nam Brathairean, the wave-washed shore-platform of Jurassic strata suddenly became a location hailed by the press as one of Britain's most important geological sites. Large footprints of a massive dinosaur were found impressed into the now solidified layers of clay and, so far, this is claimed to be the only such discovery in the entire British Isles, despite the international fame of Dorset's "Jurassic Coast". I wonder if this humble stretch of Scottish coastline will ever become as big a tourist attraction as the Giant's Causeway? If it does then the Isle of Skye Council will face an even bigger headache in their future plans of dealing with the tourist influx.

On looking back, as I write this missive from my home in East Anglia, I now realise that although I had spent so many hours tramping around Skye's convoluted coastline when noting its complex geology, I had actually spent very many more hours further south on another large island in the Hebridean volcanic province. This was Mull and there is no better place for a holidaymaker to start an exploratory journey than in the island 'capital' of Tobermory. Many years after my first visit there, in 1956, purely as a tourist, I returned in 1972 to carry out quite detailed research for the Forestry Commission but, additionally, to collect information for my forthcoming book "Geology and Scenery in Scotland". It was on the latter visit that I wrote in my notebook "Few ports can claim so romantic a setting as Tobermory, with its curve of gaily painted quayside houses surmounted by a halo of sycamore woodland clinging to the steep lava cliffs. The [splendour] of these deciduous woodlands is deceptive, however, for not far inland it soon becomes apparent how Mull received its name, which may be interpreted [from the Gaelic] as 'high, wide tableland". I have taken the liberty of reproducing these words that were later to appear in another of my publications, "Geology and Scenery in Britain" (1992), because they were an apt description of the island scenery that entranced me when I first landed there in 1956. Thus, I must briefly turn back the clock some sixty years in order to describe my earliest impressions of Scotland's magical western shores.

I had already spent two years in my academic post in Northern Ireland and enjoyed the coastal scenery of Western Ireland, as described above, but an opportunity at last arose to set foot in the Hebrides after merely reading about them throughout the preceding years. Having driven, with my fiancée, Diane, and her parents to stay overnight in Oban, I was thrilled when I looked through the hotel window, on that Spring morning in 1956, to see the sunlight glinting on the harbour seas and the mist slowly clearing on the distant mountains of Mull, across the Firth of Lorne. I have to admit that the thought of circumnavigating this legendary island aboard a MacBraynes steamer took me back to the excitement of my first 'ocean cruise' in the form of a childhood day-trip to the Isle of Man from Llandudno pier. But by now my knowledge had been considerably enhanced by subsequent coastal experiences, and I became increasingly animated as we gazed at the distinctive shores of Mull.

It was highly fortuitous that my first venture into Hebridean waters coincided with blue skies and calm seas. However, it was not long before fellow passengers regaled me with stories relating to the fearsome storms that they had experienced on previous cruises in these parts. They told me how, in certain tempests, the Atlantic waves are capable of hurling heavy boulders far up the cliffs and that, in the Orkneys, the remnants of a wrecked fishing boat had been flung onto the top of a 200-foot cliff. I quickly learnt to avoid such 'doom-mongers' and settled myself at the ship's prow in order not to miss a moment of the unfolding seascapes as we traversed the Sound of Mull. I was conscious from my previous reading that this was the very passage that Queen Victoria had sailed in 1847 in an imposing royal squadron. The Times correspondent accompanying the 'expedition' wrote how "The sea was as smooth as glass, reflected on its surface every feature of the adjacent heights, and at short intervals, on either side, the ruins of ancient strongholds rise on the sea-side, their grim and solitary aspect calling back the mind to times of violence now past". It has been pointed out by historians, however, that the Queen was probably unaware that behind the facade of striking scenery there were serious problems in the Hebrides due to the evictions noted above. Perhaps, because of possible unrest, the Queen was not allowed to step ashore in case she witnessed the poverty of some of her subjects and she never again set foot in the Hebrides, preferring instead to holiday in Balmoral.

When we landed at Tobermory we did what all tourists do during their short time ashore, buy a postcard, visit the local gift shop, drink a hasty beverage and return rapidly to the ship. We sailed past the frowning Ardnamurchan Point, the westernmost extremity of Britain, described by Daniell as "A bluff headland, rocky, sterile and wind-worn", and were soon experiencing one of the most unforgettable coastal prospects to be seen anywhere in Britain, which the Times correspondent in 1847 described as "…far away and embosomed in the ocean [lay] the fantastic and varied forms of the adjacent islands". I was quite overawed as I saw the same panorama of mountainous islands that I had previously only read about: the distant Isle of Skye, the graceful peaks of Rum, the curious hump of Eigg and the whalebacks of Coll and Tiree. I remembered that this was the same assemblage of islands that were illustrated in the very first watercolour that I had bought as a student and which, inadvertently, my parents had thrown away. But I soon cast such thoughts aside because I knew that the best was still to come, no less than the fabled isle of Staffa. Our steamer took us as close as possible to Fingal's Cave but, not surprisingly, there was no time to go ashore. Nor indeed did Queen Victoria step onto this basaltic wonder, more than a century before us, although The Times reported how the royal barge, with the royal standard, flying, took her to the cave's furthest extremity. It is claimed that this "Cathedral of the Seas" was first 'discovered' by the eminent scientist, Sir Joseph Banks, who proclaimed it as "...one of the greatest natural curiosities in the world", when he was on his way to Iceland in 1772. His Journal records that while he was being entertained on Mull by a local clan chief he met with "...an English gentleman, Mr Leach, who no sooner than he saw us that he told us, that about nine leagues from us was an island where he believed no one in the highlands had ever been, on which there were pillars like those of the Giant's Causeway". This, of course, is highly unlikely, especially since it was so close to the sacred isle of Iona. We are told by Donald Macculloch that its very name Staffa is a Norse description for 'the little island of columns' and that the Vikings had settled in the Hebrides from 890 to 1266 (The Wondrous Isle of Staffa. D. B Macculloch, 1927). Perhaps it comes as something of a surprise to learn that such a small island has an entire book written about its undoubted merits, but I have to say that, also in my possession is a book on the tiny sea-stack of solitary Rockall, which runs to no less than 200 pages (Rockall, James Fisher, 1956).

An even greater prize lay before us, because for centuries writers, poets and mere tourists have sung the praises of Iona. I will resist any attempt to sing its praises because more accomplished writers have already succeeded in advertising both the beauty and the history of this sacred isle which, of course, has brought the tourists flocking. Our own landfall fell precisely within the latter category and we aimed to make the most of our visit and enjoy the glorious sunshine. We were told that once you have been to Iona you will come back twice more and it will be shown how we managed to fulfil this claim. Most of the passengers hurried straight to the cathedral, whose outbuildings were still being restored, but we preferred to follow the "Straid-na-Marbh" or 'street of the dead', which led to the island graveyard with its celebrated runic crosses. Here we were able to find the sort of historic tranquillity for which the island is famed. Such ambience is best summed-up by George Scott-Moncrieff who wrote: "Iona is a place of amazing beauty. A simplicitude of beauty, and a beatitude: for it is difficult to dismiss that sense as of a place hallowed, the atmosphere marked with the impress of the presence of holy people" (The Scottish Islands, G. Scott-Moncrieff, 1952). Even the critical Samuel Johnson was moved enough to comment, as he knelt at the ruined cathedral altar: "That man is little to be envied…whose piety would not grow warmer among the ruins of Iona". We then took precious moments of our time ashore to climb the island's modest hill, a mere 332 feet in height, because this was a viewpoint that allowed us to see the Sound of Iona and its romantic shoreline that Cadell translated into his most famous coastal pictures. Eastwards, across the strait, the distant deep blue and soft purple of the southern mountains of Mull contrasted with the shining red granite of the lengthy Ross peninsula; in the foreground the white shell-sands turned the encircling sea into pools of brilliant turquoise and hyacinth; westwards, the low hills of Tiree were barely visible in the pearly Atlantic haze; southwards, the surf broke uneasily on the treacherous granite fangs of the Torran Rocks, notorious in Robert Louis Stevenson's novel "Kidnapped", and beyond them the unmistakeable Paps of Jura punctuated the skyline. I was not to enjoy a comparable panorama until I stood on the summit of Mount Brandon in Ireland, as described above. Time was now running out and we paid a rapid visit to the cathedral before re-embarking. True to my vocation, I made a mental note that the stones from which it had been re-built looked foreign to the island's geology and that if we returned I would check their derivation (see below). We were reluctant to leave Iona's haven of peace and, as mentioned earlier, vowed to give any future daughter the name Fiona, in memory of this exceptional experience. And so back to southern England, but the extraordinary aura of this historic isle had made such an impression that I felt compelled to return one day.

Regrettably, the pleasure of a return visit had to wait a further fifteen years when, quite unexpectedly, in 1971, I was invited, together with my colleague Brian Goodall, to carry out a major research project on the Forestry Commission's vast estates. Their agent made it clear that, partly in response to public pressure and partly from becoming aware of the Neptune survey that I had completed a few years earlier, the Commission had decided to open up their forests for recreational use. It was true that, throughout the 1960's, an expanding population, better education, increasing affluence, greater mobility and more leisure-time had led to an unprecedented level of demand for countryside recreation. It had been noted that the United Kingdom had lagged far behind the United States in using their forests to satisfy such entreaties. It has to be said that a few British Forest Parks had already been established and these had highlighted the fact that the primary economic principle of simply growing trees was actually compatible with recreational usage. However, the big questions had remained: What type of recreation? Which type of forests would be best suited? And, finally, where should the Commission concentrate its effort, in view of monetary restrictions? I do not propose to labour through the research methodology, which is not relevant to the present volume, but merely to outline the aims of the project as published in the final 1973 report: (The Recreational Potential of Forestry Commission Holdings, B. Goodall & J. B. Whittow, 1973):

(a) To define qualitatively the characteristics of various types of forest in relation to the requirements of certain recreational activities.
(b) To assess the effect of local (intra-forest) accessibility to this relationship.
(c) To define a practical method of assessing the potential of forests for various recreational activities.
(d) To identify any future planning problems arising directly from consideration of forest recreational potential [i.e. conflict].

It soon dawned on me that the possible opening-up of the Commission's vast estates might take some pressure off the British coastline, in terms of recreation. It also became clear clear that it would be impossible to survey all the forests, so we operated on the basis of a limited stratified sample. Moreover, we had to carry out the field survey ourselves. The University of Reading was unable (unwilling) to underwrite a large body of student surveyors as had been the case during the Enterprise Neptune survey, with which it had some similarities. Although Brian and I worked together on most of the English forests, it was not surprising that I chose the Welsh and the western Scottish examples in which to carry out tests of the fieldwork. Suffice to say that the work had to be completed in the long vacations and that my dear wife, Diane, was willing to be dragged along yet again as co-driver, map-reader and field-surveyor on a virtual replication of the Neptune coastal survey. Of the few coastal forests that fell into my allocation I propose to describe only that of Mull, which had the great advantage of allowing us to spend some time on Fladda, and, above all, to re-visit Iona.

Since we would be spending much of our time away from hotel accommodation we borrowed a camper-van and set off north in time to catch the Mull ferry from Oban and make the short crossing to Craignure. The island's narrow waist, between Loch na Keal and Salen Bay, serves to divide Mull's forests into two broad groups, that in the north around the inland basin of Loch Frisa, and the southern group, occurring at intervals along the thirty-mile peninsula of the Ross of Mull, which points like a bony figure out to Iona. I was very conscious of the fact that these Mull forests were only the first of the four Scottish forests that we had to visit. After Mull we still had to drive on to Slattadale, a smaller forest near Gairloch; a medium-sized plantation at Portclair on the steep slopes of Loch Ness; and finally, the large forest of Naver, in the wilds of northern Sutherland. Therefore, time was of the essence and we had to move rapidly across the forest landscapes, testing the methodology that we had devised. But you just try to move rapidly through ranks of closely planted spruce and larch in the gloom of a deep forest. As if it were not difficult enough to surmount the hummocky terrain and the squelchy peat, we also had to force our way through a litter of broken branches that had been left on the forest floor after the periodic 'brashing' by the foresters. Let no one visualise a scene of dappled forest glades beneath attractive canopies of oak or beech, for we were working in 'economic plantations', sarcastically referred to by the public as "Sitka Slums". There was no wildlife, very little accessibility and virtually no views. Little wonder that the local Forestry

Commission workers laughed at our stumbling exploits and repeatedly asked "Why would anyone want to find enjoyment in such a God-forsaken spot? We've never seen a tourist and even the locals don't want access to our forests". Memories of Alistair Nicholson's initial remarks on our first visit to Raasay immediately sprang to mind and, especially after suffering, in a day of heavy rain on Mull, we were glad to agree with the experts. Nothing can be more soul-destroying than mapping in a dripping forest, not even those stormy days spent researching the boulder-clay cliffs of the Llyn Peninsula.

We felt that we had earned a day off and what better way to spend it than re-visiting Iona. A fine day finally dawned and we drove to the tiny village of Fionphort and crossed onto the sacred Isle of St Columba. It was almost devoid of visitors and we had time to linger in the empty cathedral and wander around the quiet village. But what I really wanted to do was to make notes on the geology and building stones for future reference. Both the nunnery and the cathedral had been constructed from pink Ross granite, local black schist and a creamy-coloured Jurassic limestone, used in the window mouldings, and brought from a Carsaig quarry on the south coast of Mull. Most striking of all was the interior decoration of Iona Marble, whose attractive greenish-white metamorphosed limestone is streaked with yellow varieties of serpentine. It was formerly quarried at the south end of the island and there, on the seashore, the old quarry workings can be seen near to Port na Churaich. This gaelic name served to remind us of St Columba's historic landfall in AD 563, after his remarkable voyage in a flimsy curragh from the Irish village of Doire (Now Derry or Londonderry). I thought momentarily about my own links with that historic Irish city, where I saw St Columb's ancient cathedral every day for three years but without giving any thought to the religious significance of the Saint's momentous voyage to Scotland. At that time my mind was too occupied with Ireland's Geology and Scenery.

Our sojourn on Mull was rapidly coming to an end, so I decided to make a rapid circumnavigation of its lengthy coastline to make notes on its geology for, like Skye, the lava flows had buried a surface of Jurassic sedimentary rocks which now peep out only where the sea has worn back the island fringes. The gigantic central vent volcano that had once existed at the centre of the island had poured out no less than 6,000 feet of lava, some 50 to 60 million years ago, in which each separate flow has subsequently been etched into Britain's best example of a "trap landscape". The term 'trap' is derived from the Swedish word 'trappa', meaning 'step' to define a topography resembling a volcanic staircase. Each of the 'treads', having weathered into a gently sloping terrace on the more friable upper surface of each lava flow, is generally covered with peat and a heathery vegetation. It follows that the more resistant lower layers of each lava flow represent the 'risers' which stand out as miniature bare escarpments. Regrettably, we had no time to visit two of Mull's most spectacular geological marvels, known as Mackinnon's Cave and the nearby MacCulloch's Tree. They can be seen, either from the sea or by intrepid walkers who are prepared to scramble some distance beneath those precipitous basaltic sea-cliffs of the western shore of the Ardmeanach headland. The cave matches the stature of Fingal's Cave whilst the fossil tree is one of only three British examples (all in Mull). High above the tumbled screes of the rarely visited 'Wilderness', I was told that one can still see the remains of the 'fossilised' tree trunk in the position of growth, a discovery dating from 1810. Since that date fossil hunters have removed much of the original trunk but the lowest part remains in the form of a silicified cylinder of fossil wood glistening with quartz crystals and surrounded by a sheath of soft, black, charred wood. It is rooted in a carbonaceous mud over a bed of red volcanic ash. As I write, the same type of volcanic inundation is happening in Hawaii, where vast outpourings of molten rock are overwhelming both forests and houses before plunging into the boiling ocean that surrounds those active volcanic islands.

Our final night was spent in Tobermory, which the internationally renowned Hugh Miller, known as "The Father of Scottish Geology", believed that: "With all its beauty, however, there hangs about the village an air of melancholy" (The Cruise of the Betsey, Hugh Miller, 1861). By the following morning we were both inclined to agree with such sentiments. Aware that in this small town it would be pointless seeking accommodation at the height of the tourist season we looked for a suitable place to spend yet another night in our camper van. Because Tobermory is hemmed in by cliffs we sought for a refuge on a neighbouring tree-covered coastal headland and found a pretty dell amidst an oak wood, overlooking a small lake. There was even a large slab of concrete on which we could guarantee a firm standing for the vehicle and, after a late supper, drowsily consumed beneath a watery sunset, we fell asleep. But not for long, because a loud thump on the van's roof startled us sufficiently to make us venture outside to look for any damage. All was calm and reasonably light in the Scottish 'simmer dim' of mid-summer. Nevertheless, we lay awake for hours, aware of strange murmurings and weird atmospheric perturbations, until at sunrise we hastily packed and drove straight away to the ferry at Craignure. Only once in my previous travels had I experienced such a spectral manifestation, during a teenage cycling trip in

Snowdonia (referred to in a previous chapter). There, we had fled from our tent on a mountain lakeshore in the early hours, terrified by the roaring of a vicious wind that lasted for only a few minutes before dying away. I was later to discover that this was a fairly common example of an 'air avalanche' caused by an accumulation of cold air in a high glacial cwm on a clear night, after which it overflowed as a torrent of air down the slope. On asking the local Welsh farmer about this phenomenon he jokingly told us about the spot being renowned for the night-time appearance of water spirits following the drowning of a shepherd. But the Tobermory incident was quite different; there were no surrounding hills and no avalanche of air, simply a feeling of distinct unease. We soon put this to the back of our minds, more intent in planning our forest researches further north in Scotland's wilderness. It was some years later that a Scottish postgraduate came to study in the Geography Department at Reading and I learnt that he lived in Tobermory. On recounting our story, he burst out laughing: "Why on earth did you spend the night there, despite its apparent beauty? Any local would have told you to avoid that place because it's reputedly haunted". He went on to explain that it was the site of a sacrificial Druid oak-grove which the locals never visited, and that during World War II the old mansion, that once stood on the concrete base on which we had parked, had been requisitioned by the War Office to house a Commando unit. Whether or not these stalwart troops had suffered similar nightmares remained unclear, but my Scottish student concluded by saying that when they left they blew up the house. "And what about the unexplained thump on the camper-van roof?". "Oh, that would be one of the swans thinking that he was landing on the nearby lake" he replied with a big grin.

Some weeks later, we had left Scotland behind to return to the humdrum urban life of southern England, where I had to put my forestry research findings into an official report. In short, we had concluded that most Scottish Highland forests were so remote and so forbidding in their 'intra-penetrability' that there would be no demand for them to be opened-up for tourist recreation, just as the local foresters had confirmed. Our mapping in the lowlands of England and parts of Wales, however, was quite another story for, clearly, that is where the major demand lay and where the largely broadleaf woodlands were more accessible and less densely planted. Our results confirmed that the latter lent themselves to a great variety of recreational experiences, many of which have subsequently been adopted by the Commission. Personally, I would have been very happy to recommend the re-forestation of certain Scottish coastlands with such native species as Scot's Pine and Birch, because they could only enhance some of their delightful vistas. My memories of the wooded coasts of north Devon came to mind, but such recommendations were not part of our brief. Moreover, it has already been described above how a planting venture on Fladda had come to grief but I hope that such an episode will not deter further coastal planting in some Scottish coastlands.

As I wrote up the report for the Forestry Commission I let my thoughts wander back to Scotland and the many memories of our recent travels because, after all, I would soon have to start writing my contracted book on "Geology and Scenery in Scotland". What was it about 'Caledonia Stern and Wild' that had influenced me most? Quite clearly, the memories of its magnificently convoluted shorelines always remained uppermost in my mind and my continuing love of mountainous environments could never be assuaged. Equally, memories of years spent indulging in the insular life on Fladda, my 'dream island', were of utmost importance because I can never forget the solitude, the tranquillity and the pure escapism from urban living. But I will also remember the wonderful Hebridean people that we met, their remarkable resilience, their steadfast life-styles and, above all, the kindness of such people as Calum MacLeod and Alistair Nicholson with their fund of stories. They provided the important links with the historic past of the Hebrides and were able to instil in me the significance of some of the tragic events of previous centuries. How divorced we are in England from such knowledge, and how little we seem to care about the value of retaining the Gaelic language as part of a culture that is swiftly threatened by exposure to the modern world and all its innovations. We lived on Fladda without mobile phones and televisions and were none the worse for it. Nevertheless, I have to accept that many islanders would disagree with my rather hedonistic feelings. I have recently purchased a volume of collected poems of Sorley Maclean, referred to above, and one of his final verses bewailed the slow degradation of the Gaelic tongue in much of Scotland:

"The mountains are speechless
if what they say cannot be understood
and the many-voiced ocean is silent
if no one knows its language".

I had experienced similar sentiments in the coastal extremities of Western Ireland and in the furthest reaches of the Llyn Peninsula of Wales, where some of my acquaintances also feared for the survival of their own Celtic tongues. Would they eventually follow the fate of the Cornish language? Who knows? But Cornwall was to be the next coastal domain that I would visit and this had long remained something of a blank canvas in my experience, ever since a childhood visit to Newquay in pre-war days. It remains something of a paradox that, although we had lived most of our married life in southern England, we had spent no time in Cornwall, one of Britain's most popular holiday destinations. Insofar as we seemed to prefer lengthier excursions to Ireland, Scotland and Wales, it is difficult to explain why we neglected the wonderful ruggedness of the Cornish coast. I can only conclude that it was because of its lack of mountainous shores, bearing in mind that, despite the lack of this attribute, Cornwall possesses some of Britain's most beautiful coastlands which have proved to be an attraction not only to casual tourists but also to droves of writers, artists, poets and composers. Manifestly, this was an omission that had to be resolved and the opportunity arose when our close friends, Peter and Kay Boulton, bought a house in the far west of Cornwall. Peter was an old school friend with whom I had lost touch over the decades until I discovered that we had both come to live on the Chiltern Hills of southern England late in our careers. Like myself, Peter had a yearning for the coast and, after his retirement they decided to move to Cornwall and offer us a great chance to explore new territory.

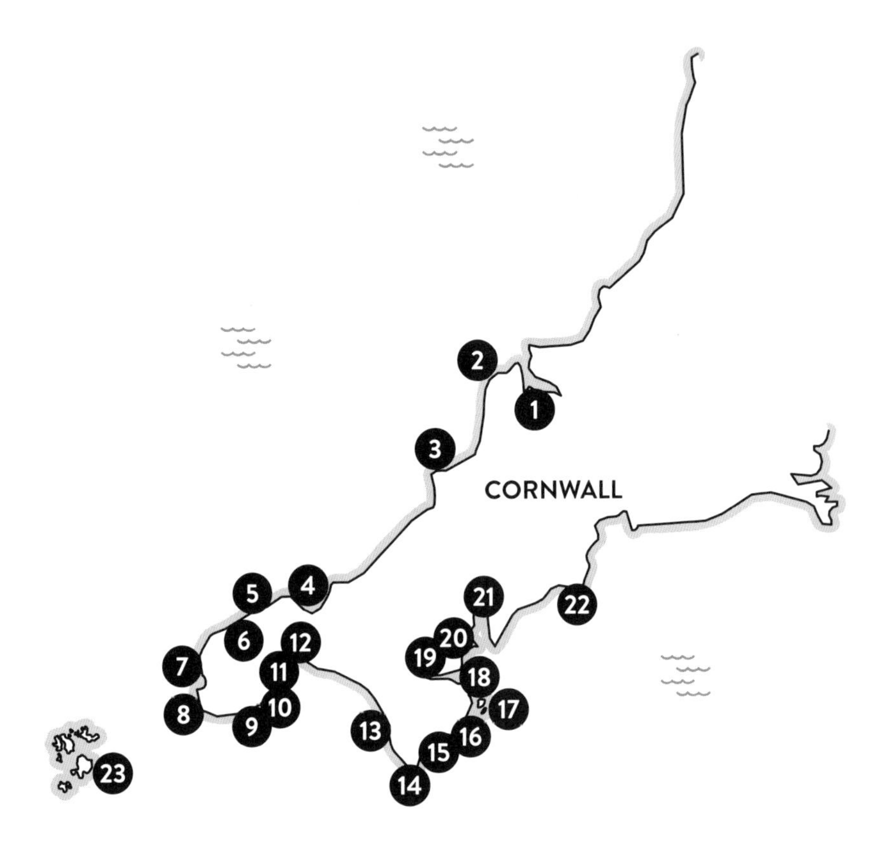

1. Padstow
2. Trevose Head
3. Newquay
4. St Ives
5. Zennor
6. Penwith
7. Sennen Cove
8. Land's End
9. Lamorna Cove
10. Mousehole
11. Newlyn
12. Penzance
13. Mullion Cove
14. Lizard Point
15. Cadgwith
16. Coverack
17. The Manacles
18. Helford River
19. Porth Navas Creek
20. Falmouth
21. Carrick Roads
22. Dodman Point
23. Isles of Scilly

8. CORNWALL

"And in the shadowless, unclouded glare
Deep blue above us fades to whiteness where
A misty sea-line meets the wash of air.
Nut-smell of gorse and honey-smell of ling
Waft out to sea the freshness of the spring
On sunny shallows, green and whispering."
(Cornish Cliffs, John Betjeman, 1966)

Ruins of an old tin mine on the coast of Penwith

Porth Navas Creek, Cornwall

Looking eastwards to the mouth of the Helford River, Cornwall

Trebah Cove, showing the D-Day Anniversary (2004)

Lizard Point and the old lifeboat station

A plaque on Falmouth Quay to commemorate the news of the Battle of Trafalgar brough by the schooner 'Pickle' on the 4th November, 1805

Cadgwith Cove, Cornwall – *See plate section for colour version*

Mullion Cove, Cornwall – *See plate section for colour version*

To understand Cornwall, I was told, you must first read the literature of both Betjeman and Daphne Du Maurier. Not her famous novels "Jamaica Inn", "Rebecca" or "Frenchman's Creek", despite their merits, but one of her last books "Vanishing Cornwall" (1967). Both these authors spent much of their lives in Cornwall and remember it from the days long before World War II. Thus, they paint a picture that has long since vanished, as Du Maurier asserts in what is little more than her revealing autobiography. Both speak kindly of this 'remote' English county and enthuse about its 'other-worldliness', but Betjeman also writes somewhat pungently about the impact of tourism: "The Electricity Board has strung the fields, villages and towns of Cornwall with more poles and wires, ill-sited and clumsily arranged, than in any other part of the British Isles. This is partly because even the remotest bungalow on a cliff wants electricity and partly because burying cables in slate or granite is expensive... Roads have been widened, blocks of houses have been taken down in picturesque ports to make way for car parks...In the holiday season lorries and cars trailing caravans and boats block lanes never intended for such heavy traffic. The County Planning authorities, hard put to it to find available sites on the coast, have been obliged to introduce caravans and chalets even to the wooded inland valleys...There is also the consolation that no one has yet discovered how to build houses on the sea" (Cornwall: A Shell Guide, John Betjeman, 1964).

I have taken the liberty of quoting Betjeman's percipient comments almost in their entirety because they summarise virtually all the reasons why, in the very same year of the guide's publication, the Neptune committee met for the first time. No one mentioned Cornwall 'per se', that I can recall, but its problems must certainly have been in all our minds. Moreover, it is pertinent to point out that, within a few years of that date, the Forestry Commission had asked me to look at their own vast estates, at a national level, in an attempt to respond to the nation's ever-increasing spatial demands for extra recreational amenities, presumably under governmental pressure. In retrospect, it appears that the 1960's was the decade in which the country awakened to the never-ending environmental problems that were being imposed upon our shorelines, such as those being faced on the coasts of Cornwall, as outlined by Betjeman. Moreover, in 1966, the National Parks Commission published their own report on "The Coasts of South-West England" in which they 'statistically' made us aware of both the vulnerability and of the possible future degradation of one of our greatest glories. It is worth highlighting that the first line of the 'Contents' in the latter's Report, baldly states: "Note on coastal eyesores". No beating about the bush in this case!

I was a comparative latecomer into what appeared to be a maelstrom of environmental-impact studies and it was, with some relief, after having built up a visionary coastal image of this remarkable peninsula (whilst editing and also colouring the maps of the Enterprise Neptune survey of 1965), that I belatedly set foot in Cornwall purely as a guest in the 1990's. I have to admit that I soon discovered the coastal scenery to be not quite as 'ruined' as Betjeman had implied, but it must be remembered that we always took our holidays in May, before the summer 'invasion' had really started, so the beaches were relatively empty and the narrow lanes free from caravan traffic. Furthermore, we were fortunate to find a quiet corner when we were able to stay with our friends, Peter and Kay Boulton, who lived 'off the beaten track', so to speak. At their picturesque retreat, Diane and I found a landscape more akin to that described so lovingly by the eminent poet, Edward Thomas, during a fleeting visit that he had made to Cornwall, before World War I.

He had discovered that "...there are sloping fields of corn and grass divided by green hedges, and woods rich and misty and warm, and the bones of the land are buried away until it ends in a bay where high and cavernous dark rocks stand on either side of blue water and level sand" (The South Country. Edward Thomas, 1909). When we arrived at the Boulton's home I discovered that Thomas's poetic description could well have been based on their very own shoreline, much to our delight. They had recently purchased a quaint house on the edge of a picturesque creek which fringed the northern shore of the well-known Helford River. A steeply twisting drive led down through overhanging trees to a series of terraced lawns and their own private quay. As we strolled down to the water's edge and gazed across to the hamlet of Porth Navas, I was immediately seized with a feeling of déjà vu, for this was a scene almost identical to that of East Hook on Pembrokeshire's Cleddau River. Each evening, as we sat on the terrace with our drinks, we played host to a family of badgers who came tamely to be fed by hand. As we watched the sun dip behind the wooded Calamansack hill we knew that we had found yet another idyllic shore, hundreds of miles from our beloved Fladda. In place of the open heather-covered island moors with their extensive views across miles of Scottish ocean, we were very happy to enjoy a very contrasting environment of extensive oakwoods whose lower branches dipped into the lazy tidal flow which crept quietly back and forth across the glistening mudflats of the hidden creek. We were soon to learn that there are two very different Cornish coasts: the northern one, carved largely from granitic rocks whose castellated headlands and tiny coves face the full onslaught of Atlantic weather; and the southern one, whose relatively sheltered shores and deeply penetrating creeks are clothed for miles in ancient woodland, with the notable exception of the rugged Lizard

Peninsula. Moreover, in the succeeding years we were also to find that Cornwall has two climates: when warm south-easterlies bring a clinging sea-fret onto its southern shores with accompanying grey skies and drizzle, a brief journey brings one into the blue skies of a cloud-free northern coast. Few British tourist-haunts can boast of such a fortuitous dichotomy.

I quickly realised, so far as coastal scenery was concerned, that I had moved into totally different dimensions of scale from those with which I had become familiar in Ireland and Scotland. Cornwall may not be a land of great mountains cliffed by restless seas and scoured by former ice-sheets. Nor is it a wilderness of endless bogland stretching down to sinuous, burrowing sea-lochs (or loughs, in an Irish context) almost devoid of habitation. No, instead, it is a rich mixture of monumental clifflines, bosky creeks, crouching fishing villages, sub-tropical gardens and sandy coves, all bathed in an ethereal Atlantic light. Such a combination of matchless scenery is, of course, why hundreds of thousands of holidaymakers are happy to consider Cornwall as the epitome of a perfect seaside destination. We also decided that this was a venue that we would enjoy for purely hedonistic pleasure. No more mapping, no more instrumental surveys, no more undergraduate instruction and, above all, always being able to shelter in comfortable and welcoming surroundings during inclement weather.

It became clear, during our annual visits, that it would be impossible to explore the entire Cornish coastline, nor would we be attempting to emulate Pevsner's blanket architectural cover. Instead we concentrated on two major regions: first and foremost, the estuaries, bays, creeks and rocky shores between Falmouth and Lands' End; secondly, the very contrasting crenellated, rugged and wind-blown coast of Penwith that lies between Lands End and St Ives. I must acknowledge that, although these beguiling shores were primarily visited for their scenic attributes, I could never escape from a life-long habit of making assessments of their geology, soils, flora, fauna and farming capability. I suppose that I was unable to forget the decades of analysis and evaluation that had been the mainstream of my academic career. When we drove, or were driven, around the mazy network of lanes between the stone-built 'hedges' that overflowed with valerian and honeysuckle, I couldn't help but drop the occasional comment about the structure of the scenery that unfolded before our eyes. The Boultons learnt about the formation of the 'raised beach' that nestles on the shoreline near Rosemullion Head and how the famous serpentine rock of The Lizard was created eons ago. Perhaps they had found such information of very little interest but were too polite to say so. But it was when Peter was able to launch his sailing boat and take us all on mini-voyages that he became manifestly enthusiastic. I remembered that it was he who had first allowed us to circumnavigate our Hebridean island of Fladda. As an ex-naval officer, the lure of the sea had led Peter to leave a house high up on the Chilterns to buy a home on Porth Navas Creek, where he was given membership of the officers' mess at the local naval air station of Culdrose. It was just as well that he was a good navigator because his new home of Tranquibar faced across the creek to the royal oyster-beds belonging to the Duchy of Cornwall. It was always essential to steer clear of their mooring stakes, especially on a falling tide. One amusing anecdote will suffice to illustrate his penchant for all things maritime. On the occasion of his wife's birthday he took us all down to his quay to proudly unveil her surprise present. It turned out to be a large metal winch to haul his boat out of the water.

All of our seaward excursions took us down the creek and out into the Helford River in which the title of 'river' is really a misnomer because, in reality, it is a flooded estuary (termed a 'ria'). This, like the other south Cornish coastal river valleys had become gradually submerged by the post-glacial rise of sea-level which, when it reached its zenith, finally demarcated the entire British and Irish coastlines that we see today. The estuaries of south-east Ireland and of Pembrokeshire, are further examples of a 'ria coastline'. It must be remembered that all the estuaries of north-west Scotland and north-west Ireland had also been simultaneously flooded by the changing level of the ocean but, in their particular cases, they had previously been greatly over-deepened by the grinding power of former glaciers which had converted them into fjords. At this juncture I find that I have reverted, once again, to an exposition on geological processes and I must hastily return to describe our experiences in our newly discovered Avalon, with its very different scenery, architecture, cultural history and life-styles from those of Wales, Ireland and Scotland. A common thread has remained intact, however, because all of these western coastlands have retained their beguiling, atmospheric magnetism that continues to appeal to 'the world and his wife'. I have often reflected on the reasons why my own wanderings around the British Isles have been preponderately along these western shores. On looking back through both the current manuscript and my own unpublished autobiography, I have discovered that I have regularly waxed most passionately about sunsets bathing the 'Edge of the Land', whether in California, Snowdonia, Donegal, Kerry or the Hebrides. I also realise that I have already begun to wax ecstatic about evenings in Cornwall and I fear that when I begin writing about my memories of East Anglian shores this type of twilight imagery will prove to be all but impossible when looking across the North Sea horizons. Perhaps, my ancestral Flemish forebears when, perched on a Beveland sand dune and gazing westwards across this same cold sea, had both relished the sunset's watery reflections and pondered on the possibility of crossing those seas to a different shore, thus freeing themselves from the increasingly life-threatening inundations caused by the rapidly-rising post-glacial sea of those much earlier centuries.

Each time we set off in Peter's boat to explore the bosky creeks I thought of the similar happy jaunts that I had shared with Bill and Helen Davies, almost fifty years ago, when we explored Pembrokeshire's breezy coastline and cruised along its tree-shaded inlets. In Cornwall, however, it was Frenchman's Creek which had to be explored on our first venture and we discovered the same haunting atmosphere described in Du Maurier's iconic novel. But even more striking in its solitude and peacefulness was the larger creek of Polwheveral which winds through mystical, oak-shrouded banks to a hidden hostelry. Another inn, which became our favourite 'watering hole', was the Ferryboat Inn that overlooks the tiny beach of Helford Passage. Here is a totally different scene, for the seaward view epitomises the lure of Cornwall as a centre of small-boat sailing. Sail boats, cabin cruisers, dinghies and speed boats, bobbed amidst their mooring buoys, and seemed to fill the haven. As we sat on the terrace, enjoying our beers and crab sandwiches, we were able to enjoy the revelry, laughter and swirling kaleidoscope of colour of the boating fraternity as they paraded across the glittering waters. I found a certain euphoric sense of wellbeing as I surveyed the scene: it suddenly struck me that this must have been similar to the feelings of those holidaymakers who, lazing on the beaches at Criccieth and Nefyn in North Wales all those years ago, may well have been puzzled by the labouring figures of two sweat-laden figures hacking at the cliff-face.

Some days we walked along the coastal path out towards the breezy ocean, past the hamlet of Durgan and the statuesque Scots

Pines at Toll Point which frame the view as if in a painting of the French Riviera. Other times we meandered down the steep coastal valleys to gaze in awe at the sub-tropical gardens of Glendurgan and Trebah, filled with exotic plants and trees that have created quiet glades of tranquility whose only sound was that of birdsong. On one unforgettable occasion, however, we discovered that the pocket-hankerchief sized beach at Trebah was a hive of activity. The bay was packed with military vehicles and was swarming with army personnel. One was immediately made aware that this was a parade of great significance, judging by the number of American flags and banners that were wafting in the sea breeze. Scores of United States 'veterans', with their badges and army caps, were strolling around the beach between the armoured vehicles, all being escorted by their hosts, a regiment of British Para's with their magenta-coloured berets. I have only recently learnt that it was Daphne Du Maurier who chose this colour at the behest of her husband, General 'Boy' Browning. Before long the parade was called to order, accompanied by military music and shouted commands. As the BBC and American TV cameras whirled and the world's press cameras flashed, a lonely British naval helicopter hove into view from behind the headland and hovered over the bay. It approached the shoreline as its winchman was slowly lowered almost to sea-level where he placed a wreath of poppies amidst the wavelets. As the strains of the American National Anthem echoed around the cove and all hats were doffed, the elderly World War II serviceman were hard-pressed to hold back the tears as this highly emotional spectacle unfolded. A brief service followed led by the British padre to the Para's regiment who, we were informed, insisted on rising from his sickbed to conduct the prayers and who, it transpired, died from cancer the following week. On questioning one of the uniformed

British soldiers we learnt that this was a ceremony for the few survivors of an American Infantry brigade that had embarked from Trebah beach on D-Day to land on Normandy's infamous Omaha Beach only to be virtually decimated. It was only at this point of the conversation that I realised that the date that day was the 7th of June. As I write these memoirs this moving Cornish scene has been replicated off the coast of East Anglia where, in November 2018, the Archbisop of Canterbury leaned over the bows of a Great Yarmouth vessel to lower a wreath onto the choppy waters of the North Sea, in memory of all those lost at sea in two World Wars. Moreover, Brancaster, on the north coast of Norfolk, was one of 28 beaches chosen to serve as a commemoration of the fallen in World War I. There, on that golden strand, a sand-sculptured portrait of a local soldier, who had been killed in that war, was drawn at low tide. It was intended to mark the 100th centenary of the 1918 Armistice in a scheme held throughout the United Kingdom and conceived by Danny Boyle the film director. It seems fitting to draw a parallel with the changing nature of our shores and the ephemeral nature of our lives, because the rising tide eradicated all 28 images as time elapsed.

After this temporary diversion into the fields of poignant nostalgia, it was time to return to that time in the 1990's when we were exploring the coasts of Cornwall. We set off on another sunny morning to visit another well-known Cornish garden and woodland, that of Trelissick whose 570-acre estate descends to King Hal's Ferry across the Carrick Roads of the River Fal estuary. Because it is one of the many National Trust properties in Cornwall it is generally thronged with visitors who wander through its profusion of azalea-bedecked lawns and gravel paths. Its colourful scenery enticed me to paint a picture as a memento of a sunlit day's visit. A local Cornish writer has recently congratulated the National Trust on its policy of buying land just behind the coastal strip (a scheme which actually started in Cornwall) and especially for its earliest efforts in the 1930's in preventing the deep waters of the Carrick Roads near Trelissick from being developed into a massive dockyard. Regrettably, the white neo-Classical mansion of Trelissick House (based on the Erectheion in Athens) is closed to the public. It is owned by the Copeland Spode family of Stoke on Trent ceramic fame but our friend Robert Copeland was not in residence. It was Robert who had drawn my attention to the original invoice of my ancestor, Benjamin Whittow, who, in 1796, had engraved the copper-plate from which the first "Willow Pattern" plate was manufactured. I am extremely fortunate that I have been able to purchase one of the first of the plates to be decorated with this well-known pattern, now 220-years old.

The National Trust owns well over one hundred properties in Cornwall, most of them on the coast and many of which have been purchased with Neptune funds. Without living in the region, we found it impossible to visit them all but made a valiant attempt to spend time in some of the lesser-known coastal tracts away from the 'tourist-trail' of Lands End, St Michael's Mount, Penzance, and Falmouth. It would be true to say that St Ives is another visitor 'honey pot' but it was a venue that I just could not ignore.

When we at last had an opportunity to visit the fabled harbour at St Ives I experienced a similar frisson of excitement that I had felt when I first set foot on Fladda. Here was a former fishing village now famous throughout the world as the home of a thriving artist's colony. I have spoken elsewhere that when I had been Warden of St David's Hall in Reading University, I numbered amongst my senior committee a number of eminent artists, foremost of whom were Terry Frost and Tom Cross. Both were latter-day members of the so-called 'Newlyn and St Ives' Schools' and I had avidly collected their books written about the region and also about their own inspirational work. By the time we had belatedly arrived in Cornwall, Terry Frost had died so we were unable to recapture the 'old times' at Reading, when one of his first abstract watercolours adorned the walls of my Warden's office. I have often wondered what happened to this very valuable painting now that St David's Hall has been converted into flats. Tom Cross, on the other hand, was, at that time, enjoying his position as President of the well-regarded Falmouth College of Art, soon to become a University. Although a lesser-known artist than Terry Frost, Tom had become renowned for his classic books on the Cornish Schools of Art, mentioned above, in addition to writing a superb account of his life living alongside the Helford River, illustrated with his own paintings. Just as we were about to renew an old friendship and walk with him along Helford's beautiful shoreline, news reached us that Tom had suffered an untimely death. Thus, I could only reminisce with his widow whom I had known as a staff member at the University of Reading. In the context of Art, I always seem to be a moment too late, either in the purchase of a painting (as described earlier) or in the continuation of earlier friendships.

When we finally drove along the acclaimed waterfront of St Ives, where the former 'sail-lofts' have been converted into studios, we were fortunate to find this 'mecca' relatively free from both traffic and crowds. Whereupon we ourselves became tourists and followed the well-trodden alleyways and sloping streets of this lovely old town. Not surprisingly, its character has changed since the great art-rush of the 1890's when dozens of artists came to this fishing village, attracted by the legendary quality of its pearly Atlantic light.

The catalogue of famous names seems endless: Sickert, Whistler, Brangwyn, Adrian Stokes, Borlase Smart, Julius Olsen, and later to be followed, in the mid-20th century by the 'modernists' of John Park, Barbara Hepworth, Ben Nicholson, Christopher Wood, Patrick Heron and Peter Lanyon. The latter's very abstract-expressionist paintings have been described by a modern art-critic as depicting "...the reeling plumes of salty air around the area of West Penwith". It has been claimed that today's art in St Ives is so ultra-modernist "...that it has little to do with the legendary light". But the same writer, David Wilkinson, concedes that "...if one were to lie back on the rocky peninsula known as 'the Island', one could observe the progress of the sun from dawn to sunset, without lifting a brush" (Painting at the Edge. Laura Newton [Ed.], 2005).

St Ives. had once been 'quaint', as described by a writer in the 1930's: "It is a jumble of little granite houses, narrow steets, courtyards, and 'culs-de-sac'...that appear to have been thrown together anyhow. The whole thing, cobble streets and all, is old-looking and grey as the rocks around it" (The Cornish Coast and Moors. A. G. Folliott-Stokes, 1931). This is the landscape with which Virginia Woolf would have been familiar during her family holidays at Talland House, St Ives, in the late-19th century. In her acclaimed 1927 novel "To the Lighthouse", she captures the essence of the Cornish coast as if in an oil painting: "The great plateful of blue water was before her; the hoary Lighthouse, distant, austere, in the midst; and on the right, as far as the eye could see, fading and falling in soft low pleats, the green sand dunes with the wild flowing grasses on them which always seemed to be running away to some moon country, uninhabited by men". She actually set this scene in The Hebrides (where it would be equally apposite) but was clearly based on her memories of St Ives Bay. I strolled along

John Smeaton's 18th century pier in an attempt to recapture something of the scene illustrated by a multitude of canvases, painted over more than a century. The boats rocked gently at their harbour moorings, rhythmically loosening and tightening their ropes in response to the slowly creeping waves. A sudden cognisance flashed through my mind that it was such a vision that had obviously inspired many of Terry Frost's early paintings. I had no time to "lie back on The Island and observe the progress of the sun" but I lingered sufficiently long to capture a 'sense of place', as the seagulls wheeled overhead and a sea breeze set the sea-front flags and bunting into a ripple of colour. A rapid tour of the new Tate Gallery, built on St Ives 'other beach' to replace a former gas-holder, and the day-long exploration was over and I left this historic coastal scene, still redolent of fish, salt spray and oil paint, with a great number of nostalgic memories. As we drove slowly back to our host's home on Porth Navas Creek, I wracked my brain to think of another coastal settlement that could rival the setting of St Ives. I finally concluded that only the quaint but smaller Scottish harbours of Kirkcudbright, Portree and Tobermory could match anything of its scenic appeal, although the Yorkshire villages of Staithes and Robin Hood's Bay (both former 'artist colonies') would be close contenders.

Having tasted one of the beguiling fruits of Cornwall's westernmost coast, so to speak, I felt compelled to return to explore the bewitching territory of West Penwith, a mysterious landscape held in a timewarp as primeval as that of Ireland's western peninsulas. In this respect I have read the beliefs of some writers who have likened Penwith to Connemara. Insofar as its name is derived from the Cornish "Penn-whdh" which translates as 'the head at the end' there is a certain similarity, as it creates a vision of the termination of the known land at that time. But I have to point out that there can be no comparison between the regular linearity of Cornwall's western coastline and that of the meandering shores of Connemara despite both having been carved from granitic rocks. South west Cornwall's landscape has also been likened to those of Brittany whose geological structure is virtually identical. An alternative name for Brittany is Armorica, that has given its name to the term 'Armorican' which has been adopted to describe the 300-million-year old mountain-building phase which folded and mineralised the strata of southern Britain and of southern Ireland. Such an upheaval was responsible for all the contortions and fractures that characterise the remarkably varied cliff-line that extends all the way between Lands End and North Devon.

Penwith, Cornwall's westernmost toe, remains the most Celtic part of England. Its profusion of prehistoric stone monuments mimics the naturally sculpted tors and their rocking stones ('logans'), while its standing stones ('menhirs'), its stone circles, carved crosses and cyclopean burial chambers ('quoits') litter the hilltops. The grey colouring of the granite exposures is offset at the coastline because the sea-cliffs are emblazoned with yellow lichen, sea pink and thrift, interrupted by tiny coves of dazzling white sand where the disintegrating granite has broken down into crystals of sparkling quartz and spangled mica. Wherever the rock-joints are closely spaced, shingle-charged waves have ground out narrow clefts ('zawns'), whilst the intervening buttresses have survived as pinnacled headlands where the joints are more widely spaced. Many authors have likened the finely tooled cliffs and sea stacks of Penwith to architectural forms or to mystic beasts, decisions that have only added to the mystique.

On entering this sloping shelf of land that descends gently from its 800-foot heathery granite ridge down to the ragged cliff-line, constantly battered by Atlantic rollers, one turns back the clock, not by a century but for some 2,000 years, in much the same way that Sean O'Faolain had discovered in Western Ireland. The scene is one of tiny hamlets, treeless vistas, mosaics of irregular stone-walled fields unchanged since the Iron Age and overlain with a panoply of ancient stone monuments. Moreover, because of the dearth of woodland on this windswept coast the cottages are built only of stone, largely of granite and slate. This remote enclave has been termed "the finest prehistoric landscape in Europe" but having become familiar with the 'beehive' architecture and numerous dolmens of Ireland's Dingle Peninsula, I find it difficult to concur. Second only to the county of Wiltshire in the wealth of its ancient monuments, however, this part of Cornwall can still be regarded as a tiny remnant of primeval England. Even this contention has been denied by a writer who believes that: "Although of England it is quite un-English…Cornwall, surrounded on three sides by the sea…was isolated from the rest of England" (Cornwall. W. G. V. Balchin, 1954). Moreover, West Penwith is even more distinctively remote because it is almost separated from the rest of the county by the protective granite ridge of Penwith Moors which, even at this reduced scale, loom like mountains over the coastal plateau. Between the two World Wars, Folliott-Stokes (*op. cit.*) had found West Penwith to be a "…lone land, so seldom trodden by the foot of the stranger [that] it still remains one of the sanctuaries of Nature, for it is still virgin to the desecrating steel of the plough and the spade".

We decided to cross its threshold from the north, near to St Ives, and follow the sign-post to St Just. At no point does the road approach the coast so, in order to reach the remote headlands, coves and 'zawns', one must branch off along the antennae of farm tracks or follow the South-West Coast Path on foot. The artist, Patrick Heron, wrote an apt description of the only decent highway (the B3306): "A wonderful, enlarged footpath of a road, slipping and squirming between the rocks and the fields, twisting and turning through the granite hamlets of Porthmeor and Rosemergy with a total disregard for the needs of holiday traffic". But it is this very characteristic that dissuades the coach and caravan and serves to maintain the tranquil atmosphere that immediately held me in thrall. It also brought to mind echoes of my first venture into the outermost limits of another serene western peninsula, because the promontory of The Llyn in North Wales shares most of these Cornish attributes. The writer and journalist, Brian Jackman, (whom I had briefly worked with on Sunday Times publications), wrote evocatively of the merits of West Penwith: "The entire landscape, with its tumbled rocks and thorn bushes flying in the wind, has the fey eerie quality of an Arthur Rackham illustration. At Porthmeor I came upon a white goose asleep in the road. Nearby, a girl stood kissing a horse in a field, like a scene from an Irish folk tale" (Wild About Britain. Brian Jackman, 2017).

We left the road and walked down into the village of Zennor, crouching in a hollow about a mile from the sea. The day was hot and the sea breeze was little more than a feeble zephyr, persuading us to seek the coolness of the ancient granite church. We discovered that it dated from the 12th century and had withstood the Atlantic gales throughout the succeeding centuries with scarcely a change in its structure. The tourist attraction, of course, is the bench-end carving of the Mermaid of Zennor, reminding everyone of the myths and folk tales of this antique land where megalithic cromlechs, like Zennor Quoit and Lanyon Quoit stand fore-square on the skyline. My friends told me that they had seen in the local newspaper an article entitled "Bronze Age Bingo" in which a journalist had discovered 21 white-painted numbers on the Penwith rocks and ancient monuments. Enquiries led to the explanation of why they had been daubed: they were intended as orienteering markers for trainees at the Culdrose Naval Air Station. Why do the military authorities, decades after the war, believe that they still have the right to desecrate our coastal countryside?

Perhaps the ubiquitous mystique of Penwith had appealed to D. H. Lawrence when he came with his German wife to live near Zennor during World War I, although he more likely regarded it as an escape from public derision. I learnt that his former home, Tregerthen Farm, later came on the market and its sale proved to be contentious. A London property developer wished to buy it and turn it into a holiday centre. The artist, Patrick Heron, who had been in the forefront in defending the Penwith countryside from intrusive development, was quick to join forces with the National Trust to ensure that this splendid tract of coastline was 'saved for the nation'. The composer, Cecil Gray, a friend of Peter Warlock and Arnold Bax, also came ths way. From his home at Bosigran Castle, near Gurnard's Head, he composed his Celtic opera "Deidre" imbued with the sinister atmosphere of the occult. He swore that a nearby village was cursed and, during a later visit, Bax confirmed that it was "…a centre in ancient times of sacrificial blood rites and unspeakable abominations, the exhalations of which still unmistakably hover around, poisoning the air" (E. M. Marshall, *op. cit.*). After I had made a swift sketch of the Zennor church, viewed from its foxglove-fringed lane, and had reluctantly taken leave of the "Tinner's Arms", we set off southwards to enjoy "the glories of those cliff-edged, sea-encircled views" such as Bosigran cliffs, Gurnard's Head, Great Zawn and Greeb Point.

Beyond Pendeen, however, the scenery began to change into that of a countryside whose sea-fresh air had once been seriously poisoned, not by 'blood rites' but by the imposition of smoke-stack industries.

We had come to a coastline where tin and copper mining had laid waste to swathes of former ancient farmland. It is thought that tin was first extracted in the St Just area as early as the Bronze Age, some 3,000 years ago, but production began in earnest during the 12th century when Penwith became one of the four main mining areas in Cornwall which, at that time, was the only known source in the World. It is recorded, indeed, that early sea traders came from the Mediterranean, a fact versified by Matthew Arnold:

"To where the Atlantic raves
Outside the western straits; and unbent sails
There, where down cloudy cliffs, through sheets of foam,
Shy trafficers, the dark Iberians came"
(The Scholar Gypsy. Matthew Arnold)

Tin had been formed by mineralisation in the highly metamorphosed rocks surrounding the intrusive granite intrusions and was originally extracted by a process termed 'streaming' in which surface water was diverted in order to wash the mineral from the loose detritus that had accumulated due to weathering of the rocks. Tinners had the right to 'claim' a plot on any part of unenclosed land, whilst the landowner was able to charge a mere one-fifteenth 'tin-toll' on the amount extracted. In later centuries the miners learnt how to trace the surface detrital deposits back to the 'mother-lodes' and, thence forwards, shaft-mining had replaced 'streaming'. It was plain to see where the irregular Iron Age field-pattern had become replaced by the square, stone-walled enclosures within which the miners had once grown a few crops. But the greatest impact has been on the mining landscape itself, because we could discern where the soil had been stripped by the 'streaming', in order to uncover the naked rock, a process which has left ugly scars, now barely covered with wild scrub and heath.

By the beginning of the 18th century, a local Cornishman, Newcomen, had invented a pump capable of drawing water from the often-flooded workings, thereby allowing deep-mining to follow the tin lodes out to the coast and even under the sea. Such an innovation also facilitated the exploitation of the rich copper ores, some of which had been discovered when mining the tin at depth. The metal extraction industry then reached its zenith and the pit-head workings manifested themselves in the stone-built engine houses, with their gaunt chimney stacks, scores of which still litter the coast right down to sea-level near Botallack. It may come as a surprise to learn that some writers believe that their derelict ruins now enhance the quality of the coastal scenery. Personally, I am not so sure, but it is likely that I am biased, having been born in a Midland townscape overwhelmed by noxious industry. It has to be borne in mind, however, that so great is its historical importance that this scarred landscape has been designated by UNESCO as a World Heritage Site. Notwithstanding this recent accolade, the travel writer, Hockin, had once spoken bleakly, in tones reminiscent of Dickens, about this coastal zone when he walked across "...long hills piled with decaying engine houses, over disemboweled commons, across torn valleys...the running sores of adits, and, continually, past odds and ends of villages strung out along the roads round Redruth and Cambourne, tired and hard and endlessly poverty-stricken" (Walking in Cornwall.

J. R. A. Hockin, 1936). Nevertheless, it must be remembered that similar sites, such as that at Coalbrookdale, where the Industrial Revolution began, are now revered as sorts of museums. Even the mouldering back-streets of the Potteries have revived a few of their Victorian 'pot-banks' into visitor attractions. Moreover, it has to be remembered that to Cornish folk these 'scars' in the coastal scene may be regarded as a source of pride, reminding them of the time when their industry led the World. Although I remained somewhat disheartened by this strip of coastal 'wasteland' in such a realm of beauty, it is significant to note that the poet, Edward Thomas, found a natural serenity amongst its ruins, where "... donkeys graze on the brown turf, larks rise and fall and curlews go by; a cuckoo sings among the deserted mines...The lonely turf is full of lilac scabious flowers and crimson knapweed among the solid mounds of gorse". (The South Country, 1909, *op. cit.*). It has to be admitted, however, that I failed to be convinced.

Eighty years later another writer visited this mining region and tried to visualise what this stretch of coast would have looked like in the 19th century: "The air would have been filled with smoke and perpetual noise; between the the hamlets and mines would have moved a constant stream of trade and people. By the end of the last century Cornwall was running out of both tin and pilchards: mines closed; the fishing industry declined; thousands emigrated. A century ago the hamlet of Treveal supported eighty people...Now it is a single farm and home to just two families, one being the [National] Trust Warden's". (In Search of Neptune. Charlie Pye-Smith, 1990). This sad demise of a community brought back memories of Scotland's Isle of Raasay's own ignominious fortunes, but I have yet to discover a poet of the calibre of Sorley Maclean who has aimed to recapture the Cornish families' adversities – all seems to be lost in mountains of tourist literature that rightly sings the praises of this attractive coastline and its people.

The last tin mine (South Crofty) closed in 1998, but the old miners' records drew attention to the fact that during their earlier underground labours they had encountered hot springs of lithium-charged water. Currently, this mineral is mined largely in South America but the enormous global demand for lithium batteries has seen its price rocket in less than a decade from £3,000 to £12,000 per metric tonne. Satellite mapping suggests that a large area between Portreath on the north coast and Trellisick on Carrick Roads contain workable reserves that would have to be pumped to the surface in a technique similar to that of fracking. Since any new mining activity would be likely to impinge on coastal AONB's, the local authorities would have to balance the problem of increased job opportunities against the possibility of land degradation and closed access for the lucrative tourist trade. In view of the opposition to fracking in certain areas of England, it will be interesting to see whether 'development' or 'conservation' wins any potential battle. After all, this is Poldark country! On the plus side, however, schemes are well underway to utilise the area's geothermal heat, derived from deep within the 'roots' of the granite rocks, to create pollution-free sources of cheap energy to serve the local communities.

We vowed to come back another day and explore the shores of that four-mile stretch which extends down from Cape Cornwall to the 'last town' of England, that of Sennen and its celebrated Cove. The local unspoilt shore exhibits battlemented cliffs of well-jointed granite, that have been chiselled into miniature castles, butresses and spires by wind, wave and weathering. This almost architectural panorama has been recaptured in a majestic painting by Charles Napier (1882–1968) entitled

"Nanijizal Towards Lands End", one of the finest depictions of rocky cliffs that I have ever seen, especially in terms of its understanding of geological structures. To enjoy such a type of scenery, one has to follow the coastal path, for no road reaches the sea until a lane plunges crazily down to Sennen Cove. Here is an almost forgotten coast, where, since prehistoric man once wrought a windswept and precarious living, we found the silence to be broken only by the steady beat of the ocean whose waves broke incessantly on the rocky shore, except where they swashed far up the magnificent beach of Whitesand Bay. This renowned 'surfers paradise' is the only extensive and accessible stretch of sand to be found anywhere to the south of St Ives. Needless to say, such an attraction means it is a 'honey pot' for holiday-makers, and we found the tiny adjoining Sennen Cove to be packed with a cheerful throng. Because the cramped site below the cliff is able to support a mere handful of fishermens' cottages, Sennen Cove is lacking in a great deal of overnight accommodation. Thus, the visitors were almost all day-trippers, just like ourselves. Our photograph album contains a print which shows the four of us happily enjoying ice creams whilst sitting on the miniscule sea-front. A picture of the very height of decadence! It would be nice to think that when Delius visited Sennen in 1919 he was inspired to write his haunting tone poem "Sunset". What we do know with certainty, however, is that the well-known artist Dame Laura Knight came regularly to Sennen and that Stanhope Forbes's wife, Elizabeth, brought parties of student artists there from Newlyn because it is documented that: "She yearned for springtime when the students' baggage wagon could again trundle out of Newlyn, piled high with easels, paint boxes and canvases and head for Sennen" (Painting at the Edge.

Laura Newton, Ed., *op. cit.*). When that doyen of pre-war travel writers, H. V. Morton, came to Sennen in 1927 (two years before I was born) he was thrilled only by its "...little grey church... which every charabanc passes, which no motorist thinks worth a visit" Like ourselves he was bemused by the "...competition to be the last house in England, the last shop in England, the last inn in England: and as every shop, inn, and house on this piece of rock advertises this fact, quite regardless that the next-door neighbour is equally convinced, the sentimental effect is ruined". (In Search of England. H. V. Morton, 1927). It was now time for us to travel further eastwards and investigate Newlyn, England's premier fishing port and also the home of another of Cornwall's famous Schools of Painting.

I didn't quite know what to expect of Newlyn, because I had read so many conflicting descriptions. The Pevsner Guide, for example, dismisses it in a mere two lines: "The fishing harbour, the quay and the rising narrow streets [are] not as picturesque as at St Ives or Fowey or Looe"; the long-distance walker, Hockin (*op. cit.*) mentions only its "...proud and noble stink" but he obviously didn't linger there. When we turn to G. E. Mitton (Cornwall. 1915), however, we read of a different perception: "Rows of stereotyped villas in terraces now overlook the bay...But round the harbour linger still the odours of the typical old fishing village, and there are few sights more suggestive to the imagination than the scattering of the red-sailed fishing-boats as they pass at evening time out between the narrow horns of the harbour...the vision of the bay between masses of apple-blossom in springtime is one never to be forgotten". And this was written by a man who, in the same volume, had described St Ives as a town where "The prevailing tones of all the buildings are drab and grey; drab stone, drab stucco, drab paint with pale slate-grey roofs: a little red brick or tile would be an improvement from an artistic point of view". Little wonder that I was confused and tried to search the bookshops for a modern account of Newlyn. Regrettably, it was not until I sat down to plan my own book on the coast, that I discovered a splendid book by Gavin Knight, entitled "The Swordfish and the Star" (2016), described by Paul Theroux as "A marvellous and humane book…Cornish life as told by its own people – fishermen, farmers, publicans, singers, brawlers, historians, drunks, old timers, newcomers". It sounded like an amalgamation of my own memories that related to my Pembrokeshire forebears, or of Western Ireland story-tellers, or of North Welsh inns and Hebridean islanders. And, so it proved to be, but too late to guide me through Newlyn's streets some thirty years ago. It narrates stories from two of Newlyn's pubs that give a truer picture than the romantic accounts by visiting travellers of the last century. A single quotation will suffice to set the modern scene which, in fact, turns out to be not very different from that which prevailed during my first visit in the 1990's: "Newlyn is the largest deep-sea fishing port in England. Like many villages it is tribal. There are only eight or nine great fishermen who notice when and why the fish come in, and everyone else just follows them. These are the men who can tell from the cloudiness and colour of the water, or from a change in the temperature, whether the plankton levels are on the rise. If plankton multiply, the mackerel will follow, and blue sharks will follow the mackerel".

Over the centuries fishing patterns have changed in Cornwall. Whereas the smaller sailing boats once went out for hauls of pilchards and whose images have been captured in the paintings of the earlier artists of the Newlyn School, so today the heavyweight giant trawlers bring home catches of hake, halibut, cod, ling and pollock to say nothing of shark and swordfish, all of which bring in an annual turnover of £220,000,000. Not surprisingly, therefore, we drove into a semi-industrial scene not unlike the once-bustling Pembrokeshire quay of Whittow Wharf of my earliest childhood memory. I have to confess that I was slightly disappointed with Newlyn's ambience, especially after having been to St Ives, but I began to realise that this is really the truer face of Cornwall's fishing coast. The red-sailed boats are no more, massive ice-making warehouses have replaced the ancient 'fishing-cellars', many of the old buildings have been demolished, heavy lorries, bound for London, crowd the streets and creel-loaded donkeys are to be seen only on sepia postcards. Thus, after looking briefly at the Ordnance Survey's mark of Mean-Tide Level, the datum from which all of Britain's heights are measured, we rapidly left for a visit to nearby Mousehole, 'just around the corner'. Unfortunately, Newlyn's art gallery was closed and at that time we had no knowledgre of The Swordfish and The Star public houses in which I may have met and talked to some of the characters described by Gavin Knight. I feel sure that we would have met the likes of Blasket Isles' Tomas O' Criomhthainn or Raasay's Calum Macleod but I have had to settle instead with the words of Tim Hubbard, presenter of BBC Radio Cornwall, who did meet such Newlyn characters: "If you want to hear a good tale – tall or not – then a harbour is the place to be. Fishermen, fishes and fishing are the very stuff of stories, legends, dreams and, sadly, nightmares. From the memories of 'the one that got away', through a wealth of Christian symbolism to fabled monsters living in the deep, the relationship between fish and men has always been just that bit special". (A Year in Cornwall. Tim Hubbard, 2000).

I was sorry to have missed the art gallery because it houses the nation's finest collection of pictures by the Newlyn School artists, a colony founded in the early 1880's. Foremost amongst its members were Stanhope and Elizabeth Forbes, Walter Langley, Frank Bramley, Henry Tuke, Thomas and Caroline Gotch and Doris "Dod" Procter. Painting mainly at the beginning of the 20th century, such artists found that the local fishing industry provided a wealth of subjects, ranging from the idyllic charm of the fisherfolk and their picturesque surroundings, through the exertions of farming in an unyielding stony landscape, to the pathos and tragedy involved in the fisherman's struggle with an unforgiving ocean. These artists painted life in the raw, although their occasional attempts to 'romantisise' the coastal lifestyle did not disguise the reality of the poverty and squalor of Newlyn at that time. An article in the local press spoke about the "...mud and filth and rotten fish lying about and trampled underfoot. And then the smells in certain conditions of the atmosphere; the effluvia are something appalling and anyone with a delicate olfactory apparatus would barely survive the stinks and stenches" (Painting at the Edge: Newlyn. Laura Newton, Ed., 2005, *op. cit.*). Such a description echoes that of the 20th century citizens of Milford Haven who railed against the noxious smells from the smoke-houses of my ancestors on Whittow Wharf, in those selfsame years.

Mousehole seemed to be an apt description of this tiny fishing hamlet almost buried in its cliff-bound cove, although we were told that the name is derived from the Cornish term 'Mouzel', meaning 'maid's brook'. Other explanations, however, are based on a derivation from the term 'maew holh' translated as 'gull basin' which seems more likely, judging by the avian gathering we saw on all the roof tops. It's tiny mosaic of lanes and passages with their colourful window-boxes is certainly picturesque, especially for camera-festooned tourists like ourselves, but other than its charm we found little to detain us and I was more anxious to visit another coastal inlet a few miles further west. This was yet another acclaimed artists' colony in a narrow valley whose trout-stream tumbles steeply down to Lamorna Cove. Here, one is able to wander down its narrow lane, lined with alder and hazel, to marvel at the aquamarine ocean on a shore bounded by bastions of wave-carved granite hardly sullied by former quarrying. The remoteness and beauty of this serene valley had attracted a solitary artist in the 1890's and that was Samuel John Birch, or Lamorna Birch as he was later to style himself. Thereafter, a steady stream of like-minded "...painters, sculptors, etchers, writers, poets and potters" visited his home or rented nearby cottages in this lonely valley. Thus, wrote Austin Wormleighton who dubbed it as 'A Place Apart' in his delightful description of the smallest of the Cornish Schools of Art. (Painting at the Edge. 2005, *op. cit.*). Almost all of the Newlyn artists visited at one time or another but both Dame Laura and her husband, Harold Knight, were resident there for the decade that spanned World War I. They frequently played host to Sir Alfred Munnings who painted images of the Western Foxhounds on the neighbouring moors. The most notable portrait, however, is that of Lamorna Birch and his daughters, by Dame Laura Knight, which not only captures the insouciance of this remarkable man but also the appeal of his wooded valley.

Not once in all our Cornish visits did we venture to Lands End, although I had been there as a child in the 1930's when, I was told, there had been only a handful of visitors. Today it is overwhelmed. Instead, we drove to Cornwall's other main promontory, that of the

Lizard, where we were to witness a somewhat different world, in terms of its geology. We had now set foot in a new type of coastal landscape, a place where we had left behind a countryside of grey granitic scenery and had transferred to the Lizard's promontory, carved from some of Britain's oldest rocks. Here, a great mass of black, red and green serpentine, together with sheets of gabbro, had been intruded into a bedrock of hornblende schists and shining bands of mica. A similar suite of rocks can be found in such regions as Western Ireland and Western Scotland (as described above) but Cornwall is devoid of their mountainous shores. Its most comparable counterpart, therefore, has to be that of northern Anglesey whose rugged coast owes its character to a similar combination of ancient rocks.

Having driven from the oak-lined shores of the Helford River, it came as an unexpected change of scene to climb up from the tiny creek-head 'port' of Gweek and its seal sanctuary, onto a relatively barren plateau of treeless heaths at Goonhilly and Predannack Downs whose thin soils have weathered from the underlying serpentine. Such landscapes as these, together with that of the unimproved gabbro country of Crousa Downs, where myriads of boulders still litter the surface, testify to the laborious problem of former land reclamation in these parts. I found the term 'Downs' a somewhat bizarre use of a title usually reserved for the rolling grasslands which typically clothe England's chalk country. Yet, remarkably, there is substantial fertility to be found along a narrow strip that crosses the promontory, between Porthallow in the east and Mullion Cove in the west, where the soils derived from an outcrop of schists were once celebrated as producing Cornwall's finest grain harvests. But I hadn't come to see the soils and their crops but the relatively unspoilt coastline of the Lizard. Few places can compete with the curious lithology of serpentine which is the main attraction of the promontory's tourist trade. The majority of tourists make straight for Lizard town to visit the tiny workshops which produce the great variety of nick-nacks carved and polished from the green and red serpentine, a rock which dominates the southern half of the peninsula. Because its jointing is less well defined as that of granite, there are very few cottages built from this stone, although it has been extensively used to construct field walls. As a result of this characteristic some of the Lizard churches have been built from blocks of light-grey granite transported from afar. In order to reach Britain's most southerly point one must first cross the Goonhilly Downs, named from the 'goonhilly' ponies which once roamed freely amongst the trackless heath and the wind-sheared gorse. The number of scattered monuments illustrate that this wilderness was once inhabited by prehistoric man but the monument which now dominates the scene is the overwhelming array of telecommunication dishes on the highest point of the Downs. Goonhilly Satellite Earth Station is an attraction in its own right as a modern-day 'wonder', and its visitor centre now draws many of the day-trippers away from the Lizard's greatest glory that of its intricately chiselled coastline. Personally, I am not greatly in awe of this type of modern technology but Peter said that it was mandatory to view the very different attractions of the tracking station. At last, we set off eastwards, picking our way through a veritable 'cat's cradle' of narrow lanes, lined with fuchsias, wild roses and foxgloves, until we reached the village of Gillan which proved to be a wonderful viewpoint from which to enjoy a sweeping panorama from the mouth of the Helford River right across Falmouth Bay to St Mawes and Falmouth itself. We had chosen this point on the coast in order to visit some old school friends who had left our own hometown in the English Midlands to establish a small garden centre (from which we had bought a beautiful lace-cap hydrangea). After having been kindly entertained to a Cornish cream tea, I ventured to ask how many original Cornish folk still lived in such tiny coastal villages. It appeared that many had 'sold out to incomers' such as themselves but that a substantial number had continued to farm the hinterland and provide local produce for the shops and domestic labour for the hotels and boarding-houses. Moreover, those farmers fortunate enough to retain their coastal properties were said to be making a comfortable living from the camping and caravan sites, especially at Kennack Sands, one of the Lizard's few extensive sandy beaches. Not surprisingly, the National Trust has acquired more than 17 properties on The Lizard, including the popular Kynance Cove, where the serpentine cliffs reveal their wave-polished colours in all their glory.

We endeavoured to visit as much of the Lizard coastline as possible on our visits over the years but I was disappointed when we started at Porthallow to find that the gabbro quarries, extracted for their roadstone, had caused a noticeable disfigurement of this once pristine coast. Like that at Porthallow, the beach at Porthoustock is coloured grey by the quarry detritus and overlooked by derelict industrial buildings. But this proved to be the least of the worries of the fisherfolk on this rockbound shore because the nearby headland of Manacle Point has been the scene of countless wrecks over the centuries. Offshore, we saw the reef of saw-toothed rocks known as The Manacles, some just hidden and some half-awash at low tide, known as the 'ship-swallower'. In a local pub we had time to reflect on a coastline festooned with a string of picturesque fishing villages but whose graveyards are full of the bodies of shipwrecked mariners. Coverack still retained the air of a real fishing village, with its boats drawn up on the beach but, once it had become a popular place for retirement, the bungalows of second-home owners had climbed steadily up the hillside. Thus, when viewed from the shore, Coverack appears to tumble down the slope, in contrast to Cadgwith which nestles on a ledge, pinched tightly in its cove and enhanced by picturesque thatched cottages and their flowery gardens. To really appreciate such scenic delights, one should take time to stroll along the coastal path, which the walker, Hockin (*op. cit.*) describes as a "…continuous joy as it winds up and down and round and over to the always unexpected". This was how it appeared to him in 1936 and it was good to see how much of it had managed to retain its exhilarating charm some sixty years later. The main difference appeared to be in the increasing volume of the tourist industry which now caters for every type of seaside demand, from cafes and gift shops to boating and fishing trips conducted by its large number of local entrepreneurs who often depend on the summer season for much of their income. Even before World War II, Hockin had observed that "Cadgwith had more to show than flowers and does so with only one eye on the visitors, the other being on the sea". This is exemplified by the number of boats that we saw engaged in the lucrative business of netting all maner of marine crustaceans.

Mullion Cove, on the western side of the peninsula keeps both eyes on the visitors because it is well-known for its cliff-top hotels. Since it is favoured by one of the few motorable roads to reach the Lizard shores, unlike those narrow lanes of the eastern coast, Mullion town and its tiny cove is a very popular holiday resort. Its harbour crouches between dark cliffs of serpentine and, because it is owned by the National Trust, a guide book claims that it shows "...a sense of care and good taste". Apart from its own pleasant ambience, Mullion is only a few miles away from one of Cornwall's most attractive spectacles, that of Kynance Cove. Owned by the National Trust since 1935, it has been protected from the sort of commercialisation that has disfigured Lands End. Well known since Victorian times, the guide books almost run out of superlatives in their descriptions of its scenery: "Once described as the finest cove in the kingdom its beauty stems largely from the group of isolated stacks standing with their feet in the white foaming surf" and continuing by claiming that "Kynance has an entrancing beauty and variety which it would be hard to equal even on this fine unspoiled coastline". This type of beauty we had to see, but by the time we reached there, late in the afternoon, the rain was being driven in off the sea by a brisk south-westerly. Since it was a long way down to the shoreline and all four of us elderly visitors looked askance at the steep cliff-path we decided to turn for home and the shelter of the Boulton home on Porth Navas Creek. As we sat enjoying a welcome aperitif and watching the rain stream down the windows, I regaled our hosts with the story of the Best Man at our wedding, who revealed to me that he was not keen on travelling abroad, largely because he didn't like the food and partly because he "...wasn't awfully keen on foreigners". Therefore, he looked at a map and picked out Mullion because "...it was as far south as you can go and still remain in England". I believe that he continued to stay there, in the same hotel, for decades afterwards, where he was content to join like-minded bridge players. I confess that I have lost touch with him nowadays so have been unable to show him the error of his ways. But, it takes all sorts, as they say, and not everyone is such a coastal fanatic as myself.

Lizard Point itself proved to be the last of our coastal excursions in Cornwall, because the Boultons announced that they were moving on to live in a house in the Cotswolds. Thus, when we descended to the shoreline near the old lifeboat station there was a sense of finality in every sense of the word, because this was not only the end of our holidays in Cornwall but it was the southernmost termination of Britain's landmass, a veritable 'edge of the land'. Peter picked up a piece of rock from the water's edge, even though it was a sliver of schist and not the ubiquitous serpentine. He explained that he enjoyed taking 'souvenirs' from extreme points of the compass (I recall him removing a piece of Fladda's northern tip) and set me thinking about our own visits to the extreme cardinal points in the British Isles. These included Dunnet Head in Scotland, Lowestoft beach in England, Ramsey Sound in Wales, Slea Head in Southern Ireland and Malin Head in Ulster. Now we could add Lizard Point to the list, which left only Ardnamurchan in Western Scotland which, at our advanced age, seems highly unlikely to be achieved. We lingered near to the Lizard Point Lighthouse, a dazzling white beacon on the cliff edge, and thought about those mariners who must have been relieved to see its light at the end of a long Atlantic crossing. Let the last word be that of Mitton (*op. cit.*) who, at the beginnining of World War I, spoke romantically about the Lizard Light: "When the sun falls over the shoulder of the cliff, in the west, the revolving light from the lighthouse begins to flash out with a regular monotonous beat on its long night vigil. At any time after dark one can see the huge pencil of light darting round, striking the white signal station opposite, losing itself in the sea and so returning". Because Lizard Point is both the first and the last landfall in England it somehow seemed appropriate that we spent our last day in Cornwall waiting hours on Pendennis Point in Falmouth to witness the end of the Tall Ships Race across the Atlantic. As I watched a magnificent racing yacht swoop round Manacles Point and skim into Falmouth harbour I thought of the time, more than 200 hundred years ago, when the tiny sailing boat "Pickle" brought the first news of Nelson's victory at Trafalgar to the same Falmouth Quay, having rounded Lizard Point and steered clear of the Manacle Rocks.

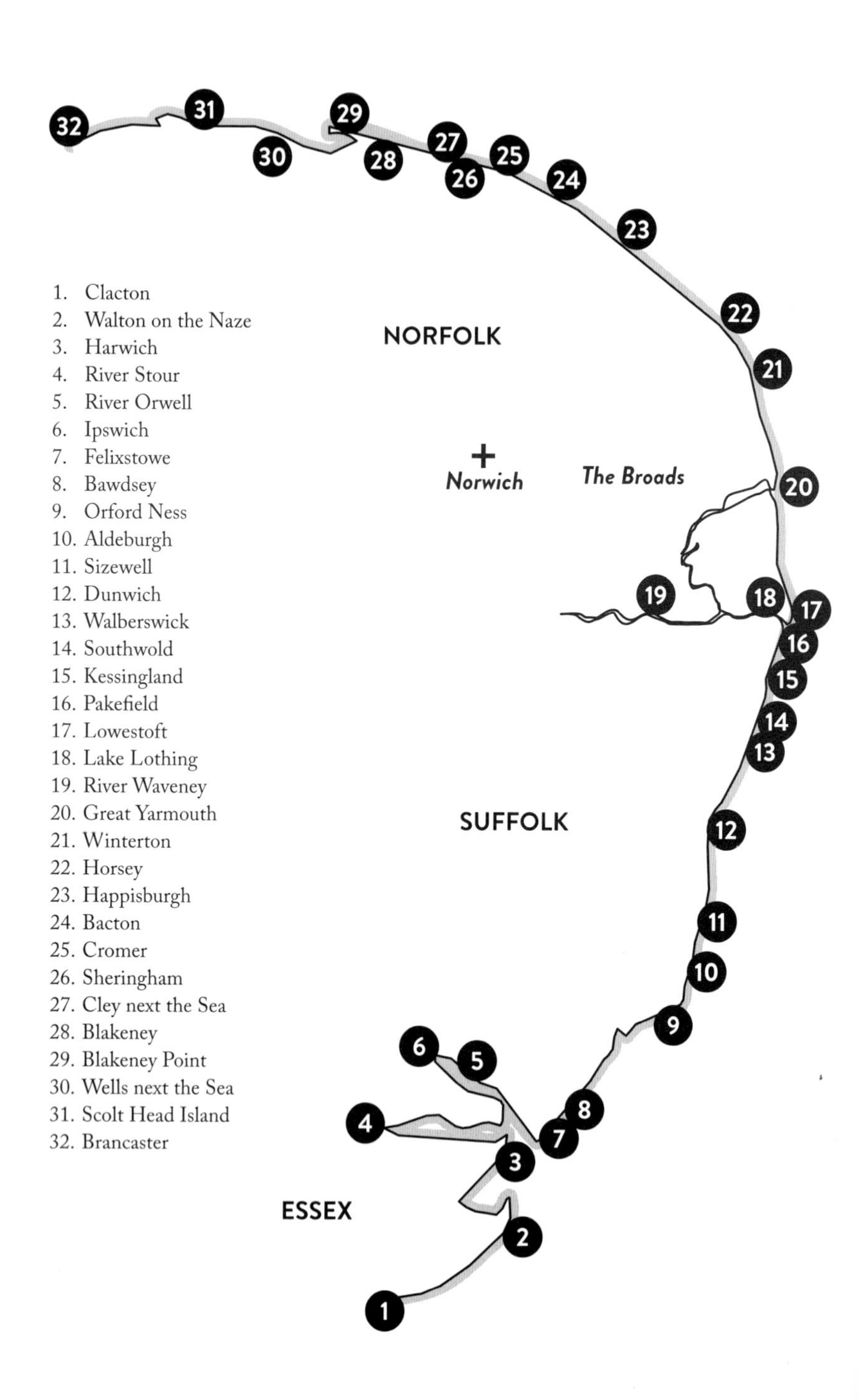

NORFOLK
Norwich
The Broads
SUFFOLK
ESSEX
1. Clacton
2. Walton on the Naze
3. Harwich
4. River Stour
5. River Orwell
6. Ipswich
7. Felixstowe
8. Bawdsey
9. Orford Ness
10. Aldeburgh
11. Sizewell
12. Dunwich
13. Walberswick
14. Southwold
15. Kessingland
16. Pakefield
17. Lowestoft
18. Lake Lothing
19. River Waveney
20. Great Yarmouth
21. Winterton
22. Horsey
23. Happisburgh
24. Bacton
25. Cromer
26. Sheringham
27. Cley next the Sea
28. Blakeney
29. Blakeney Point
30. Wells next the Sea
31. Scolt Head Island
32. Brancaster

9. EAST ANGLIA

"And here the sea-fogs lap and cling
And here, each warning each
The sheep-bells and the ship-bells ring
Along the hidden beach".
(Rudyard Kipling. 1865–1936)

Dunwich Heath and the easily eroded cliff-line, Suffolk

Orford Ness showing the abandoned 'pagodas' on the shingle ridge

Snape Maltings, Suffolk

The crumbling cliffs of glacial material at Cromer, Norfolk

Caravans on the cliffs near Cromer

Tourists waiting to board the pleasure boats at Morston Quay, Norfolk. This is where 'The Whittow' is normally moored

Blakeney Point marshes looking seawards to the fringing dunes – *See plate section for colour version*

Boardwalks to protect the dunes from trampling at Blakeney Point – *See plate section for colour version*

When we came to live in East Anglia at Christmas 2017, I began to understand what the British paratroopers must have been thinking after they had landed in the Dutch polderlands of southern Holland during the notorious Arnhem Campaign in September 1944. Everywhere was flat; rivers, canals, ditches and dykes stretched to the horizons; crossing-points were few and far between, the over-arching sky would have dominated the scene. This could quite easily be a description of where East Anglia's Broadland country reaches a similar coastline comprising miles of marshland, sandy beaches, backed by lines of dunes. After all, today these are mutual shorelines of a North Sea which, until the drowning of so-called "Doggerland" in post-Mesolithic times, did not exist as a watery strait dividing these two comparable and conjoined lowland swathes of western Europe. Of course, I did not arrive by parachute but came overland, from the hilly English Midlands to the flatlands of East Anglia over a period of some two decades, mainly on visits to our daughter and family. Like that well-known writer on the countryside, Richard Mabey, some fifty years before, I had also come to an an 'unknown country', but one which soon inveigled me into its bewitching charisma.

Its coastline could not exhibit a greater contrast to those that I have described in earlier chapters because it lacks all of those features which I have constantly praised as contributing to shores of great stature and splendour: namely, tough, ancient, gnarled and wave-worn rocks; beetling precipices and looming mountains; sea-cut stacks, arches, caves and clefts; luminous Atlantic light and fiery sunsets. These make up the very essence of the Celtic shores of western Britain and Ireland that I found both inspiring and incomparable. But this is only my opinion. Others have a life-long love of England's gentler, lowland shores where life is geared to the lazy incoming and outgoing tidal flow; the muddy creeks, reed-fringed marshes, dunes, quiet backwaters, low cliffs of crumbling glacial clays and gravels; long shingle strands and endless sandy beaches that face limpid sunrises. All combine to create an altogether different and somewhat placid ambience. Moreover, East Anglia is a land of wind-brushed, crystal-clear dawns instead of fiery storm-menacing sunsets. Such images, however, are those perceived largely by seasonal holidaymakers. The local seafarers, who brave the winter storms, will tell you otherwise and even in a calm summer the fisher-folk are often faced with a gloomy sea-fret that may blanket the coast for days. To bear this out Nicholas Crane describes one of his own seaborne journeys along the coast of East Anglia, when he tried to replicate a similar journey taken by Daniel Defoe in 1724–1726. Nicholas Crane's own captain explained, especially in a sea-fog, why this coastline was so lethal: "...the shallow waters could create steep, broken seas; the sandbanks had a habit of moving, so you couldn't trust your charts; and the shoreline was so low-lying that it was difficult to identify landmarks". (Great British Journeys. Nicholas Crane, 2007).

Nevertheless, it was the former sunlit images of Norfolk and Suffolk that stayed longest in my mind when we visited their coasts in the early years of the Millenium. These were the happy summer-times when we can still recall: strolling with Andrew, Fiona and their dog on Southwold beach; 'crabbing' with our granddaughter, Charlotte, in the muddy creek opposite Walberswick; wandering on Dunwich Heath before drinking at the Ship Inn and, above all, taking sunlit trips out to Blakeney Point on the National Trust's boat "The Whittow". These, however, proved to be the providential years which helped to lure us in to making a final move to East Anglia, far from my beloved Atlantic shores but nearer to my most distant ancestral roots in Flanders. The wheel has almost come full circle and with it has come the North Sea winter weather. Hardly had we settled into our new home, a mere fifteen miles from the shore, before we were deluged by floods, snowed-up for days in the worst blizzard 'in living memory' during a spell of weather dubbed by the press as 'The Beast from the East'. And, finally, as I write, we have endured the worst drought since 1976, when the newly planted trees have withered and died. The latter phenomenon was a final reminder that we had come to live in a region far removed from the perpetual wetness of the Atlantic seaboard; a completely new location of which The Editor of "Country Life" was soon to remind us how "East Anglia is designated a semi-arid region and [that]five out of the seven hottest years ever recorded in the world have occurred since 2010". It seemed as if Nature was testing our resolve but, looking on the bright side, so to speak, we have, so far, experienced only two days of sea fog.

It has to be said that the strangeness of this unfamiliar terrain, east of the Greenwich Meridian, has in no way been viewed as an anathema, but largely as a new challenge and a chance to view new coasts, meet new people and settle into a completely fresh way of life. This has to become a life-style unencumbered with those youthful driving ambitions when I thought of the coastline largely in terms of a research workshop, an outdoor classroom, a source for book-writing or as a fount of genealogical material. Henceforth, I will endeavor to perceive our littoral zone simply from a hedonistic viewpoint. Thus, in the last of the regional chapters devoted to memories of my seaboard perambulations, I will be able to feel much freer to indulge more lavishly in charting the aesthetic 'splendours of the shore' and thereby follow humbly in the footsteps of many writers, poets, artists and musicians who have praised East Anglia's singular elegance. It should not come as a surprise to realise that, throughout my earlier reflections, I have found it difficult not to be side-tracked too often into the 'realms of poesy'. But there is another reason why I feel unfettered; now that I have come to live permanently in the coastal zone, I can devote as much time as I want exploring, explaining and extolling its attributes. I am no longer just a casual visitor.

Essex is a county with which I have only a fleeting acquaintance. On several occasions I took Reading University students to view the northern industrialised shores of the Thames Estuary in the vicinity of Canvey Island (See chapter 12), as part of my course on Environmental Hazards. And I had once departed from the historic port of Harwich to set forth on a holiday cruise to the Baltic. Every other part of of its intricate pattern of creeks and marshes is a place that is beloved by small-boat sailors but completely unknown to me. Yet, geologically speaking, although of no interest to those yachtsmen, this southernmost stretch of the East Anglian coast is of considerable geological importance, because it exhibits the only exposures of Britain's youngest rocks, the so-called "Crags" of Pliocene/ Pleistocene age. In earlier chapters I have outlined how the British Geological Survey produces two national maps: one depicting 'solid' rocks and another denoting 'drift deposits'. It has been further described how massive ice-sheets of the Pleistocene Ice Age have left widespread layers of boulder clay, sand, shingle and mud across the underlying solid rocks. For decades geologists have tried to define the exact point in 'geological time' at which the truly 'solid' rocks terminate and the unconsolidated 'drifts' begin. This boundary has been finally recognised in the crumbling cliffs of East Anglia, especially in the vicinity of Cromer in North Norfolk (see below) but, since the official designation of the base of the Pleistocene has now been dated at 2.3 million years ago, it has left the red-stained sands of the so-called Red Crag in Essex squarely across the Plio-Pleistocene boundary, half in and half out of the Ice Age. The greatly eroded, partly slipped and heavily vegetated sea-cliffs at Walton-on-the Naze, Harwich and Felixstowe are the best places for beachcombers to find not only Red Crag fossils (whose marine forms show a gradual deterioration of climate prior to the Ice Age) but also the first British remains of true horses and elephants. Not quite as spectacular as the 'finds' on the Jurassic Coast of Dorset, perhaps, but of equal importance to someone interested in more recent geological history. As a person who has spent years tracing the evolution of the Welsh coastline from pre-Glacial into post-Glacial times, this Essex Red Crag exposure is significant because it also marks the same point in time when the pre-Glacial sea-level in the Llyn Peninsula stood at an elevation of 600 feet. At first sight this correlation will be seen as utterly confusing to a lay person. They may well ask "How can a shelly deposit at present sea-level in Essex be represented by a weathered high-level rock bench on a distant hill in western Wales?". In response, I have to remind the reader that in chapter three I described how my early mapping of erosion surfaces in North Wales was an attempt to define the coastline before the Ice Age ice-sheets abstracted water from a sea-level which stood some 600 feet higher than at present. I also described how at that time the waterless North Sea basin was continuously sinking due to geophysical forces in the Earth's crust which caused the British Isles to tilt markedly from north-west to south-east. Consequently, any littoral deposits from a formerly high strandline have now been 'downwarped' to present high-tide level along this North Sea shore. Here ends the 'sermon' on East Anglian geology but, as I now enter into my reflections on its coastal environments, it will be shown how one must always remain conscious of the underlying geology, for in every region it has always influenced the soils, the vegetation, the crops and therefore the economy, the culture and the lifestyles of the inhabitants of all British and Irish coastal zones, as I have already described on their western extremities.

I intend to start my reminiscences on the shores of Suffolk, although I have to confess that its southern tracts still remain to be travelled and explored in my new guise as a simple tourist. I once went to visit a friend in Felixstowe some years before it was overwhelmed by its gigantic container terminal and I remember travelling through acres of cornland en route to its unspoilt shore. It was this image that was soon to be confirmed on the maps of my Neptune volunteers who depicted a marsh-fringed estuary of the River Orwell leading seawards to the pleasant seaside town that was also flanked by the equally unspoiled estuary of the River Deben. Alas, no more, because juggernaughts now thunder through the countryside to service the clamorous Port of Felixstowe.

It quickly became obvious that, when describing the shores of East Anglia, I would be forced to write in a more muted style. No more mountain peaks worn by the sea into prodigious cliffs; no more caves, sea-stacks and marine arches; no more fjords; no more trackless blanket bogs; no more rocky coves and raised beaches. Above all, the geology is constricted to miles of low cliffs of unconsolidated sands, gravels and clays, all less than 5 million years old and all vulnerable to the attack of North Sea waves. There is, however, one important exception in north Norfolk where, at Hunstanton, chalk cliffs look westwards across The Wash. The reader may possibly be relieved that they are at last being freed from lengthy descriptions of granites, slates, basalts, sandstones and limestones, for example. The corollary, of course, means that without these hard rocks the coastal scenery is less diverse and the landforms are more subdued. We are no longer in the realms of the Atlantic Ocean fringe of rugged and serrated grandeur but on the perimeter of a relatively shallow sea where, on the opposite shores, those dune-fringed coasts of Denmark, Holland and Belgium mirror those of East Anglia. Thus, instead of physical grandeur, one becomes more aware of the cultural landscape where the human footprint is writ large in a region that was for centuries the most populous and most prosperous area in Britain. Moreover, because it faced across the relatively narrow North Sea, East Anglia became a magnet for European settlers and traders for a great part of early British history. Nowhere else in Britain was colonised by such a diversity of people and nowhere else did the physical shape and outline of its coast change so rapidly over the centuries. Indeed, in places its shoreline is receding more rapidly than anywhere, except for Holderness in Yorkshire, and where the storminess of climate change allied with a crustal sinking of the former "Doggerland" (at a rate of some 1.6 mm per year) has led to a constantly rising sea-level that has manifested itself in recent years by several breaches of the coastal defences. As I write, several bungalows at Hemsby, in Norfolk, have fallen into the sea. Since I am now a dweller near to the coastal zone I have become even more conscious of the vicissitudes of the North Sea moods.

All this information was in the back of my mind when I stood on the edge of the crumbling Minsmere Cliffs on a fresh breezy day, looking across the tiny lake of Minsmere whose reed-fringed banks and marshes shelter countless numbers of waders in one of Britain's most important RSPB reserves. On looking seawards, the straightness of the coastline is deceptive, however, for Minsmere was once a large coastal inlet but has now been isolated by shifting shores. Much of the surrounding heathland is in the hands of the National Trust and is a popular venue for walkers. Perhaps the coastal paths are busier now than in the days of the great Suffolk poet, George Crabbe (1754–1832) who found inspiration in this once deserted heathery wilderness:

"There thistles stretch their prickly arms afar,
And to the ragged infant threaten war;
There poppies, nodding, mock the hope of toil
There the blue bugloss paints the sterile soil".

The soil sterility stems from the underlying acidic sands that have given the area the title "Sandlings" or "Sandlands" where rainfall percolates rapidly through the heathery cover. But the coastal zone has benefitted from extensive afforestation which has added variety to the scenery in addition to providing shelter from the North Sea blast for the walkers on this exposed shore.

I wonder what Crabbe, the epitome of the bucolic poet, would have thought of the gigantic edifice that stands four-square a few miles to the south, at Sizewell, for there a nuclear power station overlooks the beach and whose warm outlowing waste water attracts myriads of fish. Whether or not the local fishermen make use of such a harvest remains to be seen and despite the assurances of the nuclear authority that the outflow water is harmless one can never be certain about possible contamination. I shall never forget that I once questioned two nuclear scientists testing the fish for radioactivity in the mill-pool of our house on the Thames following a nuclear leak that coursed down the nearby outfall from the Aldermaston experimental research station in Berkshire. I do not propose to re-enter into an appraisal of the moral and landscaping issues, as I did in the case of Anglesey's nuclear power station. Suffice to say that another power station is in course of construction on this once unsullied shore and I'm told that tourists seem attracted by this industrial innovation. No doubt in years to come this Sizewell structure will have the status of a 'Listed Building', similar to the way in which the 'Pagodas' of Orford Ness were given such an accolade. My wanderings now took me back to Orford to revisit the famous shingle spit that had been so important in the Neptune acquisitions so many years ago. I have described its bleakness elsewhere but it is only recently that I have discovered a poem by the Anglo-Welsh poet Alun Lewis, whose mentor was his fellow countryman, Edward Thomas. It is an apt description of the Ness during wartime, when Lewis was stationed at neighbouring Bawdsey. His poignant verse recaptures the desolate winter scene:

"From Orford Ness to Shingle Street
The grey disturbance spreads
Washing the icy seas on Deben Head.
Cock pheasants scratch the frozen fields
Gulls lift thin horny legs and step
Fastidiously among the rusted mines"
(Dawn on the East Coast. Alun Lewis, 1945)

Orford Ness had changed very little since my initial visit more than twenty years ago. Its shingle-formed spit, its empty marshland and its military paraphernalia all appeared to be much the same, although its renowned Nature Reserve now attracts a greater number of visitors once the military had departed and since the National Trust has managed its most expensive coastal acquisition as a dedicated conservationist should. The red- and white-striped lighthouse on the Ness has cast its beam across 25 nautical miles for more than a century and has remained a valuable maritime sea-mark. So too has the ruin of Orford Castle in the attractive village of Orford. Built in 1165, this great tower can be seen for miles around and has survived a threat of demolition in 1805 because the government insisted on its worth as a guide to coastal shipping on such a low-lying coastline. Orford itself was once a bustling planned 12th century town and seaport but the steady southward growth of the shingle spit of its Ness, due to inshore currents (termed 'longshore drift'), has caused the mouth of the River Alde to be deflected away from its initial mouth at Aldeburgh for a distance of some ten miles. Not surprisingly, once its access to the North Sea had been blocked, Orford has declined into a sleepy village enlivened largely as a ferry port for seasonal visitors to the Ness. Its demise was chronicled as early as 1586 when Camden in his iconic "Britannia" noted that on Suffolk's "crooked shore, Oreford...once a large and populous town, fortify'd with a castle of reddish stone...But now it complains of the Sea's ingratitude, which withdraws itself by little and little, and begins to envy it the advantage of a harbour". No better example can be found in East Anglia of the ways in which storm waves and tidal currents progressively erode the friable sandy cliffs in one place only to dump the loose material in another. East Anglia, therefore, has been fortunate, so far as the holidaymakers are concerned, that its lengthy coastline is characterised by a 'cornucopia' of sandy beaches. Hence, its seaside resorts are famed throughout the land as a venue for the 'bucket and spade brigade'. Shingle-shored Aldeburgh, on the other hand, is more famous for its artistic, literary and especially musical associations.

We had visited this former fishing village long before we came to live in East Anglia and I had immediately experienced a 'sense of place', although I know of no ancestral connections. I would agree with Brian Jackman that "Aldburgh is an old-fashioned town…still trapped in its 1930's time warp, it lies on the way to nowhere, a genteel backwater marooned on East Anglia's broad backside" (B. Jackman, *op. cit.*). It emanates an aura, a feeling that it is rather special, although I remain uncertain whether this image has been engendered, in my mind at least, by its cultural reputation. I was surprised to read that such a well-known author as E. M. Forster had dismissed Aldeburgh as "…a bleak little place, not beautiful. It huddles round a flint-towered church and sprawls down to the North Sea". However, we found it rather more attractive than did Norman Scarfe who described it as "…an ugly, delightful seaside resort" (Shell Guide to Suffolk, N. Scarfe, 1960). Forster admits, however, that he enjoyed staying there with Benjamin Britten in the immediate post-war years, in order to assist with the libretto for Britten's opera "Billy Budd". Benjamin Britten, the doyen of British opera, was born in Lowestoft where we learn that because of his proximity to the shore "…he continued listening to the voice of the waves all his life. Mingled with the cry of marsh birds, the sounds of his native coastline became a haunting refrain throughout his music". (East Anglia: A Literary Pilgrimage, Peter Tolhurst, 1996). His opera "Albert Herring", for example, has references to nearby Snape (see below) whilst his "Noye's Flood" and "Curlew River" were first perfomed in Orford church. Britten's greatest opera is undoubtedly "Peter Grimes" which is based on a character from one of George Crabbe's poems and the music of which recaptures the storm-bound coast of East Anglia. In Crabbe's childhood, Aldeburgh stood in what we would now call a 'depressed area'. Its overseas trade and shipbuilding had gone and some people had turned to smuggling to supplement their meagre living derived from fishing. Crabbe believed that he had been "cast by Fortune on a frowning coast" where "the soil [was] poor and sandy, the herbage bare and rushy, the trees withered and stunted". He did eventually escape from this decaying town to become chaplain to the Duke of Rutland at Belvoir Castle. But E. M. Forster believed that: "...he never escaped from Aldeburgh in the spirit; and it was the making of him as a poet. Even when he was writing other things, there steals again and again into his verse the sea, the estuary, the flat Suffolk coast and the local meannesses, and an odour of brine and dirt, tempered occasionally with the scent of flowers". When we looked at Aldeburgh's handsome main street we found it difficult to understand why later writers had appeared to agree with Crabbe's own censures. For example, Henry James spoke of a "...fourth-rate watering place that had elbowed away...the little modern vulgar accumulation" of the town; Thomas Hardy found no inspiration in the resort except for the "...sensation of having nothing but the sea between you and the north pole", thereby damning it with faint praise; Virginia Woolf was not afraid to damn it with a waspish enquiry "Why do you stay at Aldeburgh; there are East Winds there, both of God and man [in] that miserable, dull sea village?" But I would have thought that by the time of their early-20th century visits the townsfolk had moved on from Crabbe's image of:

"... a wild amphibious race,
With sullen woe display'd in every face;
Who far from civil arts and social fly,
And scowl at strangers with suspicious eye".

I can only think that these Suffolk fisherfolk must once have had feelings similar to those of the fishwives of Llangwm in Pembrokeshire when they felt threatened by 'incomers'. One of the features of Aldeburgh is the line of winches that stand like sentries along the foreshore at the head of the pebbly beach. Together with their ropes and cables they serve to haul the small inshore fishing boats above the high-water mark because Aldeburgh has no harbour and no sea wall. Since its seafront houses appear to be built on the beach itself, it stands to reason that they are extremely vulnerable to storm waves. Indeed, in 1953 the town was seriously flooded and I have just learnt that a fund has been raised to improve its sea defences. We stumbled and crunched along its almost deserted pebbly beach, more aware of Maggi Hambling's metal sculpture of an oversized seashell than we were of any fishing activity, as if the entire town was dozing in the sunshine of this windless day. It appeared to be a manifestation of the slow pace of life along Suffolk's shoreline, just so long as you kept clear of its larger seaside towns or bustling ports.

Some four miles up the estuary of the Alde the tiny village of Snape sits beside a waving sea of reeds and where seals often swim in with the tide. We didn't spot any of these creatures during our springtime visit, nor did we see many people when we entered the famous Snape Maltings. Built in the 1840's these wooden buildings were once the largest flat-floor maltings in the country and sent malted barley to London's breweries for over a century until the Maltings closed in 1965. The largest building became Benjamin Britten's well-known Concert Hall and the centre of the annual Aldeburgh Music festival and the Snape Proms. At such times this centre is overwhelmed by music-lovers but we found it on a quiet and deserted day when it was difficult to imagine the febrile atmosphere that must prevail. Nonetheless, we vowed that one day we would return to enjoy Britten's musical 'canvases' of the East Anglian coastline.

Talking of canvases, everyone knows that Suffolk is Cons... Country but to my utter amazement, after a lengthy search through his oeuvre, I have been able to find only a handful of pictures depicting the coast of East Anglia, including one of Harwich lighthouse and one of Hadleigh Castle, which is really on the Thames Estuary. It is true that he painted scenes of the coast at Weymouth and even at Brighton but, if one excludes the estuary of the Suffolk Stour, the open sea does not appear in any other of his pictures. His early correspondence suggests that he was averse to the sea despite having spent one month aboard a ship learning the mariner's art. He believed that coastal scenes "...are so hackneyed in the Exhibition and are in fact so little capable of beautiful sentiment that landscape is capable of...that they have done a great deal of harm to the art". This may well have been explained by the overwhelming dominance of the sea and the sky in this region, completely devoid of the noble trees, hedgerows and church spires, which make his paintings so popular. It must be remembered that he also spent an entire year as a miller's apprentice because his father owned a group of Suffolk windmills. Thus, he was well versed in the vacillating moods of the weather and no artist was more adept than Constable in portraying all manner of 'skyscapes'. We are told that, because of his interest in windmills, "...the wind was his business" and that "He could read the sky as a ploughman reads the field or a coachman the road ahead". (Weatherland. Alexandra Harris, 2015). It is likely that this ability stemmed from the well-known flatness of East Anglia whose landscapes always appear to be overwhelmed by the vastness of its skies. It was only when he painted Hadleigh Castle, after the death of his wife, that he seems to have come to terms with seascapes, largely because he was able to introduce a crumbling ruin in the foreground. There he was able to write, in a somewhat contradictory vein: "I was always delighted with the melancholy grandeur of a seashore". Turner, however, suffered no such constraints because two of his best known watercolours of Orford and Aldeburgh concentrate on the human interest of fishermen set against a shimmering ocean. That of Orford succeeds in capturing an abiding image of a typical Suffolk coastline, in which the fishermen are backed by the morning mistiness of the nearby marshes. Two local modern artists, Edward Seago and Edward Wesson have used similar seascapes and 'skyscapes' very effectively in their paintings, as have some of the earlier artists of the so-called Norwich School of Artists, especially those of John Crome (1768–1821), John Sell Cotman (1782–1842), James Stark (1794–1859) and John Thirtle (1777–1839). But other, less famous artists, have also found plenty of inspiration hereabouts, where they have conveyed many images of the 'edge of the land' in a variety of styles. None more so than in the small village of Walberswick.

We first saw this straggling village as we looked across the narrow estuary of the River Blyth and, apart from noting its mouldering jetties and mudflats, we were more concerned with stopping our young granddaughter, Charlotte, from falling into the creek whilst 'crabbing'. Interestingly, Walberswick is regarded as the major 'crabbing centre' of England. We were told that a small rowing-boat plied from our north-bank viewpoint to Walberswick and that the same family had been operating this ancient ferry since 1885. Dani Church is the fifth generation of this family business and has been known to make the short crossing about 100 times on very busy days. Once I had learnt that Walberswick's fame stemmed from its prominence as an art colony in the late-19th century, it goes without saying that we had to explore it at a later date. We finally chose a windless day, out of season, so that we could rediscover something of the ambience which drew painters to this relative backwater. Apparently, it boasts a luminous light that allows the rising sun to glitter across the endless sea through a clear rain-washed sky. Thus, many of the pictures at this venue were painted 'contre jour' (against the light) in the style of the French Impressionists. Not surprisingly, therefore, instead of the towering rocky cliffs and tiny coves of the Cornish artists, the Walberswick School of painters filled their pictures with holidaymakers and beached fishing boats. We drove down the rambling steet of mellow brick houses to the almost deserted shore but I failed to find the grandeur of the Atlantic shores along which I had extensively travelled. But why should I expect to? It was at Walberswick that I stopped to reflect, as we gazed across mudflats and reed-beds, that those days were in the past. I should now endeavor to stop making mental comparisons, for in East Anglia the 'edge of the land' is, perforce, dominated by a horizontality of form decreed by Nature. I reasoned, therefore, that the majority of vertical elements in any artistic scene would have to have been introduced by humankind, and these would have been set against the low horizons and an over-arching sky. Lighthouses, churches, windmills, ruined towers and military structures from all ages have always figured large in East Anglian paintings.

Some notable artists, such as Frank Branwyn, and Walter Sickert were only fleeting visitors to Walberswick, as were Walter Langley from distant Newlyn in Cornwall and Charles Rennie Mackintosh who, with his wife, was stranded here when World War I broke out. The village's most prominent figure, however, was Philip Wilson Steer (1860–1912) who arrived in 1884 to join the artist's colony of Walberswick. Some of the girls that are highlighted in his paintings, playing on the water's edge, have been recognised as daughters of the local fishermen but most other artists concentrated on the fishermen themselves, their sailing boats and the clutter of wooden shacks around the quay. From the village we looked southwards along miles of yellow sands to the distant village of Dunwich, or at least what remains of this former seaport.

So much has been written about the ocean's systematic destruction of Dunwich that we had to go and see for ourselves and observe what led Shakespeare to opine how "…the hungry ocean gains advantage on the kingdom of the shore" (Sonnet LXIV). Here, soon after leaving the dreamlike, placid, sunlit shores of Snape, Aldeburgh and Walberswick we were suddenly confronted with the grim reality of Nature's other face, that of North Sea storminess. In all the years of my coastal wanderings in which I have described how, on desolate western coastlines, people have been forced by poverty or unscrupulous landowners to leave the land, this is the most glaring example of where the land has left the people and forced them to move away. Henry James became aware of the instability of this "sinister" shoreline when he wrote how it "…moves for ever, like a ruminating beast, an insatiable, indefatigable lip" (English Hours. Henry James 1883).

Dunwich was a Saxon town and mentioned in Domesday Book as a thriving port but the fateful day came in 1326 when a tremendous storm blocked the harbour mouth and destroyed three churches. Prior to this it is recorded that it maintained "… besides eleven ships of war, sixteen fair ships, twenty barks or trading vessels to the North Sea and Iceland etc. and twenty-four small boats for the home fishery". What had been described as a 'cathedral city' was gradually destroyed by coastal erosion and by 1540 the coastline had receded as far as the market place. By 1922, a former 'landmark' for shipping, the tower of All Saint's Church, had toppled into the ocean, leaving only the desolate ruins of its Franciscan Abbey as a gaunt reminder of the former town, once regarded as one of England's major ports, even rivalling London. I have read of the numerous legends associated with its drowned remnants and the supposed tolling of its submerged church bells in bad weather. These are reminiscent of those relating to the lost lands of Cantref-y-Gwaelod in Wales, Lyonesse in Cornwall and even those of Ys, a Breton city which inspired Debussy's "La Cathedrale engloutie" (The sunken cathedral). Pevsner's Guide dismisses Dunwich simply as being set in "Fields high above the sea, fragrant in the spring and summer, wind-swept in the autumn and winter, some straggling houses and the ruins of the Franciscan Friary". There is no mention of the Ship Inn where we lunched during our first meeting with Fiona's new parents-in-law, not far from their 15th century Suffolk home.

We had spent the morning walking on the breezy Dunwich Heath, so charmingly described by Edward Thomas as "...a heaving moor of heather and close gorse up and down and ending in a sandy cliff...On the edge of this...is the ruined church that has half fallen over already". The poet Swinburne was also attracted here, from his home on the Isle of Wight, and it is largely due to him that the Dunwich ruins became something of a shrine, as Edward Thomas concluded: "He adds Dunwich to the poet's country. By observation, not naturalistic but spiritual, and by the emphasis on reverie and meditation, simple and conventional, but rapturous, he made that coast Swinburne's country par excellence". (East Anglia: A Literary Pilgrimage. Peter Tolhurst, 1996).

I saw little of merit in the remaining cliff-edge ruins but it is strange how, over the centuries, thousands of artists, writers and photographers regard such remnants with awe, as if they had all been influenced by William Gilpin's "Essays on the Picturesque" (1792). We were more concerned with the weather which showed signs of changing from a sunny morning to an afternoon of showers. I tried to visualise this cliff top during the sort of storm experienced by Brian Jackman (*op. cit.*) during a recent visit: "Outside again, with a gale seething through the bare oaks, I remembered the words of a former warden [of Minsmere nature reserve]. 'Suffolk people talk about what they call a lazy wind' he said. 'That's too lazy to go round you so it goes straight through you'". But it needed Benjamin Britten to encapsulate all of these elemental forces into his opera "Peter Grimes" in which a musical vision of a coastal storm is 'unsurpassed': "Rippling waters, the cries of the gulls, fierce swellings of waves as the wind lashes the sea into a fury, and the almost apocalyptic ragings of a full-blown storm are all present". (E. M. Marshall, *op. cit.*).

Having experienced what Henry James, in his description of Orford, expressed as "The visibility of mutilation" it came as something of a relief to enter the genteel streets of Southwold, redolent of the elegance of yesteryear and where thoughts of coastal retreat are far from ones' mind. But it was not always so, borne out by the steepness of the once wave-eroded sandy cliffs. The mid-19th century diaries of a certain James Maggs describe how the sea made several major inroads, especially at Gun Hill in the south and at the Easton Cliffs in the north. The tarred weatherboard shacks of the fishermen's cottages are now no more but, once Southwold had been discovered as a 'watering place', the substantial sea-wall and promenade have stabilised further retreat and a line of pretty pastel-coloured beach chalets now adorns the cliff-foot beneath the lighthouse. The southernmost beach, known as The Denes is a quiet dune-backed beach, claimed to be "…one of the loveliest beaches in Suffolk" (Best British Beaches. Miranda Krestovnikoff, 2009) and this is where we enjoyed taking our granddaughter to enjoy the safe and shallow seashore. As usual its appeal has also attracted a small caravan and camping site nearby but Southwold's smart Regency villas and stylish shops seem intent on resisting further change (The town motto is 'Defend Thy Rights). Because of its lack of romantic ruins, the resort "…has managed to avoid the attention of poets attracted by the melancholy beauty of Dunwich or the literary accretions that have grown around Crabbe's Aldeburgh", although George Orwell, who disliked its elite ambience, lived there throughout the 1930's (Peter Tolhurst, *op. cit.*).

From Felixstowe all the way northwards to Kessingland the thirty miles of coast and hinterland have been designated as an AONB termed the 'Suffolk Coasts and Heaths'. And no wonder, because their cliffs, marshes, meres and moorland are largely free from intrusive development and still devoid of the 'madding crowds' ever since a certain Mr Colvin, in 1885, opined that the Sandlings were "…rich neither in scenery nor associations, and all but unvisited by the tourist". These havens of peace have remained this way because there is no coastal road; the motorist has long been forced to make tedious detours down narrow lanes to reach the unspoilt beaches and, once there, has found very few car parks except at the resorts. This lack of 'honeypot' facilities has meant that the National Trust has not sought to acquire coastal properties because it has deemed that there is no longer any great pressure on this pristine coastline. It is on shores such as these, no matter whether they be in Britain or Ireland, that one is able to escape from a humdrum life and simply behold the majesty of the ocean and the ebb amd flow of its tides. Perhaps it is in such places that one will be able to find time to contemplate the 'edge of the land' with no compunction to photograph, paint, map, measure or analyse, but merely be content to gaze over the ever-changing tidal zone. This is a true margin, defined in the words of a modern writer, as follows: "Margins provide choice – food to one side, perhaps, refuge to the other. And where that margin is always shifting about, as it is on the tide's edge, within that glistening ribbon of land that lies between the high-water mark and the low, the stock is constantly replenished with new riches". (Tide. Hugh Aldersey-Williams, 2016). It is only on such occasions of deep reflection that one becomes aware of the mighty forces of the boundless ocean, which the Suffolk writer, Ronald Blythe, perceived as "…the sea on a cosmic leash" (The Time by the Sea, Ronald Blythe). It is a shoreline whose ambience is defined almost entirely by the endless tidal rhythms about which George Crabbe was inspired to write his memorable poem "Peter Grimes":

"When tides were neap, and, in the sultry day,
Through the tall bounding mud-banks made their way
Which on each side rose swelling, and below,
The dark warm flood ran silently and slow".

Only in a handful of my 'special places' have I been able to find a few moments in which to contemplate and ponder about this tempo of Nature's pulse on shores where time appears to stand still even though the 'tide waits for no man'. I can recall sunset evenings looking across to Bardsey Island in the Llyn Peninsula; gazing at the sands of Rhossili Bay on The Gower; relaxing on the coral beaches of Connemara and Skye; reflecting on the 'ghosts' of Fladda and on the desolate northen tip of Raasay; or quietly painting on the dreamy, bosky shores of Porth Navas Creek in Cornwall. All had one thing in common, they were habitats virtually empty of humanity but full of the steady 'beat' of the ocean waves.

The last time that I had visited a sizeable fishing port was a lifetime ago when, as a small child, I was taken to a rainswept Milford Haven in Pembrokeshire. Now, on the other side of Britain, I entered the busy streets of Lowestoft, Suffolk's second largest town, and renowned as one of the most important ports on the shores of the North Sea basin. Here, on a low cliff-top, protected from the ocean by miles of sea-wall, the town was founded at the former mouth of the wide Waveney valley. We know that during the Ice Age an early Waveney collected all the drainage system of Midland England, south of the great ice-sheet. Today this relatively modest river fails to reach the sea hereabouts and turns northwards to debouch at Great Yarmouth, as if it had been purloined by Lowestoft's historic competitor. A mid-19th century guidebook records that in 1844, with a population of less than 5,000: "Lowestoft ranks next [to] Yarmouth amongst the most important fishing stations on the eastern coast, and is a handsome and improving market town, bathing place and seaport…When seen from the sea [it] has the most picturesque and beautiful appearance of any town on the eastern coast" (White's Suffolk, 1844). But before that time, the old medieval town on the cliff-top had been fringed by a long line of fishing huts, boat-building sheds and net-drying posts along the shingle beach. Steep alleyways and lanes, known as the 'scores', led up from the beach to the old town. Two hundred years ago East Anglia's largest city, Norwich, was able to trade with foreign parts only through the estuary of the River Yare at Yarmouth where the high tolls and poor state of navigation through Breydon Water was proving to be a a serious deterrent. Thus, in 1827, an artificial channel was constructed (at a cost of £140,000) from the River Yare to Lowestoft which cut the distance by ten miles and turned the old, once abandoned channel of the Waveney, termed Lake Lothing, into a large seawater haven for coastal shipping. At the same time a smart new entrance to the harbour was constructed that gave access to moorings for no less than 700 fishing boats. The 'boom time' was now assured. Writing some sixty years later an author spoke of Lowestoft's flourishing fishing industry: "When all the smacks are in, the harbour presents a unique sight, bristling as it does with hundreds of masts, and with piles of fish all along the quay waiting to be sold by auction" (Poppyland. Clement Scott, 1886). There are people still alive who can recall the mountains of herrings that were brought ashore to be gutted, pickled and packed by an annual migration of an army of Scottish fishergirls. A modern account, however, records the sudden demise of this flourishing industry: "Many of the East Anglian fishermen could not believe that the herring would disappear in their lifetime – but that is exactly what happened. However, nothing could prepare them for what would happen in the final decades of the 20th century – the end of a way of life and the almost complete annihilation of an entire industry well over a thousand years old, caused firstly by over-fishing and later by government red tape and the high cost of fuel" (Memories of the East Anglian Fishing Industry. Ian Robb, 2010). Memories also returned to myself, relating to Milford Haven and the end of the Whittow family trawlers! But Lowestoft has made a remarkable recovery due mainly to its favourable position on the North Sea whose empty waters were soon to bristle with oil rigs and offshore wind farms.

It was only when I took my young granddaughter to Lowestoft Ness, to show her the easternmost point in Britain, that I became aware of the immense height of a wind turbine. The solitary one at the Ness towers over all the buildings and has become a well-known landmark for shipping. Below the now stabilised cliffline I discovered that there had once been a substantial 'Beach Town' to serve the fishing community, but this has now disappeared to be replaced by a "Bird's Eye" frozen food warehouse. I learnt this information from my next-door neighbour, Martin Graystone, a ship-construction engineer whose grandfather had once been a fisherman living in 'Beach Town'. He went on to tell me how the latter settlement's demise was symptomatic of the change in character of Lowestoft's economy from one of fishing to that of a 'Hive of industry'. When I walked to the Outer Harbour a mere handful of inshore fishing boats were all that could be seen; a somewhat forlorn prospect when compared with the bustling commercial activity that had sprung up along the town wharves just to the west. This inner harbour is termed Lake Lothing and its shores are lined with flourishing industrial enterprises. Martin, who had trained as an apprentice in one of the shipbuilding yards, explained to me how these manufacturing enterprises had transformed the appearance of Lowestoft. He proceeded to list the various well-known companies that had become established there, starting with Brook Marine the shipbuilder with whom he first worked. During the 1970's this yard was occupied almost totally by an order to construct a fleet of Russian trawlers. "The local work force was augmented by an influx of tough Irish shipbuilders from Belfast's Harland & Wolf yards and an equal number of hardy Scots from the equally renowned John Browns' of Glasgow, including my future father-in-law" he said. "There were constant whispers that the trawlers were destined to become Russian 'spy-ships' because we were in the middle of the Cold War". At a nearby yard Richards' Shipbuilders were constructing a number of minesweepers for the Royal Navy alongside a series of supply vessels for the North Sea oil rigs. Martin told me how the quays got steadily busier as new industrial manufacturers moved in: "It was not only ship repairers who flourished, because, in the large water-front sheds, gigantic modules for housing the oilmen were also being fabricated before being shipped out to the oil and gas platforms". "The Co-op canning factory was joined by such well-known names as Pye electricals, Beechams, Boulton & Paul and Shell UK, to say nothing of the accompanying service industries. Moreover, an enormous free-standing crane was finally installed to handle materials intended for the construction of Sizewell nuclear power station just down the coast". Quite clearly the Lowestoft townscape had been transformed in a decade or two and the neighbouring freshwater lake of Oulton Broad was not to escape. Once the home of George Borrow (of "Wild Wales" fame), this attractive wooded waterside retreat was to become a haven for small-boat construction. Although Lowestoft is still popular as a seaside resort, in this respect it cannot compete with Great Yarmouth, a few miles to the north.

Yarmouth is a handsome planned town built around its 12th century medieval core on a four-mile long shingle spit. It is quite clear to everyone that the mouth of the River Yare has been deflected southwards by 'longshore drift' and ancient maps show the locations of three earlier estuary mouths (1393, 1508 and 1560) before it was finally stabilised at the present outlet. A glance at a modern map will demonstate that the spit lies athwart the wide expanse of Breydon Water and it has been suggested that, at the mouth of The Broads, this tidal waterbody was once open to the sea in the form of a substantial embayment. The fishing quays line the western side of the town, sheltered from the North Sea gales but, like Lowestoft, the herring fisheries which gave Yarmouth its earlier fame have now been replaced by massive industrial units related to offshore oil, gas and wind-farm operations. Nevertheless, to many holidaymakers Yarmouth is regarded as East Anglia's most visited tourist centre, sometimes referred to as thc 'Blackpool of the East'. Miles of golden sands are backed by a line of hotels and boarding houses overlooking a foreshore crowded with amusements of every description. Out to the north the racecourse carries on the theme of 'hedonistic delight' and heralds a coastline that has been the centre of much discussion concerning the ways in which it has been developed. I once brought a party of undergradutes to visit Great Yarmouth, ostensibly to talk about coastal geomorphology, but they were far more interested in the seafront and its 'pleasure beach'. One can hardly blame them.

All the way from Lowestoft and for ten miles beyond Yarmouth the coastline has become an almost endless 'leisure centre', comprising alternating holiday camps, caravan sites, camping grounds, car parks and golf courses, all easily accessible from good coast roads. Five years before the National Trust's Neptune surveyor of this stretch of the Norfolk coast mapped it with accompanying scathing comments, Norman Scarfe (*op. cit.*) wrote a similar diatribe: "...the twentieth century has revealed its more hateful forms of unsightliness – bungalow hutches, exposed caravans, our kind of slumdum". Such haphazard, and largely unplanned, coastal development has long had its detractors and I have tried to explain, in earlier chapters how various planning and conservation bodies (including the National Trust) have reacted to such pejorative attitudes. One author, Kenneth Lindley (Coastline, 1967), has attempted to take a more balanced view than most, even when believing that "The tragedy of the situation is that the disease has become almost an epidemic, spreading round our coast like a medieval plague". He continues by saying "There is nothing wrong with either camps, caravans or chalets. It is just that they have been used to perpetrate some of the worst offences against our coastal landscape". He accepts that a well-planned and an ordered layout of a caravan site "...need do no damage to the landscape and can, in fact, enhance it whilst at the same time providing a totally new kind of holiday". I have always aimed at presenting an impartial view of this type of coastal land use, despite the critical comments made by some of the media that the 1965 Neptune Survey was biased towards a "Middle-Class viewpoint". But it has to be said that the subjective (and unsought for) comments of my team of young surveyors on their coastal maps simply echoed the thoughts of many other commentators that were being voiced at that time, more than half a century ago. More importantly, it has to be explained why this stretch of the East Anglian coastline has been developed in this way, almost in the form of a chain of major 'honeypots'.

In the preceding pages I have drawn attention to the fact that wherever there are sandy beaches there will, almost always, be pressure from tourists and how, with proper planning-control, this demand can be met in a variety of ways. I have described how the Forestry Commission reacted by opening-up access to some of their forest estate; how the National Trust has provided much-needed car parks at heavily used sites; and why the well-organised 'caravan city' at Porthcawl, in South Wales has become a 'mega-honeypot' (if you will allow me to use that awful expression) and, as such has become a tourist attraction in its own right. Almost everyone is agreed that access to the sea is a human right (with a few exceptions on security or safety grounds) and East Anglia, more than most British coastlines, has been provided with an exceptional bounty of sandy shores, resulting from the rapid erosion of its crumbling cliffs of 'soft rocks' and of their overlying mantle of glacial drifts. It has to be remembered, however, that where such materials are washed away in some places, the resulting sediments will be deposited in other locations. Pebbles can only be moved by waves, whereas sand and mud can be held in suspension while they are transported by tidal currents. Thus, because of these natural processes, the East Anglian coast has been 'smoothed off'; the mouths of its river estuaries have been blocked or deflected by fluctuating shingle spits (Orford, Lowestoft and Yarmouth); some of its northern ports have been left abandoned by the sea because of ever-shifting sandbanks and the growth of muddy marshes. Unlike the intricacies displayed by the 'hard rock' coastlines of western Britain, where bays, coves and bold headlands abound and serve to trap these deposits, East Anglia's low, linear and continuously-changing shorelines have to depend on hundreds of groynes in order to retain their holiday beaches. For example, the shores between Lowestoft and Great Yarmouth (including their suburbs) have no less than 135 of these wooden structures, built to maintain their beaches which are the primary seaside attraction for thousands of holidaymakers who make their annual pilgrimage largely to enjoy a traditional 'bucket and spade' adventure.

In terms of development, the coastline northwards from Winterton-on-Sea exhibits a remarkable change and one would be hard pushed to find more than a couple of caravan sites all the way to Mundesley. It is a relatively deserted coast of sandy beaches, dunes and coastal marshes interspersed with attractive villages such as Horsey, Sea Palling and Happisburgh. Only at Bacton, the site of Britain's first natural gas terminal, is there any industrial intrusion. Therefore, this is the sort of coastline that the National Trust would regard as 'pristine', but it has few properties there because it has already been protected from major development by other conservation bodies. Behind Winterton Dunes a partly wooded Nature Reserve is a virtual wilderness where successful planting of sea buckthorn and a rare species of marram grass has succeeded in stabilising these very old dunes. At the northern end of the reserve, current Ordnance Survey maps still carry the name Winterton Ness, which indicates the site of a foreland. In fact, it provides an excellent indication of the magnitude of East Anglia's rapidly shifting shorelines, because the actual Ness has now moved southwards for more than a mile. To the north of the reserve the outer limits of The Broads National Park reach the sea at Horsey where the dune belt is so narrow that it is vulnerable to breaching by storm waves. The area around Horsey Mere, owned by the National Trust, was formerly the estuary of one or two Broadland rivers and as such is merely a stretch of grazed marshland below sea level. It came as no surprise when storm waves tore great breaches in the dunes in 1938 and again in the notorious storm surge of 1953, both of which flooded the farmland and almost reopened the ancient estuarics of which Horsey Mere is a remnant. In view of the rising ocean-level and the sinking North Sea basin it appears to be only a matter of time before this particular fragile coastal tract becomes permanently overwhelmed. Daniel Defoe became aware of previous catastrophies along this shore during his 1724–1726 perambulation. He must surely have heard tales of the great storm of 1665 when not only the coastline itself was overridden but dozens of ships were wrecked at The Ness. He was told how it was "...well known to the mariner as the most fatal headland between Scotland and London". It is not difficult to visualise this low shoreline as a hazard to shipping when easterly gales blow or when sea fogs blot out the landmarks. Defoe went on to describe the poverty of the local fisherfolk when he noted how "...there was scarcely a barn or a shed or a stable... but what was built of old planks, beams, wales and timbers and the wrecks of ships, and ruins of mariner's and merchant's fortunes" (A Tour Through the Whole Island of Great Britain. Daniel Defoe, New Edition, 1986).

One is tempted to describe the wonderful scenery of Broadland (especially because I now live on its fringe) but in truth it is not strictly coastal and it is almost impossible to view its waterlogged landscape from most coastal viewpoints. Since much of it is tidal, I pondered this question for some time, and remembered how I had previously lingered awhile on a lengthy description of the mighty Cadair Idris in Wales, but its foothills actually reach to the shore and it can be seen for miles along the coast. But is this special pleading and an example of my bias for preferring the rockbound shores of western Britain? I finally decided to base my decision on the rules of the 1965 Neptune Survey which led to The Broads being ignored because they were located inland from the 'Lowest road-bridging point'. Such a decision relieved me from 'the horns of a dilemma', so to speak, but one can rest assured that there is a whole host of literature on The Broads, on their history, on their wildlife and especially on their tourist attractions. It is now time to move on in order to convey thoughts of my experiences on the exceptionally fine shoreline of north Norfolk which I had already been able to explore in considerably more detail over a number of years.

When I first came to Norfolk, several years ago, it was this northern coast that quickly captured my interest, for few places display such fine examples of coastal geomorphological processes. I admit that I was also impressed with its attractive scenery, that has been described much more successfully by many other writers. H. V. Morton, for example, spoke almost poetically of how "...the tide goes out for miles and returns at a canter. It is desolate. The wind whispers. The sea birds cry. No men but naturalists disturb the solitude of the salt marshes". This is certainly my sort of country, although I have to admit that, by bringing groups of students here, I did disturb the solitude.

We first stayed on holiday at the Blakeney Hotel, right on the seashore although the sea was nowhere to be seen. Apart from the handful of boats standing high and dry on the narrow muddy channel one would hardly know that this was a tiny harbour. We set off to walk along the harbour wall and were astonished when the tide came 'cantering' in at more than a 'trot'. "One minute the oozy banks are dry; the next they are alive with a brown snake of water that writhes and bubbles, lapping the bright fringe of samphire at the edges" (In Search of England. H. V. Morton, 1927). In the 1920's he spoke of Blakeney as desolate; we found the town bustling with holidaymakers and crammed with traffic and mobile homes being towed through its narrow streets. It struck me then, and has done so ever since, that these pretty flint-faced coastal villages deserve a better fate than that, but over the decades nothing has been done to alleviate the overcrowding. And yet the crowds do not come to enjoy a 'bucket and spade holiday'. Visitors descend on dear old Blakeney, and its neighbour, Cley-next-the-Sea, simply to enjoy the scenery, walk miles along the distant shingle beaches, revel in its bird life or simply potter about in boats. It seemed like a million miles from the piers and amusement arcades of Yarmouth and Lowestoft because this is a different kind of resort. It is one which appeals only to naturalists, artists, writers and photographers and, of course, to the occasional angler and those holidaymakers who wish to chug out in fleets of hire-boats to the distant offshore sandbanks in order to view the seal colonies. But we soon discovered that Blakeney has its own treasured and peaceful coastline, that of Blakeney Point, known only to the more discerning as one of England's finest shingle spits which, unlike that at Orford Ness, has remained quite unsullied by human despoliation. As a teenager Richard Mabey spoke lovingly of his first Blakeney experience when "The Point was always our goal. We could not get enough of it and we struck out for it like the promised land...It was our Coral Island, an enchanted oasis of lagoons and shifting dunes, where seals basked and the air was full of the clamour of oyster catchers and redshanks" (Places: An Anthology of Britain. Ronald Blythe [Ed].1981).

Like most of this bracing shoreline, Blakeney is a birdwatcher's paradise because North Norfolk is a rendezvous for numerous birds (more than 375 species have been recorded) on their seasonal migrations either from north to south or from east to west. I have been fortunate in being able to obtain a book written entirely about Blakeney Point by a local author who has the sort of extraordinary feeling for nature that I had met previously only in the works of Pembrokeshire's Ronald Lockley. Andy Stoddart writes compellingly of how "Blakeney Point has always been at the forefront of knowledge and new ideas. It has reflected our understandings and perceptions of nature, holding up a mirror to how we view the natural world, but it has also been a pioneer, inspiring us to extend what we know and to explore new ways of seeing and thinking. Today Blakeney Point remains an intellectual testing ground, a laboratory of the imagination. It asks us not only what we know about nature but also how we think of it, how we value it and how we might best be part of it". (Shifting Sands. Andy Stoddart, 2013). These sentences neatly summarise my own philosophy which I have tried to explain not only to generations of students but also when attempting to express my own lifetime's coastal perceptions and experiences as I write this volume. Unlike many other books, Stoddart's slim volume is one that I read in a single sitting because it so closely reflects my own feelings for everything coastal. Here was someone who holds the same sense of values as my own; a person who perceives the coastline as a wonderful gift of nature and one that should be conserved with the utmost vigour.

After several visits to Blakeney, from the distant Midlands of England, my own personal apotheosis came in 2008 when I was delighted to hear that the National Trust had honoured me by naming the Blakeney Point Warden's boat "The Whittow" in recognition of my decades of voluntary coastal work and advisory information that I had contributed, ever since I had helped to found Enterprise Neptune in 1964 (See chapter 2). I immediately felt the urge to travel across country to set eyes on this sturdy vessel and, if possible, make a trip out to sea. The great day finally arrived and we were instructed to drive to Morston Quay where we were met by John Sizer, the National Trust Director of Norfolk's coastal management. It was a bright and calm day, with 'fair weather' cumulus clouds drifting lazily across the sky, as we wended our way across the marsh to the mooring-post in the muddy creek. Diane, unselfishly, decided to stay ashore with our daughter, Fiona, thereby allowing my son-in-law, Andrew, and my granddaughter, Charlotte, to accompany me on the journey across to the Point. Our easy-going boatman steered a careful course through the maze of winding channels and across the calm waters of the capacious harbour that is sheltered from the open ocean by the grey-green outline of the lengthy shingle bank of the Point itself. A rapid walk along the inner beach, a few photographs and a chat with the staff at the Old Lifeboat House (The Warden's visitor centre) and we had to hasten back before the out-going tide left us stranded. We just had time to arrange for a much longer visit out to the Point before we had to return to our home in the Midlands. The second visit was planned to be a much more formal affair, to meet National Trust officials and to make recordings of our discussion on coastal affairs in general and those of Norfolk in particular.

Before we made our second excursion I had time to read more literature about one of the National Trust's earliest coastal acquisitions (1912). The four-mile long shingle spit is so important, from an ecological standpoint, that it has become one of Britain's most heavily protected areas. In addition to its status as a Site of Special Scientific Interest (SSSI), it is Norfolk's oldest Nature Reserve and is situated within the AONB of the North Norfolk Coast. Such a prestigious list of accolades made me doubly proud to have the Warden's boat named in my honour because these were the environmental and conservation fields in which I had been seriously involved throughout my academic career. I was very pleased when Diane was able to accompany me on this second trip, together with a young intern from the Trust who was there to record the discussion for the Trust archives. As a matter of fact, I had already made a much lengthier recording of my earliest work for the Trust some years previously, but this was the first recording to be made in a coastal location. After our trusty boatman had landed us on the pebbly beach we tramped the several hundred yards to the iconic blue-painted Lifeboat House (built in 1898 and de-commissioned in 1935) where three gaily striped deck-chairs on the wooden verandah added colour to the scene. We discovered that the wardens were, in the future, to be termed rangers, as we were welcomed by a bright young lady, Victoria Egan, and her assistant, Ajay, who was resident at the Point at that time. We were seated around a table and served tea and a large cake which Ajay proudly announced that they had bought specially for the occasion. Victoria told me about the Trust's work on the coast and about the recent marine flooding of the Trust's car park at Cley. We talked at length about the restoration and re-planting schemes on the dune coast and it set me thinking about the similar methods that I had seen demonstrated on the Jutland coast some fifty years ago. After a short excursion to examine the newly-built 'board-walks' on the nearby dunes we returned to the Lifeboat House to discuss the educational programmes that had been arranged at the Point, before we said our farewells and set off to return to the boat. It had been quite a 'brainstoming' episode and I asked the young intern if the recording had been successful. Much to everyone's horror we discovered that the tape-recorder had not been activated and, despite a request to repeat the entire exercise (an impossibility), the boatman reminded us that "Time and tide waits for no man". Therefore, we had to be content to listen to the sound of the seagulls, recorded as an entrée to the discussion in which we had learnt about the significance of the Suaeda bushes on this lonely beach which enticed the extremely rare avian visitor, the Bluethroat, to call here en route from Scandinavia during its winter migration to Africa. Such an explanation only served to highlight the continuing value of Blakeney Point in the Trust's conservation programmes. As we drove home I thought about the way in which another important record had been lost, but this time by the Department of the Environment, when our 1965 photographic survey of the coastline (commissioned by the Ministry of Housing and Local Government) seems to have disappeared (See chapter 2). Undertakings such as these can never really be properly repeated but, I have to admit, that I felt so sorry for the intern after the recent misfortune.

Although Blakeney has continued to be a 'special place' now that we have come to live in Norfolk we have had plenty of time to visit the north coast's other remarkable coastlines. At first, I had viewed the north coast with the eyes of a geomorphologist because, with the possible exception of the Moray Firth in Scotland, there is no other British coastline that can match the complex configurations to be seen between Sheringham and Hunstanton. Professor Steers, my former mentor, spent much of his early career mapping and explaining the genesis of the intricate network of sandbanks, shoals, berms, spits, bars, islands and marshes which give so much character to this lonely shore. It is a landscape fashioned not only by waves but also by tidal currents. The most common current is that known as a 'tidal stream', which is simply a response to the oscillating flood-tide and ebb-tide, and which carries sediment in and out of creeks and estuaries. More complicated is the 'longshore' current which carries material laterally along the coast (as its name denotes) and, where it meets an obstruction, turns offshore in the form of a 'rip current'. It is the latter that creates an unseen hazard to swimmers, such as in the episode that I described on Blackpool Sands in Devon (See chapter 1). A combination of wind-driven waves and fluctuating tidal currents has helped to create such offshore elongated islands such as Scolt Head which is an example of a 'barrier island'. This is an offshore bar high enough to permit dune growth and to protect the lagoon mudflats and coastal marshes from severe wave erosion. Professor Steers has demonstrated that at Scolt Head Island there is a westward flow of the current until two hours before high water and, following a short break, the tidal flow then turns eastwards until approximately three hours after high water. Because of such vicissitudes around Scolt Head, the silted up harbour channels of Burnham Overy Staithe have been turned to the west and those of Brancaster deflected to the east. Similar offshore ridges are developing at Stiffkey and at Holkham Gap.

Despite the fact that we had settled in Norfolk only a few weeks previously, I couldn't wait to see this coastline to the west of Blakeney about which I had not only read but had also had it explained to me by Steers himself almost sixty years ago. Thus, we booked a hotel at Holkham in January 2018 with the intention of exploring the shores. We couldn't have chosen a worse time to walk on the exposed beaches, for a strong northely wind, straight from the Arctic, brought tears to our eyes. No wonder we were the only ones who battled out beyond the line of trees at Holkham Gap, planted by the Earl of Leicester to stabilise the dunes and act as a windbreak for his rushy fields. A harsh lesson but one very different from that of Patrick Barkham, a Norfolk naturalist, journalist and author, who had spent happy childhood hours on this very shore, even though on his first visit he admits to having been underwhelmed when he perceived Scolt as "...an empty island of tawny sand dunes and flat grey-green marsh [that] seemed bereft of anything live or arresting. Why would people come here if they could visit Cornwall?". This viewpoint came close to our own feelings on that bitterly cold January day. However, Patrick came to love this coast as he continues: "But North Norfolk has a subtle charm that seeps into you like the trickle of an incoming tide, less bombastic than awesome cliffs but both soothingly and strangely uncompromising". (Coastlines: The Story of Our Shore. Patrick Barkham, 2015). I got to know Patrick when he was commissioned by the National Trust to write about the historic beginnings of its coastal acquisitions including, of course, the story of the Neptune campaign. I shall always recall the moment when he handed me a signed copy of his book at Whiteford Burrows on The Gower, where many of us gathered in 2015 to celebrate this first coastal purchase from money raised by the Neptune campaign. Diane and I had already entertained Patrick when he had interviewed me to discover the background to the 1965 mapping experiences. It was then that I had recounted to him the over-critical subjective comments made by the Norfolk surveyor who noted that part of it was "...Unworthy of any attempt at protection or redemption – it is completely past it, except perhaps for a small buffer area to the north of Winterton". His book describes my reaction when I responded: "Just finding that Norfolk assessment made me laugh because that's effectively writing off the county. Everyone has their own perceptions and the students weren't trained enough to be objective".

Once more, in Patrick, I had met someone who had a remarkable feeling for and a great affinity with the 'Edge of the Land'. Of course, there are many others who share such sentiments but whom I have never met. I find that Anna Pavord, a journalist, broadcaster and former chairman of the National Trust's Garden Panel, is a person who understands the very essence of landscape. Her perception of the minutiae of a shoreline is exceptional when she writes of the ways in which tides have sculptured a North Norfolk beach: "In some places, the sand was mounded in gritty slopes, thick with shells: mussels, oysters, finely fluted piddocks and clams" (Landskipping: Painters, Ploughmen and Painters. Anna Pavord, 2016). A Norfolk artist, Liz Mcgowan, also sculptured the sandy beach at Brancaster, in which she created what she termed a "Sea Heart" as an indication of the rhythmic pulse of the ocean. This type of 'sand-art' was to be copied on Rememberance Sunday 2018 (as described in the previous chapter). The earlier effigy was commissioned by the National Trust but her other conceptual art constructions, at an exhibition in Norwich Cathedral, entitled "Force of Nature: Meditations on the Norfolk Landscape" were created from a collection of natural and 'objets trouvées' painstakingly gleaned along the shorelines.

And then there is Hugh Aldersley-Williams (*op. cit.*) who had the patience to sit at Blakeney Quay to "…watch the water for twelve or thirteen unbroken hours" in order to monitor the tidal flow as part of a scientific exercise that demonstrated a tidal-range of more than 18 feet. One would think that such an experimental data-collection (like my own on the glacial cliffs of North Wales) could result in a bout of very dull reading, but not a bit of it for, like Anna Pavord, Hugh breathes life into the different colours, shapes and habitats of the littoral environment as it changes over time. These are the sort of people who must have looked carefully at the details of our landscapes from childhood days, just as I had done when I gathered beach pebbles on Llandudno's shore and set in train my own early wonderment of the coastal scene.

To fully appreciate the extensive panorama of the flat North Norfolk coastline we found it essential to follow a lane inland that would take us up onto the gentle slopes of a coastal ridge above Stiffkey. This area is termed "Poppyland" and over the years that we had visited our daughter's home in Norfolk I had always been impressed by a picture entitled "Poppyland" that had been given to her and her husband as a wedding present by Jeremy Barlow, an eminent local artist. In it one can look across a dream-like field of poppies down to the hazy line of Blakeney Point and to the blue sea beyond. What we saw, on that bleak winter day, was devoid of this vibrant colour, to be replaced only by a khaki-brown and olive landscape and a grey sea beyond, together with a feature that was missing in Barlow's painting – a collection of windmills at a distant offshore wind-farm. It became apparent that these bleak slopes must really be visited on a calm summer's day when one can pause to admire the view, for this is a coastal scene not to be hurried.

Below us lay the tiny village of Stiffkey, famed for the aberrations of its vicar but even better known, perhaps, for the cockle women wandering along its tide-lines. They were there in H. V. Morton's day and he writes at length of the deep impressions that they made on him: "Slowly, heavily, they come with dripping sacks of 'Stewkey blues' on their backs. Most of them are old women, who belong to a tougher generation. The salt spray drenches their short skirts, the wind lashes their bare legs, as they come plodding in over the marshes". (H. V. Morton *op. cit.*). That was a century ago and one cannot help but compare those stalwart women with the cockle-pickers of The Gower or with the fishwives of Pembrokeshire. From Morton's description of their black-shawled images one is also tempted to compare them with some of the old women that I had encountered on Achill Island in western Ireland. Such characters are now no more and their dwellings, like other small cottages along this shore, are now likely to be the second-homes of many wealthy incomers. For today this is a fashionable region in which to live and has led to some of East Anglia's highest house prices. Thus, the seaside towns have undergone remarkable changes from sleepy fishing villages to vibrant coastal resorts with their restaurants, boutiques, gift shops and 'superior' hotels. We discovered that the bars were crowded not with local farmers and fisherfolk but with holiday makers in trendy outfits, with not a black shawl in sight.

The ridge on which we stood becomes wider and higher as it is traced eastwards, reaching an elevation of almost 400 feet in the steep hills and wooded valleys between Weybourne and Cromer. This feature is termed the "Cromer Ridge" by geologists and geomorphologists, for it is known to be a conspicuous glacial 'end-moraine' marking the southernmost limit of the last ice-sheet advance into East Anglia. It is characterised by an abrupt northern slope, broken by steep-sided post-glacial valleys, and a gentler south-facing slope comprising extensive outwash fans of sands and gravels poured out from the former ice-front. The place names of Salthouse Heath and Kelling Heath testify to the sandy moorland that has subsequently flourished on this outwash material. Immediately after the ice-sheet had disappeared a wide plain would have stretched far across a lowland which would have connected with continental Europe, but once the sea-level started to rise then tides would begin to drive the shoreline back until the waves would have attacked the moraine itself. This is why geologists flock to the cliffs around Sheringham, Runton, Cromer and especially Happisburgh, because there are ever-changing glacial cliff-sections exposed by the accommodating waves. So important are these exposures that such names as Sheringham, Paston and Cromer have become the official 'type-site' nomenclature in the Geological Survey's classification of Ice Age stratigraphy. The most famous is the so-called "Cromer Forest-bed" where layers of peat, buried beneath boulder clays and contorted gravelly sands, contain some of Britain's finest mammalian remains dating from the later stages of the Ice Age. Analysis of the pollen trapped in the layers of peat has shown that there had been several fluctuations of climate during their accumulation, a time now termed an 'Inter-glacial' between the major ice-sheet advances. Such climatic changes are illustrated by vegetational differences, when birch and pine forests indicate cooler conditions while warmer eras are defined by forests of oak, elm, lime, alder and hazel. The remains of bison, elk, elephant, rhinoceros, hyaena and mammoth have been discovered in the Cromer Forest-bed since the middle of the 19th century and 'fossil trading'soon became a common practice. One assiduous local collector, Alfred Savin, sold his impressive collection to the Natural History Museum in 1897 but the search has continued along this coastline in an effort to discover the earliest evidence of human occupancy.

The crumbling 30-foot cliffs at Pakefield (just to the south of Lowestoft) are known to thousands of holidaymakers who flock to its holiday village and the many caravan and camping sites above the long sandy beaches. As I had found many years previously, on the shores of Criccieth in North Wales, the vast majority of visitors would show little if no interest whatsoever in the exposure of the Cromer Forest-bed. Indeed, they would have been warned of the hazard of continual cliff collapse. This problem did not deter the intrepid geologists at Pakefield who, in 2005, discovered a handful of flint artifacts, fashioned by early humans about 700,000 years ago, mixed in with animal remains, and all interbedded in the peat. From all this evidence it has been possible to reconstruct the early environmental conditions of that time: a climate similar to that in East Anglia today and a slow-moving freshwater river with no evidence of saline conditions. This has been taken to represent the course of a very early River Waveney during an inter-glacial break between ice-sheet advances. Several miles along the coast at Happisburgh, villagers have lived happily for centuries without knowing that beneath their feet was evidence of Britain's earliest settlers. That was until a local resident, Mike Chambers, whilst walking his dog, came across a humanly knapped flint tool embedded in the foreshore mud. Archaeologists and geologists were quickly on the scene to set in motion a lengthy series of excavations on the beach, both to the south of the village and at another site just below the caravan park. The finds have proved to be even older than those at Pakefield, demonstrating that the very crude tools were fashioned between 950,000 and 850,000 years ago. Furthermore, it was found that the associated gravels included far-travelled erratics – quartz and quartzite pebbles from the Midlands in addition to 'puddingstones' from Hertfordshire and cherts from rocks in Kent. Such an assemblage gave further proof that the very earliest Thames flowed north across this region and, after joining the very earliest Waveney drainage system, continued northwards to link up with an early Rhine at a time when the southern part of the North Sea was dry land, as described above. An even more exciting discovery was to be made here in May 2013, following months of severe storms. Several fossil footprints of adults and children were found in the compacted mud. Photographs were taken before the prints were destroyed by the waves, but it is claimed that: "This unique insight into a moment's activity by a family group provides a very tangible link with the past. Evidence of this type is incredibly rare, Happisburgh being the oldest outside Africa" (Early Humans. Nick Ashton, 2017). Footprints such as these, like the ancient dinosaur prints on Skye (See chapter 7), make one realise that it is largely along the constantly mobile coastal zone at the erosive 'edge of the land' that discoveries will continue to be found, even if they are always at risk of subsequent wave destruction.

The rapidly eroding cliffline on the north Norfolk coast, although it continues to provide fresh exposures of valuable geological and archaeological material, at Cromer itself the coastal retreat has been halted by hefty sea defences and a cliff-top promenade with its façade of smart hotels. In the time of Domesday Book the present town did not exist but the village of Shipden stood nearby as a major North Sea port on the coast at that date. The ruins of Shipden now lie beneath the waves almost half-a-mile offshore, giving a measure of coastal retreat within historic time. By 1806 a visitor was describing how Cromer was then to be "...considered as a watering place with observations on the Picturesque scenery in its neighbourhood", implying a somewhat elite resort. By the time that we visited in the spring of 2018 this demeanour had changed because its streets were thronged with day trippers, its car parks were overflowing and its streets were full of typically modern-day seaside features such as bars, betting shops, fast-food cafes and gift shops. Some reports say that it has become 'rather shabby' but its fishing boats, drawn up on the shore, testify to its continuing renown as a centre of a thriving shellfish industry, whilst 'Cromer Crab' features on every menu in the region. We had recently bought a watercolour of Cromer's stately 160-foot church tower, painted by Henry Ninham, a reputable artist of the Norwich School of artists, and we set out to discover the original viewpoint in a street of fishermen's cottages. The tower remains but the street is now lined with modern chain stores and charity shops, just like most latter-day high streets throughout the realm. This disappointment, however, was off-set by the extensive cliff-top views, for it is is rare in East Anglia to find such a high viewpoint along its low-lying shores. Here we could understand why this 'high' cliff had inspired artists to illustrate the acres of well-maintained grassland enhanced by Cromer's prominent lighthouse and its majestic pier. I still find it difficult to understand why I almost always expect seaside development to remain in a time warp of smart Victoriana. It very rarely does and seasides will continue to evolve as Britain's population grows exponentially and the demands for camping and caravan holidays will bring increasing pressures on their suburban coastlines.

Here, such demand was clearly shown by the number of mobile homes to be found between Cromer and the 'pleasant' cliff-top resort of Sheringham. However, the planners seem to have insisted that they had to be located inland away from the Norfolk Coast Path and that they must be set amidst woodlands, swathes of rhododendrons and heathlands of gorse and heather. From a visual standpoint this seems to have been an excellent example of environmental coastal planning.

Our final excursions led us back to the more peaceful muddy creeks and lonely marshes of Cley and Wells-next-the-Sea. As I have already described, these are areas of seabirds, wildfowl, seals and sheer emptiness, an ambience that some people find almost hypnotic and irresistible. Although Wells has its tourism and industry it still retains the image of a flint-faced fishing village of yesteryear. Both Cley and neighbouring Blakeney have developed an air of exclusiveness, almost devoid of their former port activities because the open sea is out of sight, although some folks stroll leisurely around their streets wearing knitted sweaters and yachtsman's hats as if they had been part of the former fishing heritage. In fairness it has to be said that the talk in the pubs is not of the 'one that got away' but more on the rising prices of houses and motor-boat fuel. I simply sit and listen and venture no opinion, very much aware that I am a comparative newcomer.

I have now reached the end of my coastal memories over a period of some eighty years, but now that we have finally come to live so near to the 'edge of the land' I am certain that there will be many more anecdotes to add to the list and a few more truly coastal characters to interview. In the next chapter I will recount how I decided that it could be of interest by looking at the coastline from a different perspective, that of viewing the shoreline from the sea. Diane and I have sailed for thousands of miles in every ocean except for those bordering the Poles but rarely have we spent much time voyaging around our own shores. That deficiency was soon to be overcome, as I will endeavour to relate.

The Hebridean Princess off the Cuillins of Skye – *See plate section for colour version*

10. VOYAGES AROUND THE BRITISH ISLES

"I am about to take my last voyage, a great leap in the dark"
(Last Words. Thomas Hobbes (1588–1679)

Presumably, countless thousands of holidaymakers and coastal dwellers have spent a great deal of their time simply gazing out to sea and, perhaps, reflecting on the 'wonders of the deep'. Fisherfolk will be contemplating a good catch, sailors a fair wind, beach-lovers a calm sunlit sea but, more than anything, passengers boarding a cruise liner will be anticipating vistas of new shorelines, quite unlike those with which they have long been familiar. Cruising experiences are somewhat different from those of anyone taking a ferry; the latter is a means to an end and usually entails only a brief glimpse of receding or approaching shores. Conversely, to passengers on a cruise ship the voyage is an end in itself. They can forget the hustle and bustle of the car-deck and the duty-free shop and simply look forward to leisurely changes of scenery as their vessel glides slowly along ever-changing coastlines.[1]

Once an individual has left our shores they will undergo a completely different perspective of the 'edge of the land'. Anyone looking seawards is, generally speaking, in a static position and, unless there are coastal ships, oil rigs or wind-farms, the empty ocean will appear to be both featureless and limitless, devoid of points of reference until it is truncated by a flat horizon. Once aboard a moving vessel, however, the shoreline can never appear to be stationary and unchanging – the motion of the ship, on the majority of occasions, will generate a feeling of visual instability as the skyline appears to move up and down; the eye will be forced not only to adjust to this moving image but also to adapt to a change of scale as once-familiar points of reference on the land now become diminished in size. The excitement of a coastal cruise lies in the knowledge that one would never be too far offshore and therefore

1 Some locations in this chapter can be seen on the map on page 276

would be able to look forward to viewing many new shoreslines without the monotony of gazing over endless empty oceans. And yet, it has to be acknowledged that there is something in the British psyche that encourages the shorebound holidaymaker to pay more for a 'sea view' from their bedroom window because in their own minds the whole point of their holiday is geared to being able to gaze out to sea, no matter how featureless.

On returning to examine the advantages of coastal cruising, it hardly needs emphasising that when one looks landwards, the shoreline is almost always embroidered with intricate patterns of human occupation. All of these varying land-uses, of course, were the very 'raison d'etre' of the Neptune survey that I have already described in detail. Even where this 'footprint' is missing, Nature has provided a bountiful collection of natural coastlines around the British Isles. During my own far-reaching journeys along these same fringes I had been able to build up a fairly comprenensive knowledge of their remarkable attributes but it came as something of a surprise, some years after my retirement from all things academic, when an unexpected phone call from the cruise line Noble Caledonia, asked if I would like to be a lecturer on one of their 'Round Britain' voyages. After responding positively to their enquiry, I travelled to their London office to discuss the details. It transpired that my name had been recommended in view of my work for the National Trust and also for my published books on British and Irish scenery. It was agreed that Diane and I would join a cruise due to leave Leith (port for Edinburgh) in late-May 1999. A month or so before our scheduled departure, however, our fortunes had taken a turn for the worse. We had just found a purchaser for our house, that had been on the market for several weeks, when an almighty crash indicated that the dining room ceiling in our ancient Thames-side home had collapsed, an hour before a final viewing. Builders had to be hastily assembled and, in view of our impending excursion, the estate agent would have to be left in charge during our absence. An even greater disaster had already impacted on our lifestyle when Diane had recently suffered a triple fracture of the upper arm. A very complex injury of this type should have been sufficient for us to withdraw from the intended commitment but Diane believed that we should not forgo such a unique opportunity to circumnavigate our island shores, coastlines that we had previously enjoyed only from a landlubber's perspective. In hindsight I really believe that discretion should have over-ridden such valour on her part, but we had cruised the World over and believed that we would be able to cope with another shipboard adventure, especially because it would start by exploring our beloved Scottish islands with their intricate forms of geology and scenery. It was to be my job to explain these landscapes to the shipboard passengers. Moreover, I had been told that the cruise was to be themed partly on coastal gardens, so would I kindly include material on natural coastal flora and fauna. It seemed to be quite an undertaking, especially bearing in mind that the majority of our fellow tourists would have little if any knowledge of coastal processes or of the geology and varied landforms that they were going to see. But, on the other hand, there were going to be those who had already visited some of the selfsame coastlines of Britain and Ireland and had driven there to enjoy walking, angling or beachcombing on the sands. If so, they ought to be well aware of the changing moods of our unpredictable weather, when the placid jade and turquoise tones of the shallow-water coves can rapidly change into the colour of beaten pewter that often heralds the approach of an Atlantic storm when the sea's surface would soon be rent into a maelstrom of white-water breakers. The ship's captain and crew, of course, would be well versed in such rapid transformations and would be well aware of how the scenic shore that we had all been admiring could soon become a hazard and when sea-sickness could be the least of their worries. Little did we know, when we set sail, that inclement weather was to be the norm on this fateful cruise.

Such negative thoughts had rarely been in the forefront of my mind when I had previously embarked on numerous ferry-crossings to and from Britain and Ireland, either on 'business' or pleasure trips. It was interesting to recall the names of the British and Irish ports from which I had departed over a lifetime and I was rather astonished to discover the length of the ensuing list. Moving clockwise from London's Tilbury (en route to East Africa) they included: Dover, Newhaven, Portsmouth, Southampton (en route to New York and later to Australia), Ryde (IOW), Fishguard, Holyhead, Llandudno, Douglas (IOM), Liverpool, Heysham, Oban, Uig (Skye), Tarbet (Harris), Thurso, Stromness (Orkney), Newcastle, Hull and Harwich. In Ireland there were only three: Wexford, Dublin and Belfast. All of these comings and goings had been spread over many years but we now had an opportunity, in merely a fortnight, to add many more 'ports-of-call' to this lengthy list.

We finally boarded the Scottish express train at King's Cross, with Diane gamely struggling along because, by then, her arm had been pinned, screwed and supported in a sling. A taxi whisked us from Waverley station to the wharf where the Caledonian Star awaited us. This sturdy little ship was moored alongside the beautiful Royal Yacht Britannia, harshly de-requisitioned some years previously. We thought about the happy times once enjoyed by the Royal family when they had left their ship to picnic on the coast of Raasay, just across the channel from our island of Fladda, but alas no more. As we laboured up the gangway of our cruise ship, dutiful deck hands helped Diane aboard and others carried all our luggage, amongst which were rolls of maps and diagrams that I had drawn specially for the occasion. In addition, I had compiled a detailed guidebook for the itinerary (for my eyes only) because I had been informed that whilst the ship was moving I would be expected to give a running commentary from the ship's public address system. This entailed frequent visits to the bridge where I had regular opportunities to converse with the First Officer and the Norwegian Captain. Having made their acquaintance I became doubly assured that such officers would be well trained in navigating the convoluted shorelines of the Scottish islands and sea lochs.

Our cabin turned out to be the special guest-suite that was almost as spacious as that in a normal home. We also felt privileged to be allocated seats at the table of the ship's doctor, a friendly middle-aged and courteous gentleman, who vowed to look after Diane at all times whilst we were aboard ship. Following a pleasant afternoon tea in the lounge the passengers crowded on deck to witness the departure from the quayside, always a rewarding spectacle of thrashing screws, mooring ropes and busy little tug-boats. The distant skyline of Edinburgh slowly faded into the distance as we sailed down the Firth of Forth, setting course for the open sea. In no time at all the dinner gongs were ringing and we took our seats in the restaurant to look out over a calm sunlit sea basking beneath cloudless evening skies. Our first surprise came when the engines stopped, the anchor chains rumbled and we came to a halt within the shadow of the towering 420-foot sea-stack of the renowned Bass Rock, near to the mouth of the Firth. I had described its geology in my Scottish book but, thank goodness I wasn't required to give an exposition during the meal. There was really no need to because the cliffs of this ancient igneous pyramid were alive with thousands of gannets who broadcast their own cacophony as they swirled around the cliff that had been whitened by their guano. I had already learnt that the island had once been a 7th century hermitage, similar to that of Skellig Michael, a far more isolated sea-stack in south-west Ireland. We hoped that this first coastal vista might prove to be a good omen for the remainder of our cruise and we remarked to our table companions how unusual it was to be eating an evening meal with such a striking panorama just beyond the ship's bows. The other diners, in addition to the doctor, were a couple of genteel ladies from Sloane Square in London, who had come largely to visit the maritime gardens and professed little interest in the scenery. But, no matter, there were at least a further hundred passengers who might be quite interested in the coastal landforms.

The next day we awakened to a glorious sunrise and looked out over the bustling quayside of Aberdeen's harbour. We were all to be taken in a fleet of coaches to Royal Deeside, not only to visit gardens but also to some of the stately castles. I was soon appraised of the fact that we would be so far inland that I would be excused from commenting on the scenery, except for a few words about the granite architecture of Aberdeen and the local Rubislaw quarry from which the stonework had been quarried. We sailed from Aberdeen that evening and, following a peaceful overnight crossing, we discovered that because of the amount of shipping, our ship had been allocated an anchorage way out in Kirkwall harbour, facing across to the sandstone-built capital of the Orkney Islands. To reach the shore entailed a journey in a large type of inflatable, termed a Zodiac. The weather had by then taken a distinct turn for the worse and waves were breaking along the quays. Because we had been here previously, several years ago, Diane chose to stay on board but I was committed to join other passengers on the coach tour.

By the time we had walked around the attractive town and admired the cathedral, the rain had steadily increased to a real Scottish downpour and we tumbled, steaming, into our coaches, bound for the west coast and a visit to Skara Brae on the Bay of Skaill. Once there, we all assembled in the visitor centre to learn something of this remarkable Iron Age village that had been unearthed from a cover of blown sand and note how wave erosion had left it perched on the edge of the ocean. I led an intrepid group, swathed in wet-weather clothing, out to the beach to explain how the superbly built structure had been fashioned from the local sandstone which splits into excellent flagstones. By this time my words were being swept away by gale-force winds that drove the rain horizontally into our faces. It was intended that we should walk a few miles along the cliff-top to see the monument erected to Lord Kitchener who was drowned near here in 1916, when his ship, HMS Hampshire, had sunk after hitting a mine when en route to Russia. Leading a bedraggled group such as this reminded me of the countless treks in the rain that I had endured with student parties, so I was quite relieved when no one volunteered to make this windswept journey. Instead, we all continued on our trip to visit such tourist attractions as Stromness, the standing Stones of Stenness, the Ring of Brodgar and the tomb of Maes Howe where we crawled along its stone-lined passage. By then most of the passengers had decided to remain in the coach and view the countryside through rain-streaked windows. I was able to explain that, despite these northerly latitudes, the Old Red Sandstone from which the islands are composed has weathered into fertile soils that can be tilled with comparative ease. Thus, fields of young barley and oats, swaying like ocean waves in the the gusting wind, were interspersed with extensive emerald green pastures well stocked with cattle, although I had to ask them to envisage the scene in high summer, a request that was almost impossible to perceive because of the stormy weather. I began to sense that an atmosphere of ennui was setting in, the elderly group were becoming tired of trekking through the driving rain and, to be honest, so was I. Back on board the ship, Diane was glad that she had opted out of the excursion but, surely, we could look forward to more rewarding outings once the weather had improved. Unfortunately, it did not relent and, if anything, it became even worse, to such an extent that the proposed trip by Zodiac to the Balfour Castle gardens, on the nearby island of Shapinsay, had to be cancelled.

Our next stop was Lerwick, the largest town in the Shetland Isles where we were able to berth alongside the quay. The harbour facilities had been greatly improved following the North Sea oil bonanza and we thought that the affluence would be reflected in the town itself. However, we were rapidly disillusioned because, sadly, this was not the case and, rest assured, to be in a rainswept Shetland town on a Sunday, when all the shops are closed, left a lot to be desired. We wandered around the forlorn streets and finally found a small hotel where we could obtain a drink of coffee before joining an afternoon coach tour to see the 'sights'. The rain had eased off when we made the short drive to the historic fishing port of Scalloway with houses which looked more like those in Bergen than in Scotland. It was a timely reminder that we were now nearer to Norway than we were to England and that our archipelago of some 117 isles was ruled by Norwegian kings until 1469. We were told that many Shetlanders are proud of their Viking ancestry but felt quite isolated from the rest of Britain.

I went for my customary morning visit to the ship's bridge, expecting to have to give a lecture on the ship's tannoy as the vessel left the quay en route to our next stop, the isolated but nonetheless renowned Fair Isle, midway between the Shetlands and the

Orkneys. To my surprise, the Captain explained that the Harbour Master had advised him to stay in port because storm-force winds were expected that morning, reflected in the fact that the entire fishing fleet had returned to Lerwick's sheltered haven, an almost unknown occurence. This created something of a dilemma for it meant that I would be forced to re-arrange my lecture notes in order to accommodate a hastily arranged coach tour of the Mainland. An alternative tour had also been arranged to visit the airport at Sumburgh together with an exploration of the ruins of Jarslhof, which dated to pre-historic times and was one of the earliest-known settlements in all of Scotland. The latter party would be travelling far south along the narrow peninsula that culminates in Sumburgh Head. My own coach party was destined to travel to see something of the convoluted northern coastlines. I thought that Ireland's Connemara had the most complex shoreline in my experience but that was before I came to Shetland with its multitude of islands, skerries and sea-stacks, a veritable treasure house for a coastal geomorphologist like myself.

There is a well-known Scotttish dictum that the Orcadian is a farmer with a boat, while the Shetlander is a fisherman with a croft. Shetland's greater land area has only about a quarter of the arable and grassland acreage of Orkney so we were all conscious of seemingly endless peat bog, moorland and rush-covered fields when we drove northwards up the centre of the main island. This is a waterlogged landscape exacerbated by the impenetrability of the underlying metamorphic schists and gneisses. As we looked morosely at the drabness of the dun-coloured fields and olive-green bogs, slashed with black peat cuttings, I couldn't help thinking of western Ireland. It was difficult to engender very much enthusiasm until we returned to the coastline where I pointed out that nowhere in Shetland is more than four miles from the shore. At last the cameras appeared, in order to photograph a Shetland pony sheltering in the lee of a croft whose garden had daffodils fully in bloom at the beginning of June. But at last the rain eased off and we were able to leave the coach at a place with the unprepossessing name of Mavis Grind. It was here that I was hoping to talk about the efficiency of marine erosion in carving out deep narrow inlets termed 'voes', that had previously been scoured out by glaciers which had made use of the interface between granitic and gneissic rocks. So successful had been the post-glacial wave erosion that we were now standing on a narrow rocky ridge, only a few yards wide, that separated the North Sea from the Atlantic. It was clear that in future centuries the sea would break through to create separate islands. From this windy vantage point, however, it was the view to the west that transfixed our eyes because we saw mountainous waves breaking right to the tops of the ocean cliff-line in marked contrast to the relatively undisturbed seas in the leeward shelter of Sullom Voe that stretched away to the east. It was not difficult to read the minds of my fellow travellers as we stared at this oceanic inferno – how can we possibly sail out into a storm of this intensity? I knew that it wouldn't lighten their mood if I informed them that the highest ever recorded British wind-speed was recorded here in northern Shetland in 1962, at no less than 177mph. Instead, I told them that they were now standing on some of the oldest rocks in the British Isles (4,500 million years), the same age of those in Labrador. The majority took in this information with courteous nods but one grey-haird gentleman ventured to ask "How do you know their age?". I was never really sure that he really cared and was simply showing some polite enthusiasm during my windswept lecture, reminiscent of the one that I had endured on Jutland's dune coast in 1960 (See chapter 2). I was forced to enter into the obscure realms of what a geochemist would call 'Potassium-Argon dating', at which point it was quite obvious that all of us were getting right out of our depth. No invitation was needed to hurry back to the shelter of the coach and move on to something considerably more interesting – the famous oil terminal at Sullom Voe whose shores were lined with tankers. By now it was raining again, the coach windows were beginning to steam up and, apart from a few words concerning the genesis of the North Sea oil-fields, the greatest interest appeared to be in watching a family of otters bounding around in the surf. I was quite relieved when it came time to return to the Caledonian Star. In all my years of lecturing I cannot recall a more depressing episode, although I have to admit that any initial enthusiasm had appeared to dissipate once the party had viewed the intensity of the Atlantic storm. The chatter was all about the weather as we clambered back on board the ship, just in time to change for the evening meal. At least we were able to enjoy this excellent food, cooked by our Filipino chefs, especially since we were safely moored in Lerwick harbour. At the end of the meal the public address system crackled into life and the Captain's voice swept through the restaurant. "I hope that you enjoyed your dinner and can look forward to the evening lecture on Scottish gardens. Because of the loss of a day in our cruise schedule I regret to inform you that we shall be unable to land on Fair Isle but will set sail this evening across to Cape Wrath before heading southwards on our way to Ullapool on the west coast of the Scottish mainland". That turned out to be only part of the bad news, for he continued: "I have to advise all passengers to remain in your cabins overnight, because we shall be encountering strong headwinds and there will be a considerable amount of movement. But do not worry, this ship is built to withstand such storminess and we will be entering calmer seas later tomorrow". Amidst the groans of disappointment, I could sense the feelings of apprehension throughout the passengers, most of whom were elderly.

We set sail as a watery sunset lit up the renowned 2,000-year old round-tower, termed a 'broch', on the tiny island of Mousa, built from the same sandy flagstones that we had seen used extensively on Orkney as building material. At this time of midsummer, the sun never dips far beneath the horizon in these northern latitudes, reminding us that we were a mere 400 miles from the Arctic Circle. I opened the official guidebook to read: "This is a season in Shetland that one is not likely to forget. This twilight…is poetically known as the 'simmer dim' [when] the long horizontal rays of light produce a remarkable effect on the landscape, especially by the side of the lochs. Everything – heather, grass, the few flowers and the water itself – seems to become luminous, to show colour more strongly than at midday". I concluded that the writer had not been here in the weather conditions that we were now experiencing. Before returning to our cabin I climbed up to the bridge where the Captain was navigating around Sumburgh Head before heading out into the open Atlantic. I asked him about the weather forecast and he drew my attention to the TV screen which showed the Radar chart. "See for yourself" he said. "Once round this headland and we will hit a Force 10–11 on the Beaufort Scale which, as you probably know is classified as 'Storm Force'". I was already aware that wind speeds could rise to 70–80 mph that is indicative of a 'Violent storm'. He continued "If I was you, forget an evening lecture and try to get some sleep while you can".

Diane and I had experienced severe storms in the Indian Ocean and an unforgettable hurricane in the Australian Bight, when the large P&O liner had been forced to 'hove to' for 24 hours before proceeding. Not surprisingly, few if anyone had any sleep that night, as cabin furniture hurtled across the floor and we heard the crashing of glassware and crockery from the ship's galley. A grey morning saw us bucking head-on into giant waves that were breaking over the ship and there were few passengers on deck. One doughty fellow said to me "I sat up all night and was delighted to see the flashing light from the Cape Wrath lighthouse", A passing crew-member grinned and responded "No Sir. That was Fair Isle. We haven't rounded Cape Wrath yet. We're running several hours behind schedule". When we finally reached this notorious cape, my mind went back to that idyllic day that we had once spent on the beach of Balnakeil Bay looking across a calm sunlit sea to this famous headland (See chapter 7). But my visit to the ship's bridge now confirmed that there was an unseasonal deep 'Icelandic Low' anchored not far to the north and that its presence would have a malign influence on our weather for the foreseeable future. Late in the afternoon we entered Loch Broom where the anchorage of Ullapool was crowded with fishing boats seeking shelter from the storm that had only marginally subsided. The public address system came into action once more, informing us that we had overcome the worst and were now in calmer seas, sheltered by the Outer Hebrides. However, we had now missed the planned shore excursion to nearby Inverewe gardens and learnt that the sea was too rough to launch the Zodiacs, even in this 'sheltered' sea-loch. The passengers seemed to take this bad news with apparent aplomb, no doubt pleased to be safe and sound at last. In my case it looked as if I would have to conduct an unexpected slide-show on British coastal scenery. There was a very good turn-out in the ship's lounge but I became well aware of the nodding heads after a sleepless night. At least nobody had the discourtesy to snore!

The number of missed venues now totalled three but we ploughed on to the remote island of Rum, a fabled place to the south of Skye around which we had circled during the night. This was unfortunate, from by viewpoint, because I had been looking forward to seeing the Cuillins from the sea. As we anchored in the shelter of Rum's Loch Scresort I looked back across the Sea of the Hebrides hoping to catch a glimpse of those unforgettable mountains but their summits were wreathed in cloud. So too were the equally elegant peaks of Rum whose precipitous slopes had been carved from similar volcanic and granitic rocks. Before we went ashore I was asked to say a few words about the island's features and then the Zodiacs took us across the cove to enable us to visit Kinloch Castle. No expense had been spared when this sandstone mansion had been built in 1891 and it remains redolent of Edwardian opulence. The Bullough family, from Lancashire, having made a fortune from designing milling machinery, had bought the island's entire 26,400 acres and turned it into their holiday home which they then called Rhum. Once they had stocked it with extensive herds of Red Deer the island became an exclusive deer-stalking centre for wealthy sportsmen. There are few private islands of this size in the British Isles and the press were soon to label it "The Forbidden Isle". A tiny population, of a mere forty people, remained, after the crofts had been cleared, but in 1957 the island was bought by the Nature Conservancy who have retained it as a Nature Reserve. They soon removed all the sheep and continued annual culls of the deer because it was found that the vegetation was being over-grazed. All of this historical information was relayed to us by the curator when we entered the imposing Great Hall of the castle and he later chastised me for turning the pages of the iconic leather-bound "Game Book" which included the signatures of certain Royal visitors. But before we dispersed to ramble along the roadless island, I fulfilled my obligation by providing our party with a few comments on the bird-life (hastily gleaned from my private guidebook). Because of the absence of both tourists and predators, it appears that this is one of Britain's great bird-watching sites. Over 150 species have been recorded, including such rare species as golden eagles and sea eagles. Moreover, Rum has at least 54 breeding species, with 130,000 Manx Shearwaters, numerous peregrines, merlins and kestrels. To preserve such a wonderful wildlife the Nature Conservancy allows entry only by appointment for naturalists, geologists, ornithologists and climbers. Having listened to these facts and figures our party dispersed in all directions. Diane and I set off boldly in an attempt to walk to the western cliffs where, we were told, waterfalls fall vertically into the sea. Many years previously I had bought a large watercolour of these cliffs which included a three-masted ship heading into a gale-force wind. How rewarding it would be if we could visit the actual site. However, it was not to be and, although the wind had decreased and the sun had at last managed to break through the scudding clouds, we were forced to turn back about half-way across the utterly deserted island interior where we had been surrounded by towering mountains as spectacular as the Cuillins themselves. As we retraced our steps we were joined by two lively ladies and we began to exchange pleasantries and opinions about the cruise. It transpired that they were both retired officers in the WRNS and were coping with the stormy seas better than most. From then onwards we struck up a companionship because they remained cheerful whatever the weather gods decided to throw at us. As a personal joke we always saluted each other each morning when we met on deck.

The next morning, as we sailed southwards, the seas had abated and the awful pitching movement of the vessel had given way to a steady rolling motion in response to the mighty swell that trundled endlessly in from the open Atlantic. More of the passengers were now venturing out onto the open decks which had been virtually empty for the preceding few days. From there they would now be able to enjoy better prospects of the coastlines that many of them had come to see. The visibility had also improved and the squally showers had moved on to the Scottish mainland. Here was a splendid opportunity to talk about the islands that were now beginning to appear on the port bow. Once more I used the public address system and began to sense a new-found interest amongst the fellow passengers once the visibility had improved and the seas were calmer. The first island of any great interest was that of the curious outline of Eigg whose horizontal basaltic plateau was seen to be topped by a prominent ridge of even harder rock. As we progressed past the white-painted crofter's cottages of Cleasdale, looped around the attractive Bay of Laig, I asked the passengers to note how the prominent central ridge had become even more spectacular when we were able to view it end-on from its southern extremity. From this angle it had visually transformed into a majestic spire-like pinnacle rising 1,290 feet above the ocean. I explained how this rocky protruberance is the remains of a gigantic flow of lava that had coursed down a valley many millions of years ago, burying vegetation on its way. Today, this remarkable feature, known as "An Sgurr" is a Mecca for geologists, partly because the fossilised wood beneath the lava flow not only gives us a date of the volcanic eruption but also provides an idea of the vegetation of that time. I further explained how the lava flow itself was so much more durable than the surrounding rocks that what had once been the infilling of a valley has now been left standing as a ridge as the the surrounding strata have been weathered away. Little did we know at the time that the crofters were shortly to gather together as a community in order to buy the island for themselves. It would be governed by an elected council and would be seen to be in sharp contrast to the former autocratic control of neighbouring Rum. There was not much to be said about the tiny Isle of Muck except that its soils are one of the most fertile of the Hebrides. I explained how this was because the type of winds that we had just experienced had succeeded over the centuries in blowing shelly beach sand across the low-lying island. This was reflected in the richness of its pastures and I suggested that those passengers with strong binoculars might be able to see the dazzling array of purple vetches, blue cornflowers and golden marigolds, because we were sailing quite close inshore. At least I felt rather justified that I had mentioned something about coastal flora, as requested, because to date there had been very few opportunities to examine such detail on both barren, wind-torn and rain-blasted shores. Shortly we rounded the massive headland of Ardnamurchan Point whose lighthouse, on the brink of the mighty volcanic cliffs, represents the westernmost point of the British mainland. It was just as well that we skirted its tidal-race and wave-beaten shore at speed because it would have taken hours to explain the geology and landforms of one of Scotland's most complex landscapes. Furthermore, it was no use telling my colleagues about the wonderful view that could be obtained from its cliff-top because this was not on our cruise itinerary. If it had been, the guide book tells us that the coastal prospect "...is as magnificent as any that you will find on the main body of Scotland". Instead, there was a palpable feeling of excited anticipation amongst the viewers because we were now entering the Sound of Mull before making a landfall at Tobermory.

Here was a town that Diane and I knew very well and we were looking forward to making a return visit. Curiously, as

I write these very words one Sunday newspaper carried a travel article extolling the virtues of a 2018 holiday in Mull. It spoke of "…a preposterously pretty kaleidoscope of colours above a harbour packed with fishing boats" and this is precisely how we found it in our present visit when the seafront houses still flaunted their pastel colours as an eye-catching spectacle. What we did not experience on that Noble Caledonia voyage were the "…galleries galore and cracking local produce in its gastro cafes" because, at the time, Mull had not become "…one of the artiest corners of Scotland", a label that filled me with dismay. Instead 1969 Tobermory still appeared as a traditional Hebridean working port that was only slowly awakening to the demands of mass tourism. But unlike Skye, with its road bridge, Mull seems destined to remain truly insular and, to my knowledge, there has been no recent talk of bridges or tourist taxes. Our party of visitors was keen to get ashore and, like all 'day-trippers', make the most of the few hours of 'quality time' without being harangued by myself. There was not sufficient time to see much of the town's features and we ourselves were content to purchase the odd post-card and look for a quiet coffee shop. We certainly had no desire to re-visit the nearby wooded headland where we had experienced such misgivings, many years previously during my work for the Forestry Commission (See chapter 7).

The rain continued to hold-off and, in due course, the entire complement of passengers piled into coaches in order to view the renowned Duart Castle that stands foursquare on a coastal crag of black basalt, at the south-eastern corner of the island. Guides showed us around this 13th century stronghold and told us of the history of the Clan Maclean. From its topmost tower I was asked to say a few words about the magnificent views in all directions, especially along the narrow Sound of Mull. To Diane and myself that particular view was quite special, for this stretch of water had been where we first became aware of the 'Call of the Isles', forty-four years previously, after sailing from Oban. Our next stop finally fulfilled the frustrated desires of the many garden-lovers, for we had driven to the nearby mansion of Craignure with its impressive loch-side gardens – the first we had seen since Royal Deeside. The chatelaine herself served us tea in her splendid drawing room and told us how the cattle drovers once swam their cattle to the mainland from the shore at this point, although this quiet spot was to be where the new car-ferry was to be sited in future years. After spending the night in Tobermory harbour we set sail for Iona which many regarded as the highlight of the Scottish itinerary. The relatively calm passage along Mull's lengthy southern coast was something for which I had long been prepared – not only was it a cliff-line of great scenic beauty and wonderful bird life but it also displayed an unusual array of geological phenomena. Here for many miles, layers of light-coloured calcareous sandstones can be seen at beach-level underlying the black basaltic cliffs. These fine building stones are especially well exposed in the cove of Carsaig Bay and had been quarried centuries ago to form the doorways, pillars and windows of Iona Abbey. Furthermore, on the shores of Loch Spelve, I was hoping to point out the place where moraines mark the last glacial advance of the British Ice Age some 12,000 years ago. I climbed to the bridge to relay this information throughout the ship only to be met by rather dignified smiles from the helmsman who invited me to look ahead. Wreathes of sea fog were beginning to unfold across the steel-grey waters and the sun was slowly disappearing. Within minutes the nearby coastline had become blotted out and so it remained until we reached Iona. Disappointment for myself but probably a welcome relief for the majority of the passengers! Would our meteorological woes never cease?

It ws really gratifying to be back on Saint Columba's sacred isle, especially as we approached from the south and were able to pick out his original landing-place and the remains of the island's marble quarry. I resisted the urge to relay this information, knowing that everyone had gone below decks to get ready for this momentous landfall. Because of the shallowness of the strait the ship was forced to anchor almost a mile offshore and we were taken to the jetty by the fleet of Zodiacs. As we strolled around the historic village, and the majority flocked to the Cathedral, we were surprised to discover signs that tourism had arrived on a much greater scale since our previous visits some years previously. There were one or two places to eat, even if they were not 'gastro cafes', and we noticed that craft shops had opened on the street. Naturally enough, they quickly became crowded with our large party of visitors and I stopped to think that Iona had inevitably become a 'honeypot'. As if to exemplify this newly-found commercial status we were astonished to find an antiquarian bookshop. Now this type of shop had always proved to have magnetic properties for us both and we spent much of the time ensconced amongst its shelves. I was delighted to discover a first edition of the New Naturalist series, "Sea-Birds" by James Fisher & R. M. Lockley, that was missing from my collection, but we had dallied so long that all but two other visitors had already returned to the ship. A member of the crew hurried us down to the jetty where the last Zodiac awaited us and it was then that we noticed how the weather had changed. On our previous visits, the village on Iona had always appeared to be sheltered from the westerlies, a feature that helped to give it its idyllic charm, but now an approaching storm was sending enormous swell waves driving northwards up the narrow channel. Our helmsman was quite worried that with only four passegers the Zodiac would be unstable so he ordered us to sit in the bows to offset his weight at the rudder. By this time a typical Scottish 'smir' (drizzle) had set in as we crashed head-long into the waves. We crouched in our streaming anoraks, me with my precious book tucked into an inner pocket, one hand clinging to the safety rope and another trying to safeguard Diane from lurching awkwardly on to her strapped-up arm. In all our world voyages this became the worst maritime experience of our lives, as the waves broke over us. At one point we were driven backwards until the American helmsman wisely decided to steer laterally along the troughs and then flip over the wave-crest under the shelter of Iona's cliff. I looked ahead through the murk and saw that the ship's anchor was being hauled-in as the Captain attempted to bring the vessel nearer and to slowly turn it broadside-on to give us a wind-shield. My final view was of passengers' faces crowding the rails and the deck-hands waiting at the port, half-way up the ship's side. Our helmsman skillfully steered us close-in and the three of us guided Diane to the opening, as a ten-foot wave lifted the flimsy craft sufficiently high for the ship's doctor and two stewards to grab her safely aboard. My two helpers and I quickly followed and thanked first the crew, then the helmsman and finally our 'lucky stars' for our safe return. I later went to the bridge to apologise to the Captain and he explained that he had advanced as far as he was able until the ship was touching the sea-floor. I began to feel that we really shouldn't have accepted the invitation to cruise in the first place, because not only could we have exacerbated Diane's injury but possibly lost our lives. The captain re-assured us that "worse things happen at sea" but it certainly taught me a lesson that has stayed indelibly in my memory to the same degree as the traumatic time when I lost my climbing colleague on the high glaciers of an East African mountain. Back in the cabin I had time to ponder the ironies of fate – we had been to Iona three times and on two previous occasions had left with feelings of nostalgic memories; on this occasion, however, we had experienced the darker side of the normally idyllic atmosphere of this legendary island. But, having spent so many years on Fladda, we should not have been surprised at the vagaries of Hebridean weather.

Overnight we moved away from our treasured Scottish shores at a high rate of knots, bound for the equally familiar shores of Ireland. Next morning, I was astonished to find that, owing to such excellent progress, we were gliding past the the tiny sea stack of Ireland's Eye just before turning into Dublin Bay. I learnt that the entire day was to be taken up with garden tours and that I could sit back without being called upon to comment on the scenery. Personally, I would have preferred time-off in Dublin itself because there was still so much for us to see of this historic city despite our previous visits. Instead we spent hours on country roads in the scenic Wicklow Mountains whose gentler profiles were in stark contrast to the majestic Scottish peaks that we had left behind. Moreover, because we experienced not a single glance of the sea, this felt more like a day-trip to the interior rather than a coastal voyage. But, since the weather remained fine, a great number of passengers happily indulged themselves in trailing through beautiful bowers of trees, magnificently-designed gardens and acres of early-summer colour. Who was I to complain? After all, this was the main theme of the entire cruise and it was good to have some time away from my notes and not even be called upon to comment on the flora and fauna. The highlight of the tour was a visit to the mansion of Powerscourt which displays one of the finest formal gardens in Europe and epitomises all that was best of Georgian elegance in Ireland. Regrettably, the great house itself had been gutted by fire but there were more than enough features to enjoy in its wonderful scenic setting. I had hoped to have had time to travel south to the magical valley of Glendalough, a deep glacial trough amidst encircling mountains. This is where I had once attended a geological symposium and where the Irish round tower, silhouetted against the two valley lakes, had left a lasting impression on my mind. But we had dawdled too long at Powerscourt and I was informed by the coach-driver that it would be daunting enough to get back in time at the height of the Dublin rush hour. I found it quite strange to hear talk of road-traffic problems when we in the midst of a coastal cruise but, after days of visiting remote and almost uninhabited island shores, such statements simply demonstated that there are few places along the periphery of the British Isles where one can avoid the human imprint of cities, towns and ports. And it was another Irish port that was to be our next destination. This was the ancient town of Waterford, located far up the winding estuary of the River Suir.

Having sailed through the night we arrived off the long promontory of Hook Head to await the pilot boat. As we paused in the capacious jaws of so-called Waterford Harbour, I reflected on this somewhat curious title because I knew that the city was sited some fifteen miles up-river. After a brief consideration it struck me that such apparent anomolies are not really unusual for I had to acknowledge that Port Glasgow is a similar distance down the Clyde from the city centre itself. However, the time it took to cover this distance, along a narrow estuary, gave everyone a wonderful opportunity to stand on the ship's deck and watch a tidal shoreline glide past almost within touching range. Thick oakwoods, green pastures, grazing livestock and pretty villages soon brought out the cameras, as did the herons in their statuesque postures on the waterside boughs. All this pastoral serenity suddenly ceased as the city loomed into view and we docked at the quayside on which a brass band gave us a rousing reception. I wondered if we represented a rare visitation of a cruise ship or was such a welcome commonplace. We were soon to learn that this is typical of the modern Irish Tourist Board (Borde Failte), one of whose representatives climbed the gangway and introduced himself as the coach-tour manager. On hearing him speak I realised that here was not only a very cultured academic lecturer but also someone with an infectious sense of Irish humour. For an entire day he had our party reeling with laughter at his amusing anecdotes interspersed with the factual information of the true tour-guide. It was to be a long time, until our next coastal cruise, before we would have the pleasure of listening to such a beguiling speaker. Jack Burtchaell was a raconteur in the long tradition of the 'Oidheche Sheanchais' (Irish Story teller) akin to those of Achill Island and the Blaskets, described above, but with the added advantage of speaking in English (See chapter 6). I learnt later that he had a joint degree in History and Geography from Dublin University, confirming my discovery that he had a widespread knowledge of the evolution of the Irish landscape, so here was a man after my own heart.

The cruise programme was intending to look in detail at the landscape of southern Ireland together with an extended visit to Lismore Castle and its renowned gardens on the River Blackwater. The latter mansion was owned by the Duke of Devonshire but was available to rent to particular parties. We spent a very pleasant sunny morning strolling around its grounds and I was impressed by the presence in our group of a blind lady who listened patiently to the guide's descriptions of the specimen trees before asking pertinent questions about their colours, as if she could envisage the actual scene. He gave her a leaf of the so-called "Handkerchief

Tree" to help her with her conception of foliage. Our journey took us through the quite mountainous country of the Comeraghs and the Knockmealdowns where I was invited to explain the creation of the conspicuous glacial corries that dated from the last periods of the Ice Age in Ireland. When we reached the small town of Cappoquin, Jack Burtchaell requested the driver to park at the roadside and invited the passengers to look out at the River Blackwater and the way that it suddenly veered from its east-flowing course and turned southwards through a deep gorge, leaving its former valley manifestly abandoned. I knew that this was a classic example of 'river capture' and I had previously written (in conjunction with Gordon Davies) a scientific paper explaining the geological reasons for this particular diversion that I later incorporated in my Penguin Book on Ireland. Imagine my amazement, therefore, when our guide reeled off a perfect explanation of the complex phenomenon which we were viewing. At the end of the excursion, back in Waterford, I quietly asked him how he had acquired such knowledge and he replied that he was using a textbook on the subject. With a smile on my face I enquired if he wished me to sign the copy which he now held in his hand. We retired to the ship's bar and, over a glass of Guinness, had a good laugh over the whole affair. Just before we sailed away, Jack dashed back on board to hand me a copy of his own book on "The Famine in Waterford" and in turn I requested his signature. As we left the Irish coast, little did I think that our Waterford visit would prove to be my last landfall in Ireland, a country where I had trodden most of its remarkable shorelines and revelled in its unforgettable scenery. I was surprised at the nostalgic memories that remained and how, as I write this book, the images of its landscapes and its people have been so easily recalled.

Our journey now took us out into the open Atlantic and, together with all our colleagues, we fervently hoped that our voyage would prove to be considerably calmer than that in the open ocean off North-west Scotland. In fact, we had all become used to the gentle motion of the ship and the cruise director thought that it was stable enough for me to give an illustrated lecture on Irish Landscapes. I have retained the notes of that evening lecture and have discovered that I showed 57 colour slides to a reasonably receptive audience. I well remember how the setting sun had streamed through the ship's windows, before it dipped beneath the dark silhouette of the receding coastline of County Cork, and how the stewards had been forced to draw the blinds to enhance the viewing. At the time the glare appeared to be slightly irritating but a few days previously we would have given anything for such welcome sunshine.

In the early hours of the morning we awakened to the rattle of chains as we anchored in a coastal environment that I had only read about but never seen. The sunshine that had caused problems for the previous evening's lecture now heralded a serene day of blue skies, calm seas and an almost sub-tropical ambience, exemplified by the palm trees which lined the shores. Around us lay the archipelago of the Isles of Scilly and we were as eager as everyone else to clamber into the Zodiacs to make our way to the quayside of Hugh Town on St Mary's. We commented to each other that the short journey was considerably less nerve-wracking than the last time that we had used this mode of transport at Iona. It was the height of the holiday season when we roamed the flower-decked streets of this granite-built town with its gaily painted houses and tourist shops full of seaside souvenirs. Holidaymakers sunbathed on the beaches or swam in the jade-coloured sea, providing the most glaring of contrasts to our experiences in the Shetlands only a week ago. It seemed as though the anxiety and gloom of the Scottish part of the cruise, with its storminess and missed landfalls, was simply a dream and that we had now sailed into a sort of Avalon at the first of the English venues. It struck me that those unfortunate episodes were a cause for very great regret because, in my mind, the Scottish shorelines offer some of Britain's most majestic landscapes, coasts upon which we ourselves had often spent endless weeks of hedonistic enjoyment. But that was then and this was now and we looked forward to visiting the famous gardens on the neighbouring island of Tresco. A fleet of small ferry-boats transported us across the far-reaching 'lagoon' of The Road and there was a hilarity and anticipatory chatter amongst the party as we stepped on to this heavenly sanctuary of exotic flora. We wandered freely around the Abbey Gardens, marvelling at the profusion of the entirely introduced species of plant-life that had been brought to this once amost barren hump of granite by a former owner of this idyllic isle. We felt a great feeling of euphoria envelop us as we relaxed on a seat, soaking up the hot sunshine in a secluded spot away from the crowd. Here we had time to unwind, to let our minds wander and let happier memories drift in and out of our mind's eye: the serenity of Connemara's coral beach, the serendipity of a calm evening on Fladda, the solitude of Balnakeil Bay near to Cape Wrath. But almost as a repetition of the way in which that latter experience had been shattered by an aircraft's bomb blast, so was our Tresco haven of peace suddenly broken by a sudden and unexpected downpour that had crept up on us without warning. Because of the lack of cover our entire party became thoroughly drenched, except for those who had managed to crowd into the tiny shop. As we sat on the wet seats of the returning ferry, in gently steaming clothes, I could only smile at the image of one of our Sloane Square table-companions who was sitting primly upright beneath a pretty umbrella, entirely untroubled by the elements. The image was so reminiscent of Kathryn Hepburn striking a similar pose on a tiny river-boat in East Africa while a grimy Humphrey Bogart struggled to restart the engine. This had been one of the most memorable scenes in a recently released Hollywood film entitled "The African Queen". Our time in these colourful isles was far too short for us to fully appreciate their truly remarkable atmosphere, because we were informed that on the following morning we would be departing for another isolated outpost of the British Isles, none other than the tiny isle of Sark in the Channel Isles.

Since we were nearing the end of our eventful voyage the cruise-director asked me to say something about the south Cornish coast as we entered the English Channel. I responded by informing him that I had brought along a film, on loan from the National Trust, that illustrated some of their recent Neptune acquisitions. Thus, it was back to the ship's lounge and the stewards lining up the chairs. I timed the delivery to perfection so that as we rounded Lizard Point the image of the Lizard's white-painted lighthouse on the screen was replicated in reality on our port bow. I was extremely gratified by the ripple of applause for this was my 'piece de resistance' for the entire exposition. Henceforth we would be out of sight of land until we reached the Channel Isles and no doubt the passengers would be relieved to be left in peace to enjoy a cruise across a calm sea and on a windless day, probably making use of the deckchairs on the 'sun-deck' for the first time since we left the Firth of Forth. It also gave me time to take stock: this was how an early-summer cruise was meant to be with many hours spent on deck with camera and binoculars scanning the fascinating coastlines, their wildlife, their antiquities and above all their special gardens. In fact, the cruise was proving to be an illustration of the 'sang froid' of my fellow passengers who, in times of disappointment and discomfort, had always managed to "Keep Calm & Carry On", as our wartime poster campaign had exhorted the nation. Perhaps I was more disappointed than most because I was aware of what they had all been missing during the first half of the tour. Moreover, I personally, was sorry to miss out on Shapinsay, Bressay and Fair Isle, to say nothing of the scenic coast of Wester Ross. No matter, the Irish excursions and the Isles of Scilly had been delightful and now we had the rarely visited island of Sark to look forward to.

We were enjoying the antics of several porpoises, surfing alongside the ship, when the public address system broke into our reverie: "This is the Captain speaking. The Guernsey Coastguard has made contact to inform us that thick fog-banks are persisting in the Channel Isles and that we must not attempt to approach Sark. Instead we must anchor offshore from St Peter Port, the capital of Guernsey and wait for the fog to clear". A few hours later, to the doleful moan of foghorns, we were eventually informed: "The Coast Guard believes that there is no sign of a clearance in these windless conditions. Therefore, I regret to say that we shall be unable to land on Sark. Those passengers who wish to go ashore in Guernsey will be ferried in the Zodiacs for a limited visit". What we would have given for such windless conditions in Orkney and Shetland and now, in the southernmost fringes of the British Isles, we were becalmed with yet another missed venue. Furthermore, we couldn't even see the shoreline and we ourselves decided not to venture ashore. I could hardly believe that yet another island coast would remain untrodden and unseen in a circumnavigation that had promised so much when we had sailed away from a sunlit Edinburgh. During the evening meal I sensed that spirits had dipped to a new low, especially since, by the following morning, the cruise would be terminating on the south coast of Devon. Sure enough, by the time we landed at Totnes the Heavens had opened and we were taken to a soggy and mist-shrouded shore. Thus, a cruise that had started with a glorious 'bang' at Bass Rock finished with a 'whimper' in a less than 'Glorious Devon'.

Over the succeeding years both my energy and my mobility have gradually decreased, especially after having had both hips replaced. Apart from taking a Baltic cruise to St Petersburg, our voyaging became restricted to European river tours. It was not that I had lost my 'sea legs' but I had become less stable when the ship began rolling or pitching. But at least we were passengers and were able to sit back and listen to other guides and lecturers. I had completely left behind the days of using the ship as a floating classroom, although memories persisted of our British and Irish circumnavigation. Henceforth, we never missed a landfall on the river banks of Europe's mightiest rivers, but river banks lack the atmosphere of a maritime coastline despite their rapidly changing scenery and the plethora of artifially constructed landscapes. Long gone were the wild landscapes and seascapes of Scotland and Ireland – on the riparian shores there were no towering sea-cliffs, sea-stacks, shingle beaches, hidden sandy coves, seabirds, seals, porpoises, otters and Zodiacs. Instead, we landed on solidly built quays, where we were whisked away on coaches, trams or enticed onto cablecars to the modest hills. In most places the passing river craft were massive, heavily-laden commercial barges – not working trawlers and drifters or even picturesque yachts. Above all, we had lost the smell of the sea, the beat of the waves and the open vistas across the ever-changing oceans with their reflected sunrises and sunsets. Of course, we enjoyed the spectacular architecture, the shops and cafes, the exotic food and the wine-tastings, but I was always conscious that we were almost always in the built-environment. I was always content to widen my experience of foreign venues but the relatively undeveloped shorelines of the British Isles remained my first love, especially the wilder ones of rock, peat and heather. It came as no surprise, therefore, when we responded to a brochure advertising the unique blandishments of Hebridean cruises. Here lay a wonderful opportunity to return to the beguiling shores of Western Scotland in an attempt to recapture the pleasures of yester-year.

Once we had contacted our very good friends, David and Su Starkie, we all decided to reserve our places on one of the company's end-of-season cruises. We realised that we would be taking a chance with the weather in early-November but the itinerary appeared to be following coastlines that were virtually unknown to us. David and Su had previously been co-owners of the Fladda cottages and I knew that they too had succumbed to 'island fever', especially when associated with the Hebridean isles. None of us was enamoured of 'Big-Ship cruising', which we had experienced together, and now we could all look forward to joining a ship with less than fifty passengers and a crew of forty. We were not to be disappointed for the smart little vessel, the 'Hebridean Princess', was the epitome of luxury. The next week was equivalent to a sojourn in one of London's top hotels with their excellent personal service. Little wonder that the Hebridean Princess was once hired by the Royal Family, following the withdrawal of the Royal Yacht 'Britannia'.

By the time we had been driven from central Glsgow to the quayside at Greenock it was too dark to see the port or even the ship but, as we were shown to our cabin on the promenade-deck, we were able to judge that the quality of the décor was of the highest order. We had chosen a forward-looking cabin just below the bridge so that we had a wonderful view across the boat-deck in order to appreciate the unfolding coastal vista, almost as good as that of the helmsman on the bridge just above us. The sensation must be similar to that of sitting in a 'driverless car', but without the windscreen wipers. We were later told that this was the cabin chosen by Prince Edward during the Royal family cruise. Our friends, David and Su, found themselves ensconced in the cabin once occupied by the Duke of Edinburgh, towards the stern of the ship. The evening meal in the candle-lit restaurant was in sharp contrast to that of our Round-Britain cruise when, for our first meal, we had been seated admiring the sunlit cliff-face of the Bass Rock. By the morning, however, when we sailed out into the Firth of Clyde, a panorama of Highlands and Islands filled the horizon, and we were also blessed with a fair wind, sufficient to break up the clouds but insufficient to cause more than a choppy sea. Our spirits rose as we followed the same route that many thousands of Glaswegians had previously taken 'down the water' on Sunday excursions. I have to admit that, once the shipyards and industry have been left behind, the view on the Clyde' estuary is considerably more entrancing than that seen on a trip down the Thames estuary. I feel that I must include a pertinent quotation at this juncture, by an Edwardian author who was making a case for taking a Clyde excursion in the winter: "A Clyde steamer in July is like a section of Sauchiehall Street…but at this time of year it is pure Highland, a thing apart, as dignified as a mountain, and as full of 'real characters' as a clachan…[when] men talk in the accents of Ardrishaig about hogs and herrings". (The Clyde. Neil Munro, 1907). Leaving aside the 'hogs and herrings', I absolutely agree with his sentiments.

Before long the well-known, white-painted lighthouse at Cloch Point had faded from view and our vessel had turned southwards into the widest part of the Firth. Ahead lay the wooded Isle of Bute and that was to be our first landfall at the attractive port of Rothesay, with its seafront of smart hotels. We were told that, before this town became a fashionable resort for Victorian holidaymakers, Rothesay had been famed for its five cotton mills driven by water-power from nearby Loch Fad. Despite all its eye-catching buildings we were astonished when our guide took us first to Rothesay's most visited attraction – no less than the Public Toilet Block renowned for its stunning marble and ceramic tiles. But it was not these features that we had come to see, nor even the prominent pink sandstone ruin of its medieval castle, because only a few miles away down the coast lay the mansion of Mount Stuart, at the centre of the estate of the Marquess of Bute. The entire cruise had an underlying theme of 'castles and mansions' and the red sandstone late-19th century Mount Stuart was one of the finest examples of 'Scottish Baronial' architecture to be found anywhere in Scotland. The usual guided tour of the palatial interior illustrated how the opulence had been based on wealth acquired largely from the coal and iron industries of South Wales but one has to remember that the family dates back to Robert the Bruce and the first Stuart King of Scotland.

From Rothesay we were informed that we would shortly be turning northwards for a lengthy journey to the head of Loch Fyne, which at 40 miles in length is one of Scotland's longest sea-lochs. I was desperately hoping that we would sail through the narrow passage to the north of the island, the so-called Kyles of Bute, famed for their arboreal beauty, but this was not to be, and we circled round the southern headland before setting forth on our overnight voyage. It was at this point that the weather returned to its more characteristic mode as rainstorms swept in from the Atlantic, thereby depriving us not only from seeing much of the wild and mist-shrouded shore but also of sighting the dolphins.

seals and basking sharks which appeared to have emigrated as the winter months closed in. Instead we listened to stories of the famous herring fisheries and the epic 19th century confrontation on Loch Fyne between traditional drift-net fishermen and the newly arrived trawler-net fishermen from the Kintyre Peninsula. This was one of several evening lectures aboard ship, with the most rewarding being presented by our guest lecturer, David Burnett, on Heraldry and Coats of Arms. As the official Ross Herald of Scotland, he held us in thrall at his explanations and anecdotes relating to Royal visits 'North of the Border'. I sincerely hoped that my own cruise lectures from several years previously had approached David Burnett's eloquence, although I doubt it. But there was another David on board, no less than the Pursar who, every evening after dinner, talked about the programme for the following day. In addition, he entertained the passengers with the finest fund of stories and anecdotes that I have ever heard, even surpassing those of our Irish guide at the Waterford venue of our previous cruise. Those passengers who had been on earlier cruises on the Hebridean Princess had already warned us that David's story-telling was one of the highlights of the entire programme and before long his eloquence and wit had everyone in fits of laughter. What I found so impressive was the way that he had learnt everyones' names and how he greeted us each day as if we were all old friends.

By the time we neared the head of the loch the wind had increased to a significant squall and we were informed that the landing stage at Inverary was unfit for purpose. Such an unexpected setback meant that anyone going ashore to visit the well-known castle would have to be ferried ashore by the ship's lifeboats and then taken a few miles on coaches to see this remarkable edifice. When Diane and I saw the visitors dressed in oilskins and lifejackets our minds went back to our frightening experience in the Straits of Iona. We also had to remember that, with my artificial hips and Diane's metal-braced arm, climbing up and down to the boats could prove hazardous. For the first time in our lives we declined to make a landfall, especially when we saw waves breaking over the lifeboats as they battled ashore. Our colleagues, David and Su, were made of sterner stuff and told us on their return about the remarkably grand home of the Duke of Argyll, that we would have thoroughly enjoyed. On the credit side, we were able to share a very quiet ship with the handful of people who had stayed on board and were able to make full use of the library, the coffee and the pastries. It also gave us time to talk to the officers and crew, before we set sail in the late afternoon. On asking a grizzled deck-hand on which of the Hebridean islands he had been born, he surprised us with his response: "Not any of them, my family lives on the Falklands., but I love Scotland". He continued by telling us how the Royal Family had asked similar types of questions and how much they had enjoyed their time aboard.

There are some islands that excite me more than others: Achill is one, Rum and Skye are others and all because their high mountains swoop down to the seashore. The island that we were now about to visit is one that also falls into this category and has the added attraction, at least from my viewpoint, that it exhibits some of Britain's finest geological features. No other British island exhibits such geological complexity for its size. Several years previously I had written: "The variety of its rocks, ranging in age from Precambrian through Palaeozoic and Mesozoic formations to the widespread Tertiary igneous phenomena…make Arran a geologist's paradise, for in a sense it represents a microcosm of Scottish geology". (Geology and Scenery in Britain. John Whittow, 1992). And now I was going to be able to make a leisurely tour of this remarkable island whose towering peaks form one of the most dramatic skylines in the Firth of Clyde. During earlier conversations with David, our Pursar and guide, he had enquired about my publications and, since I had brought along a copy of the book noted above, he was grateful to receive my signed copy for the ship's library. Judging by my shipboard companions, it is doubtful if it will ever be opened! No matter, I sat back in the coach as we commenced a circular tour of the island and I was able to revel in both its landscapes and its seascapes. What made this one of my most memorable experiences was the autumnal colours of the seaboard, highlighted by intermittent shafts of sunlight that transformed the surrounding ocean into myriads of flashing diamonds in its reflections. The braes were a mixture of russet-brown bracken fern, purple heather and yellow gorse, as if Nature had purposely laid on this kaleidoscope just for our benefit. I quickly realised that the 'cold front' of the previous day, that had resulted in the stormy weather in Loch Fyne, had now fled far to the east and had allowed an inrush of colder bracing air to create the wonderful visibility that we were now enjoying.

The narrowness of the roads, with their regular passing-places, meant that our rickety bus was forced to drive slowly along the seashore, and I mean seashore, because in most places the road-verge was the rocky beach itself which gave us many opportunities to enjoy the birdlife and the seals basking on the inshore skerries. This was the sort of wilderness that I have always found most appealing but imagine my surprise when our first stop was at a small hotel at Blackwaterfoot with its adjoining golf course. We had time to stretch our legs and admire the empty shores of the Kintyre Peninsula across the water but, unfortunately, not sufficient time for me to visit the nearby Drumadoon Point, one of Arran's most visited geological features. To me it seemed almost incongruous that on such a wild and apparently untamed coastline, golfers were cavorting on what was almost a microcosm of Staffa's volcanic landforms. To the north lay a terrain of high rugged peaks that also replicated another famous volcanic landform, because the cluster of jagged summits surrounding Goat Fell's elegant pyramid mirrored the majesty of Skye's Cuillins. All this information kept crowding into my head and I had to constantly remind myself that I was not the tour guide. But, in any case, my fellow passengers would almost certainly have had no interest in any of this knowledge. Nevertheless, the scenery of northern Arran was something which I had long wanted to experience at first hand and to my mind it was the highlight of the cruise.

Our next stop was at the picturesque Loch Ranza, near the northern tip of this remarkable island, and which was to be the venue of our mid-morning al-fresco coffee break. We were now to witness an unforgettable culinary experience. The ship's stewards quickly erected a couple of tables, adorned with white table linen, upon which large flasks of coffee, croissants and other delicacies were soon displayed, together with flasks of brandy and whisky. Such elegance on this remote shoreline! Apart from the ancient castle tower, there is little else to show that this had once been an important haven for shipping because of its protection from southwesterly gales. In the early-19th century William Daniell visited Loch Ranza and his painting depicts the roadstead packed with shipping against a dramatic background of rugged mountains. He described how: "In point of gloomy grandeur no British bay surpasses Loch Ranza, in Arran: dark ridges hem it in, and an ancient castle, formerly an occasional residence of the Scottish monarchs, occupies in the midst of it, a central and commanding position, on a green projecting slip of land". (W. Daniell, *op. cit.*). The Royal Navy also made use of these waters during World War II and there, on the shore, is a poignant war memorial to the entire crew of the submarine, HMS/S Vandal, who perished just off the coast of north Arran in 1942. I left my fellow visitors and wandered down to the kelp-strewn tideline, intent on collecting a couple of pebbles of Arran granite to add to my collection of rocks and pebbles. It triggered a momentary vision of the time, some seventy-five years previously, when I first collected pebbles on Llandudno's beach. An approaching shower was a signal for everyone to retire to the coach prior to ascending the mountain pass leading back to Brodick. It was only then that I had a sensation of being awakened from my reverie and thrust forwards into the 21st century, because looming up in the mist was the Arran Distillery. Our guide stated that this was the only 'legal' distillery on Arran (shades of Donegal) and was established in 1995, after a survey had been carried out to find a suitable location. As in the case of vineyards, certain 'terroire' and water factors are essential requirements in order to achieve an acceptable standard. In my book on Scottish geology and scenery I had explained how the stream water in Speyside has to travel over granite and be softened by a cover of peat before it attains the necessary quality. Arran's new distillery appears to have been successful in this respect for in 2007 it was voted 'Scottish distillery of the Year'. Personally, I would have preferred a visit to taste the whisky but instead we were taken, as night fell, to the display of 'Arran Aromatics' in Brodick, a floodlit perfumery that seemed rather out of place in ancient Brodick.

We sailed next morning from Brodick, on a fine morning which allowed us to enjoy a magnificent view of Goat Fell, bathed in sunlight. Before long we were abreast of the remarkably conical Holy Isle, separated from the mainland of Arran by a mile-wide strait.

We were informed that it had a long religious history, dating back to the 6th century, when a saintly hermit lived in a cave in which runic writing has since been discovered. In 1992 the island had been purchased by a sect of Tibetan monks, thereby carrying on the island's eponymous name. We were also told that a unique species of the whitebeam tree flourishes on the steep slopes of this small island but from the ship it was difficult to distinguish this particular tree from the other woodland species. Such detailed information about a feature that we were unable to see, set me thinking of the numerous times that I too had 'purveyed' similar facts and figures to a captive audience. I then began to ponder on the depth of information that a tour guide needed to convey and began to realise that one first had to distinguish between an educational cruise and a leisure cruise. My 'Round Britain & Ireland' cruise clearly fell into the former category whilst the current voyage was basically a 'sight-seeing' experience. My presence on the former required me both to describe and to explain the scenery but I finally concluded that this Scottish cruise had to be regarded as a much more light-hearted affair which required only a modicum of description from the crew themselves. The curators of the castles and mansions that we visited were, of course, proficient enough to answer all the the questions that were posed. It was at this juncture that I realised how an on-board lecturer can purvey too much information and that some passengers could be annoyed by the chatter of the ship's public address system. Yet another salutary lesson.

A breezy crossing from Arran took us into the open ocean before we docked at Campbeltown, the 'capital' of the lengthy Kintyre Peninsula, as isolated by road as almost any reasonably-sized town in western Scotland. Indeed, the locals refer to their town as 'the nearest place to nowhere'. As we walked around this pleasant little port we were quite unaware of its remote situation because its fine houses and its towering obelisk at the head of the main street combined to breathe an air of prosperity more akin to the larger cities of the Scottish Lowlands. It was only when we met two long-distance lorry drivers on the quayside that we became fully aware of Campbeltown's inaccessibility. They told us how they had just delivered parts of a wind turbine that was to be erected at Campbeltown airport, a few miles away on the western shore of the peninsula. As they leaned against their two gigantic vehicles, enjoying a quiet smoke, they explained how they were now faced with 260 miles of narrow twisting roads before they reached Glasgow and then a further 410 miles before returning to their headquarters in Kent. Afterwards, when I looked at a map, it was revealing to discover how far south we were, because the nearby southern headland of the famed Mull of Kintyre was almost at the same latitude as that of Newcastle on Tyne in Northumberland. The problem lay in the massively circuitous detour that a driver would have to make in order to pass around the deeply penetrating Loch Fyne. On reflection, I don't know why I was so surprised at such distances because for years we had driven similar distances around Scottish sea-lochs in order to reach our island of Fladda.

Our colleague, David Starkie, because of his professional interest in air transport and airports, was keen to visit the local airport on the shores of Machrihanish Bay, one of Scotland's finest sandy beaches. I was reminded that it was on this very strand, open to the full force of Atlantic storms, that, in the 1880's the great Scottish 'impressionistic' artist, William McTaggart, set up his easel and left for posterity a series of paintings that epitomise British wave-beaten shores in all their majesty. Few people have succeeded in capturing the vitality of a breaking wave in all its manifestations, phenomena which Vaughan Cornish (*op. cit.*) compared with living beings: "For while they move, they live and have a being, which, like our own, is but momentarily associated with the matter of which they are formed". But enough of this philosophical digression because we were supposed to be on a pleasure cruise not in a lecture theatre. Of considrably more interest to most of our colleagues was the planned tour of a whisky distillery, one of only three survivors from the time when Campbeltown once boasted no less than thirty-four. As on Arran, there were neighbouring peat-bogs to add the essential flavour to the noble liquid but, since there once was a flourishing local coalfield there had been no need to use the peats themselves to fire the stills. In late afternoon we started our tour of the distillery, only to be told that we would have to forego a visit to the 'malting floor' which had been flooded by overnight rain and had not yet dried out. Nonetheless, we all learnt the basic principles of whisky production and some left the shop with precious samples to taste at a later date. On enquiring why there had been such a dramatic decrease in production I learnt that demand had fallen markedly in the United Staes during the Great Depression and the years of Prohibition. It was a reminder for me, at least, of the degree to which the remote coastal dwellers of western Scotland depend for their livelihood on exports of such products as whisky and Harris Tweed.

The last few days of the cruise were spent 'port-hopping' along the Ayshire coast which proved to be a very great contrast to the days that we had spent along the wilder shores further west. The fact that rain showers had reduced visibility and that we spent more time on coach tours than gliding along the coastline, in my opinion, reduced the quality of the scenic experience. This was now a coastline 'redolent' of industry and commerce, in the strictest sense of the word, because chemical works, a major airport and 'smokestack' structures now filled the skyline. Despite its miles of dunes and sandy beaches, behind which international golf courses flourish, the shoreline that stretches from Troon to Ardrossan bears a massive human 'footprint' that reduces its scenic attractiveness. This is because the industry grew up on the fringe of the once flourishing Ayshire coalfield but, judging by my own impressions during our fleeting visit, there has been little if any improvement of the disfigurement. The Firth of Clyde's beauty remains, however, in the wonderful seaward prospect, which may be experienced from any high vantage point on the hinterland. From the hilltop tower of Dundonald Castle, we were able to enjoy one of Scotland's finest seascapes, for spread before us lay a panorama of the islands and distant shores of all the landfalls of our unforgettable few days. I have to admit that our mainland visits to the stately homes of Dumfries House and Ardgowan House were amongst the highlights of the entire cruise schedule, and we will never forget the hilarious coach-stop for afternoon tea at the tiny settlement of Dundonald. I ask the reader to imagine a coach-load of cruise passengers arriving at the local bowling club, an episode that was rather more than the local members had expected when we trooped around their well-kept greens. Although the manager had prepared a delicious spread of cakes and stong tea, poured from a gigantic brown pot, we were startled when a local tenor broke into a rendition of operatic arias, much to the utter bewilderment of the few Sunday afternoon club 'diehards' who had remained drinking at the bar. To the accompaniment of a piano we were then invited to dance on the highly polished floor of the clubroom, a request that was met with amused compliance and enjoyment by some of the younger members of the party. The older members, like ourselves, seemed more content to sit admiringly on the sidelines, perhaps too tired after our strenuous climb up to the nearby castle. Overall, it was a thoroughly engaging and memorable ending to our cruise and an admirable exhibition of Scottish hospitality. As the Scottish song intones "Will ye no come back again?". At the time of our quay-side farewells in Greenock, it seemed very unlikely that we would ever re-visit Scotland and we felt that its magnificent coastlines would have to remain simply as wonderful memories. However, life is full of surprises and an invitation arrived from a former student, now living in Glasgow, inviting us to spend a few days with her and her husband, during the following summer.

This vacation proved to be a real bonus, for it allowed us to see something of the north bank of the Clyde estuary. Deborah Willey had been one of my most promising graduates at Reading University and, after gaining post-graduate qualifications, she had secured a very responsible post in planning in the County of Stirlingshire, Scotland. Together with her husband, Kevin Murray, former President of the Town Planning Institute, she lived in a pleasant western suburb of Glasgow. They were only too pleased to take us to see some of the few stretches of Scottish coast that I had not been able to traverse in my wanderings. The first of our visits was to Dumbarton Rock, an ancient volcanic 'plug' which, like that of the Bass Rock, rises vertically above the waves and is one of the Clyde's great landmarks. Its prehistoric earthworks have been replaced over the centuries by more ambitious stone structures when it gradually became transformed from being the capital of the Kingdom of Strathclyde in the Middle Ages to being an important military garrison and finally a museum. Next it was Helensburgh, a planned 18th century town of grid-iron pattern, rising behind its grassy promenade and line of stately Victorian villas. We had really come to see the Hill House, designed by Charles Rennie Mackintosh and now owned by the National Trust for Scotland, and we found it a delightful place to escape on a wet Sunday morning. Diane and I agreed that it was considerably more rewarding than our previous visit to a Lerwick hotel on an equally wet Sabbath some years previously. Next it was along the coast westwards to the deep waters of the Gare Loch whose once pristine shores have now become one of the largest military bases in Britain. It is here at Faslane that Britain's nuclear submarine fleet is based and, as one would suspect, the entire shoreline is totally out-of-bounds to the likes of us. The only view that we could get of this establishment was from the neighbouring mist-shrouded mountain. Unlike many military developments on the British coasts, this is one that is very unlikely to be de-commissioned for the foreseeable future. There was just time for us to look in at the western end of the Forth-Clyde canal where it debouches into the Clyde estuary near Old Kilpatrick. Here, squeezed between a railway, a main road and the shore, was a new development which Kevin was proud to show us as one of his commissions. He explained how a once derelict site was being converted to a smart array of shops and other amenities around a long-established dock, soon to become a fashionable marina. Wearing my 'Neptune' hat, although this was not applicable to Scottish coastal development, my surveyors would have mapped this as industrial wasteland. Enlightened thinking, however, will upgrade this coastal stretch that will not only provide a welcome social amenity but will also enhance the scenic view from the estuary. Our final tour was to the celebrated region termed "The Trossachs", the lakes of which I had long wanted to explore. A memorable trip aboard the famous old steamship "Sir Walter Scott" on Loch Katrine was yet another type of 'voyage' and, together with a trip along the shores of Loch Lomond, served to fulfill a longstanding personal desire to explore some of Scotland's most acclaimed watery shores. I had been to Loch Lomond several decades ago when I was acting as external examiner to a Higher Degree student at Glasgow University. It transpired that her research had been in the field of the recreational potential of Loch Lomond's shores and was similar to the work for the Forestry Commission in which I myself had been previously engaged (See chapter 7). Returning to view this celebrated water body once more, demonstrated that her recommendations must have borne fruit because I discovered that its shores were crowded with tourists at specially created 'honeypots'.

11. SON OF NEPTUNE

"There is a tide in the affairs of men,
Which, taken at the flood, leads on to fortune"
(Julius Caesar. William Shakespeare)

The coal-strewn beach at Easington Colliery, Durham before National Trust ownership – *See plate section for colour version*

The same beach after National Trust reclamation – *See plate section for colour version*

Golden Cap, Dorset, where the 50th Anniversary of Enterprise Neptune was celebrated

The Thames Barrier built to protect London from flooding (Under construction)

An example of 'Managed Realignment' devised by the National Trust as an enlightened scheme to 'work with nature' instead of attempting to control rising sea-levels

The approach of the fiftieth anniversary of the founding of Enterprise Neptune, now known as the Neptune Coastal Campaign, was heralded by a report entitled 'The Year of the Coast 2015'. It was written by Catherine Weaver, an officer of the National Trust, partly to consider the future strategy for coastal acquisition and partly to emphasise the ongoing 'mind-shift' of the Trust itself. The latter is demonstrated by the opening paragraph of the report: "When people think of what the National Trust means to them, many people immediately picture country houses and manicured parkland, but these days the Trust is becoming increasingly well known for its stewardship of hundreds of miles of coastline around England, Wales and Northern Ireland". In a national questionnaire in 2010, two-thirds of the respondents stated that visiting the coast is vital to their quality of life (Coastal Values Survey 2010). Based on this premise the Trust decided to embark on a new phase in its history whereby its intention will be to give a greater focus on the 'Outdoors' in which the strategy will "...aim to shift perceptions, build awareness and support for what we do as a conservation charity and communicate the visitor experience by 'Bringing Our Places to Life'". The report continued by stating: "The campaign which gave our coastal work its voice fired the imagination of the British public, and continues to benefit from unrivalled fundraising support and success. The time has come for the National Trust to put our coastal work at the forefront once again, and 2015 seems the fitting time to celebrate our achievements and set new goals". Moreover, the aim will be to give "...the general public sustainable access to the coast for the future, and an opportunity to explore maritime culture and the inshore marine environment". Such aims seemed to encapsulate all the lifetime endeavours that I have spent pleading for a recognition that the 'edge of the land' must be acknowledged in its totality, not only as an onshore and offshore ecosystem worthy of conservation, but also as an essential requirement in terms of a sociological necessity; in the words of Adam Nicolson, in his article for The Guardian newspaper a decade earlier, the coastal experience is a "good worth having".

In order to discover the extent to which coastal changes had taken place over the fifty-year span since the 1965 survey, which initiated Enterprise Neptune, it became imperative that a second survey should be planned. I have already described how my conversation (in the precincts of Westminster Abbey) with Peter Nixon, Director of Land, Landscape and Nature at the National Trust, had led to a decision by the National Trust Council to underwrite a further commission. The objectives of the second survey would be:

1. Identify the extent and nature of new coastal development.
2. Identify localities where the original development has been rolled back (e.g. through industrial decline) and replaced by other land uses. The latter context naturally raises the question of what sort of replacement use has emerged.
3. Identify potential ares of future acquisition by the Trust.

It became perfectly clear at the outset that any attempt to survey the coast on foot would be undesirable and highly unlikely for a number of reasons: First, I would find it quite impossible to assemble a similar team of volunteers; secondly, the attempt to remain totally objective in the 1965 survey had been shown to be not completely successful. Moreover, there had been a small number of errors and omissions; thirdly, by 2013, several technologies were available that could provide a completely objective collection of the data required.

The National Trust decided to proceed by establishing a small working party which comprised:

Two National Trust officers, Phil Dyke (Chairman), Huw Davies (Head of Conservation Information); a consultant, Adrian Woodhall; and two advisors, David Pinder and myself. After a number of meetings in Swindon and in London it was decided to invite applications from academic institutions and ask them to describe the type of methodology to be used in their proposals. A short list of applicants was drawn up and Professor Alexis Comber from Leicester University was appointed after he had made an impressive submission based on the technique known as 'Google Earth', in which the results would be compatible with the 1:25,000 scale of the 1965 maps in order to make viable comparisons between the two surveys.

After about a year the new team of four researchers at Leicester University's Department of Geography had produced the first handful of maps from which a selection was made that covered the coast of Wales. The working group decided that Adrian Woodhall and myself should meet a few of the Welsh coastal rangers from the Trust at a venue where Alexis Comber and his assistant, Sarah Johnson, would present some of their results. On a fine autumn day Diane and I drove across the Cambrian Mountains towards the calm sunlit waters of Cardigan Bay. The gradual unfolding of the panoramic view of a shoreline that I knew so well retrieved many of the varied memories that I had accrued over a lifetime. But a rhetorical question remained: Would this be my last visit ever to the "Land of my Fathers?". We chose to stay at the attractive historic town of Aberaeron, where we renewed our acquaintace with Adrian Woodhall. He had worked assiduously for many years in support of Enterprise Neptune and, some years previously, had made a lengthy recording of my views on coastal affairs for the National Trust archives. On the following day the small party assembled at one of the Trust's mid-Wales' properties, the handsome villa of Llanerchaeron, designed by John Nash in 1796. There, amidst the birdsong of the dense Arcadian woodland, we also spent most of our time listening to Alexis's exposition and holding conversations with the Trust's officers, all in an attempt to test the veracity of the 'Google' results for the Welsh coastline. Because of my intimate knowledge of North Wales, I was asked to talk to the rangers from this region and question them about any changes that they had monitored over the years. To our delight they confirmed that the new maps were a true representation of the current state of the coast and that all the changes had been accurately represented. This was found to be a very reassuring signal that the remainder of the new maps would be equally accurate and that valid comparisons would be able to be drawn in the near future and that a final report would contain valuable information at a national level.

The report, written by Huw Davies, appeared in time for the Golden Anniversary of Enterprise Neptune in 2015 and was met with universal acclaim. I felt privileged to be invited to write the Foreword to "Mapping our Shores: 50 years of land-use change at the coast" and was pleased to discover that one of the 1965 Welsh maps, surveyed by Diane and myself, had been chosen to demonstrate the changes that had occurred in the vicinity of Llandudno over the intervening half century. The report showed how, of the 900 miles that I had recommended for acquisition, 775 had now been taken under National Trust authority, assisted by many valuable gifts and a fundraising that had already reached a total of £65 million. Huw Davies wrote of "…some large changes that have occurred in the balance of land use at the coast [and how] the results broadly show the success of the planning system in protecting it from the kind of threats that were prevalent in 1965. It's good to think that the Neptune campaign helped to raise public awareness of the coast's importance and the related shaping of planning policies over the years". He concluded his Introduction by emphasising that "…built development is shown to be almost entirely irreversible, and once open countryside is gone – it's gone". But the report also looks ahead and lists the principles that are desirable if we are to continue our national vigilance and to maintain our coastline as a worthwhile public inheritance:

1. The coastline to be clean and healthy, predominantly shaped by natural forces.
2. The sheer beauty and diversity of our coastline to continue to inspire and refresh generations of people.
3. Wildlife to be rich and abundant, not squeezed into a narrow margin.
4. People to enjoy walking on every stretch of coastline, not just land managed by the National Trust.
5. A coast rich in reminders of our heritage.
6. Coastal resources put to good use, contributing to the economy, in a way that is respectful and sustainable.

No matter how admirable these principles, they have to be viewed against the report's key findings which demonstrate that 'open countryside' has decreased by 4.2% since 1965 – equivalent to a loss of 14,800 hectares, which is greater than the size of Bristol. Even more worrying is that shoreline urban/built-up areas have increased by 42%, an area that would cover the size of a city such as Manchester. Thus, the nation has been made aware that without rigorous protection our 'open' shores will continue to dwindle inexorably. But there is some good news! Almost the entire coastline that my volunteers mapped as 'pristine' in 1965 (3,342 miles) is now reaping the benefit of some degree of protection from further development. If one examines the Northern Ireland statistics apart from the overall findings, however, the situation is somewhat more unsettling because its coastal 'open countryside' has decreased by 7.9%, at a rate almost twice that of England and Wales, although the actual loss in area is only one-seventh of that in England and Wales. Nevertheless, it has to be said that in the last fifty years the built-up areas on the coast of Ulster have more than doubled (an increase of 116%). Turning to other changes in land use there are some significant gains and losses: There have been welcome increases in the amount of coastal woodland and in land vacated by the Ministry of Defence; the area described as 'shack settlement' has been reduced considerably. On the other hand, coastland devoted to industrial and transport is shown to have increased markedly. One has to accept that in the United Kingdom the fifty years in question have seen a massive growth in population that has sparked both a housing 'boom' and a growth of industrial infrastructure some of which has, of necessity, had to be located along our island coastlines. The report emphasises, however, that industrial changes have to be seen in the context of what is termed 'churn' in which some regions have been characterised by a decline (e.g. coal mining, quarrying, iron and steel), whilst others have witnessed substantial increases in port activities (e.g. Holyhead and Felixstowe). It must be remembered that in 1965 the United Kingdom had not yet entered the European Union nor fully joined in a North Sea oil bonanza so that its East coast ports were still renowned largely for their fishing industry. In this respect the report in question measures an enormous cultural and economic change that has seen some of our coastlines transformed. All the more reason that we continue to protect the best of what is left and, in this respect, it is heartening to record that the National Trust surveys have served to demonstrate that more than two-thirds of our precious coast (69%) remain undeveloped. As Peter Nixon, Director of the National Trust's Land, landscape & Nature, so aptly states in the report's conclusions: "Some of the threats of 1965 have receded. That's not to say that some threats have gone away, but society's ability to manage them has improved".

The report was given a fair degree of media coverage and I felt a modicum of elation to have lived sufficiently long to have been able to help with the second Neptune survey. Even more gratifying was to find my name as one of the co-authors of a detailed scientific paper that described the technology of the 'Google Earth' survey, published in the Transactions of the Institute of British Geographers under the title "Mapping coastal land use changes 1965–2014: methods for handling historical thematic data". It's concluding paragraph gave me food for thought when it was concluded that the methods of the second survey "…suggest the need to accept the original boundaries between thematic classes where possible, to consider the concepts underneath the class labels driven by measurements and changes in survey objectives, and to flag any inconsistences or errors in the original data when they are suspected. In short, they suggest adopting the mind-set of the original mapper". I felt honoured that my original concepts and classifications of mapping coastal change had been accepted in this way but was somewhat amused to find that the original Neptune maps were now being regarded as an historical archive – such an assessment really did make me feel my advanced age!

The National Trust marked the 50th anniversary not only by publicising the report's findings in their own literature but also by arranging a series of publicity events at a number of different venues. The first was held, quite appropriately, on the stretch of coast that represented the first to be purchased with Neptune funds. This was at the western tip of the Gower peninsula of South Wales on the beautiful dune-fringed shore of the Whiteford Burrows, referred to in a previous chapter. Its acquisition by the National Trust in March 1965, has subsequently led to its recognition as a National Nature Reserve (NNR) and a Site of Special Scientific Importance (SSSI). We drove down narrow switchback lanes to this remote spot to find it crowded with Trust operatives and their guests, before being led on a tramp across the dunes and the long sandy beach. I have to confess that after an hour I had to turn back as my energy had drained away and I was very grateful to Phil Dyke who kindly guided me back to the base via a short cut. Here, amidst the cool of the pine trees, I had time to think back to the time when I had been able to walk for miles along coasts like this without flagging, and how the new survey had been carried out without having to set foot on the coast. I pondered on the remarkable advances that new technology had brought, when one-eighth of the manpower had been able to obtain comparable results to those gathered in 1965. But what my team of volunteers had achieved in a few summer months in all weathers had now taken two years to complete from the safety of an office, and at a cost some ninety times more than that of the 1965 survey. However, there was no doubt in my mind that it had been a worthwhile task and one that had succeeded in providing so much valuable information to the public at large. It was good to be able to relax at this Welsh coastal site and even more wonderful to meet up again with some of the National Trust officers of earlier years, to reminisce about 'the old days', to listen to the speeches and to enjoy a 'power-point' slide show, created by David Pinder, which traced the history of Enterprise Neptune.

Not many weeks later a second invitation arrived, requesting our presence at another coastal function, this time on the famous Jurassic Coast of Dorset. Memories crowded back – this is where Neptune first started, the wheel had come full circle. It was exactly fifty years ago that I had brought my team of staff and students to Dorset in order to conduct the pilot study for the 1965 survey. How things had changed. Tourists now thronged this magical coastline; Chesil Beach and Lulworth Cove have now become major 'honeypots'; new hotels had opened; coastal lanes were seen to be heaving with cars hauling unwieldy caravans, whilst holiday parks had been opening-up at new venues. Our 1965 survey had served to forecast such changes and gradually, over the succeeding years, the National Trust had responded by acquiring more than thirty parcels of land in the vicinity of the outstanding headland of Golden Cap. And this is precisely where we were heading for an important Golden Anniversary event beneath a panoply of marqees on the cliff-top. We drove carefully up the narrow lane, full of anticipation of seeing the panorama of Lyme Bay unfold before our eyes, but we were to be disappointed because a Channel fog had descended along the coastline and we were glad to seek shelter and a cup of coffee undercover from the swirling mist. However, the sun broke through and, after introductory speeches, in which we learnt that the Trust had acquired no less than eight miles in the local area of this precious coast and had opened-up 25 miles of footpaths to the public, we were invited to join one of a number of parties to learn more of the attractions of the Jurassic Coast. Not surprisingly, we decided against the steep climb up to the 617-foot summit of the highest cliff on England's south coast, where the glowing yellow sandstone top had given its name to this well-known landmark. Instead we chose a gentler walk along the heath-covered cliffs that enabled me to see, for the first time, the major landslips near to Charmouth.

Eventually, everyone re-assembled for refreshments and to hear the Chairman's eulogies, after which I was delighted to be presented with an autographed copy of a book by Patrick Barkham, a feature writer for The Guardian, who had been chosen by the National Trust to write "Coastlines", the definitive account of the Neptune story. We had previously entertained Patrick at our home, to which he had travelled to gather material for the publication, and we were later pleased to be invited to his book launch in London. It was just before the memorable Golden Cap function had been brought to its conclusion, that I was introduced to Mark Harold, the National Trust Director for the South West region and I took the opportunity to discuss with him a possible future Neptune acquisition on the Dorset coast. The matter had been drawn to my attention several years previously by the former Director General, Dame Fiona Reynlds, who sought my opinion on the stretch of coast that formed the western tip of Portland Bill. This had been heavily disfigured by stone quarrying over the centuries but it was also the site of an important 'raised beach' of Pleistocene age. She told me that the Trust had been approached as a possible purchaser of this important piece of coastline which contained the quarry from which the stone had been taken to build St Paul's Cathedral. Indeed, there still remained a few blocks of this iconic white stone that bore the initals of Christopher Wren. After a site visit and weeks of negotiations the National Trust decided that the acquisition would not be worth the asking price and so an opportunity to add an extra portion of the Jurassic Coast was lost. On learning of the size of the asking-price I was more than happy to agree, although the decision on its purchase was none of my business and lay, quite obviously, entirely within the hands of the Trust's finance committee. As we drove slowly back home to Midland England I had hours to reflect on the extraordinary events of the previous fifty years and how, what had been originally conceived as a limited venture by the National Trust's Council, had blossomed into their most successful fundraising scheme of all time. The entire exercise had also led to an acknowledgement that the British public love their coastline, a fact which had always seemed fairly obvious but, for the first time, people had demonstrated this ardour by contributing huge sums of money to aid in its protection. I felt privileged to have played a role in the launch of this major enterprise and very happy to have witnessed the spirit, energy and foresight of the National Trust officers as they had 'kept the ball rolling' over the 50-year span.

Neptune celebrations continued throughout the summer and a further invitation arrived enquiring if I would like to journey down to Kent to attend a function to celebrate the acquisition of another substantial stretch of the White Cliffs of Dover. Over the years the National Trust had purchased five miles of these famous cliffs, in addition to the South Foreland Lighthouse, but the two were separated by a privately-owned section. A Neptune fund-raisng campaign achieved the £1.2 million asking-price and the cliff-tops are now under permanent protection for the public to enjoy. I reluctantly had to decline the invitation but was pleased to contribute to the required funds. The final invitation was one that I could not ignore for it represented the grand Neptune finale at Somerset House on the banks of the Thames in London. All the campaign participants were there and were joined by celebrities from the media to listen to the final accolades and admire a 'Neptune Bell' cast on the beach in Cornwall. I managed to obtain tickets for my cousin, Hugh Whittow, Editor of The Express, and his family, for this was billed as the last event of the Golden Anniversary. And soon it was all over – mission accomplished – no more mapping and no more landscape appraisals, but simply a matter of reflection on the magnitude of the achievement of a lifetime's obsession. We made our final handshakes and bade our goodbyes to some of the colleagues with whom I had worked for decades, at which point the thought suddenly struck me that my official links with the National Trust were over and that I would now return to ordinary membership. As I stood with Diane in the twilight, looking across the Thames to the Houses of Parliament, we both reflected on the efforts and exploits during our countless coastal jaunts in sunshine and in rain. Was it all worth it? Yes, of course it was. I only have to remember the figures: £65 million had been raised and 775 miles of beautiful shoreline saved for the nation to enjoy. What more could one ask? Furthermore, the exercise had also allowed me to relish the joys of visiting new coastlines and meeting like-minded people, some of whom had gifted part of their estates to the National Trust to be held in perpetuity. In this respect, it was gratifying to talk to landowners who believed in the concept of coastal acquisitions and in giving access to the nation's walkers. If nothing more, these landowners were able to be reassured that their adjoining shores would be left in a pristine state and continue to be conserved by future practices of good management. Finally, in the last chapter, I must turn to look briefly at what the future holds for our coastline, because the one certainty in life is that things are unlikely to stay in a static timewarp, especially in the dynamic environment at the 'edge of the land'.

EPILOGUE

"In my beginning is my end"
(East Coker. T. S. Eliot. 1888–1965)

This is a volume of memories, but memories are not the same as an autobiography because this book is a story of selective memory. At the outset I claimed that 'memories are a window to one's soul'. In exploring my own soul, I have found that I had been on a voyage of discovery – not only along our shores but also into the depths of my own persona.

After a lifetime of introspective thinking, I have finally concluded that some of my innate characteristics have been mirrored in my obsessive interest in all things coastal. I believe that I am impatient; inquisitive; impulsive; impressionable; investigative; indomitable; imaginative; indebted; occasionally indulgent; I'd like to think inspirational and influential, but that is for others to judge. (It seems that the I's have it, to misquote parliamentry procedure).

On looking back, I think that I have visited every coastline of the British Isles, although I failed to set foot on the Channel Isles or even St Kilda! Each of these different venues has been a test of my eleven perceived attributes. Impatient? Countless are the times that I bemoaned how distant was the departure date for my childhood seaside holidays. Inquisitive? Memories remain of collecting and pondering the origins of the pebbles on Llandudno's beach because this is where my obsession began. Impulsive? How else could I explain the foolish sea-cliff climbing (sometimes alone) on Donegal's daunting shores? Impressionable? Some of my most treasured memories arose from listening to the Gaelic speakers on Achill Island and on Raasay, although the stories of Welsh coastal wildlife, told by my early mentor, Alf Sharrocks, on a mountain above Conwy, must rank highly in my impressions. Investigative? I was not satisfied until I had roamed the beautiful shores of Pembrokeshire in order to write the family history in the "Land of my Fathers"; Indomitable? Seemingly unending mapping of the coasts of North Wales on three occasions tested my endurance and became somewhat tedious, especially in driving rain; but the sea-floor mapping from a pitching vessel in a stormy Clew Bay in Western Ireland required both ardour and good sea-legs. Imaginative? Some of my most golden memories relate to 'dream island days' on our beloved Hebridean island when I could visualise the former life-style of the former islanders. Moreover, the mysterious ambience of Penwith in Cornwall is where I discovered that 'ghosts' could linger in the mind on a coastal tract that hasn't changed its identity for thousands of years. Indebted? To so many people that have assisted me in my coastal wanderings and especially to my former friends at the National Trust for their goodwill and their decision to name the Blakeney boat in my honour. Indulgent? Perhaps the cruise on the Hebridean Princess was a luxury, but what a wonderful way to revive my happy memories of Scotland's unforgettable shores, in the twilight of my life. Inspirational? Nothing has pleased me more than teaching generations of students to understand the ways in which our coasts have been fashioned and the extent to which they are currently valued by society. Perhaps a few of my 'bon mots' have caused them to perceive our shorelines in a different light. Influential? Having spent half a lifetime in advising the National Trust on coastal affairs I feel honoured and proud to have made a small contribution to a campaign that will conserve for the nation one of its most important glories.

Despite the long-running Neptune Campaign and the ongoing endeavours of numerous conservation bodies the new millennium has been a time when the British coast has remained the scene of numerous pressures. The threats are twofold; one from the ever-growing impact of humankind, the other from the vagaries associated with climate change. On considering the former pressure the most significant change occurred once the Government responded to the century old public demand for access to the countryside (the so-called right-to-roam) by introducing the Maritime and Coastal Access Act in 2009. Its aim was to "...improve coastal access to, and enjoyment of, the English coastline by creating clear and consistent public rights along the English coast for open-air recreation on foot". Its manifestation was to be in the form of a 2,800-mile Coastal Path. It has to be said that Northern Ireland and Scotland (with its 7,375-mile coastline) had their own schemes and Wales had completed its own Coast path, of 870 miles, by 2012. At the outset it had been calculated that 70% of England's coast was already accessible to the public (including National Trust land) but the Ramblers Association pointed out that as long as those parts of the coast owned by private landowners broke up the shoreline into disparate parcels there could be no continuous footpath. They claimed that access to the coast was our birthright, although they conceded that local needs must be taken into consideration. Such demands had already been anticipated by the Government when they had introduced the Countryside & Rights of Way Act in 2000 (the CROW Act) at a time when the National Trust asked for my advice on the ways that this would influence their own coastal acquisitions. The Act identified a 'Coastal Margin' in which public access would be allowed with two exceptions: First, where land was under crops or was occupied by buildings, their gardens and 'courtyards'. Secondly, stretches of coastline that were unsuitable for a footpath such as salt-marshes and mudflats. The latter distinction was largely due to pressure from the naturalists lobby to protect the unique flora and fauna of those habitats, but it also reflected the hazards that would face walkers when trapped by the tide in a relatively remote environment that would be inaccessible to inshore lifeboats.

The question was posed: who actually owns the coast? In terms of the foreshore (the zone between mean high- and low-water) the Crown Estates own 55% but the remaining 45% belongs to a variety of owners, including the National Trust, the Duchies of Cornwall and Lancaster, the Church, the Ministry of Defence, together with countless numbers of private landowners and farmers. The 2009 Act, followed in 2013 by the Coastal Access Scheme, recognised that a balance must be reached between the public rights and the interests of owners and occupiers and that a number of constraints would have to be incorporated in the legislation. This was to be a footpath, therefore no vehicles (including bicyles) would be allowed; there would be no camping or lighting of fires, dogs must be kept under control and litter should be taken home. I had raised pertinent questions with The National Trust concerning the maintenance of the path itself which would, of course, suffer from excessive trampling and, in places, loss from coast erosion. It seems that, as in other Trust properties in mountainous areas, the footpath maintenance is regarded as the responsibility of the owner. Moreover, I have searched the literature and have yet to discover a definitive statement on compensation, although a Parliamentary Inquiry, at the outset, had suggested that landowners should be compensated if the introduction of the Coastal Path left them out of pocket. The scheme immediately led to an outcry when it became clear that the onus lay with the landowners to prove that they had lost out financially. This was particularly true of the farming community who were concerned about making miles of field boundaries proof against dogs worrying their livestock. The National Union of Farmers (NFU) quickly highlighted the lack of an appeals procedure although the Government's refusal to include clauses referring to an appeals procedure was welcomed by the Ramblers Association whilst the NFU had to agree that the CROW Act already provided land managers with rights of appeal and the ability to implement footpath diversions and restrictions. Nonetheless, individual complaints continued to surface in the Press throughout the succeeding decade, including one against a cabinet minister who was accused of blocking access to the coastal path, which he had previously endorsed, where it impinged on his own riparian estate. Then the country was hit by a monumental economic recession followed by an endless trail of governmental 'cuts' that we are still enduring as I write. Some funding was scaled down or withdrawn from the coastal path programme, encouraging the Country Land & Business Association, which represents half of England's landowners, to claim that such a misguided scheme should be scrapped. But the English coast path is on course to be completed by 2020, or so the Government leads us to believe, but who knows what will happen in the post-Brexit era?

The plans to exclude salt-marshes and mudflats from the course of the coastal path have recently caused a furore in Norfolk, after Natural England, the Government quango, deemed that many of the salt-marshes between Holkham and Blakeney would become out-of-bounds to the "surge of ramblers" in order to protect birds and other wildlife. A local resident complained that "Our marshes have been used by local people for generations, for gathering mussels, crabbing and collecting samphire. They are part of the local economy and culture". This is a stretch of the coast that I know well and I have been aware of the controversies for some time, especially since many of them pertain to National Trust land. It is not only Norfolk that is witnessing such conflicts, for one hears stories from the estuarine coastlands between Lymington and Beaulieu and from many other muddy estuaries which are renowned as refuges for some of our most endangered wildlife. Many years previously the Nature Conservancy Council had listed twenty-four estuary sites where the wildlife was at severe risk of degradation or even destruction. These included: three sites in Northern Ireland; five in North-West England; five in Wales and South-West England; four on the South Coast and seven on the East Coast. By pointing to the ways in which the container terminal at Felixstowe had wiped out an important wetland site, conservation bodies have highlighted some of the ways in which an expanding economy might impact on our coastlines in the future. These will include the growth of industry (a possible resumption of potash-mining on the North York Moors, for example), port extensions, barrages on our coastal bays and estuaries, to say nothing of extra provisions for sewage and other waste disposal.

It is difficult to believe that some fifty years ago the same conservation bodies were fulminating about the siting of caravans and camping sites on our coastline. But because most of the issues of inappropriate siting and sprawl have now been tackled by the local planning authorities and by the strict standards of the Camping and Caravan Clubs, these are no longer regarded as major problems. Furthermore, it has to be remembered that the Second Neptune Survey (2014) showed that 'shack settlement' had declined by more than 81% in that fifty-year span. However, other environmental issues have become increasingly important in recent years and have been trumpeted by the media who write and talk unendingly about "geese and golden eggs", so to speak. It would be rewarding to think that the National Trust's efforts in publicising the apparently unceasing threats to our shoreline have had a lasting effect on public opinion.

Leaving aside, for the moment, the changes wrought by trampling and vehicles, the most serious human-induced impacts on the coastline can currently be seen as: litter, sewage, plastic and pesticides. Additionally, it remains difficult to forecast the ways in which the future development of alternative energy supplies, such as wind, wave and nuclear power installations, will impose on our shores, as our dependence on fossil fuels gradually diminishes.

Litter has long been a scourge, not only on our beaches but also in our streets and country lanes, because we have become a 'throw-away' society. It is a culture that is constantly being derided by the media, and the 'Keep Britain Tidy Campaign', but seemingly with very little effect on public attitudes. We are reliably informed that litter, dog excrement and fears of contamination from sewage outfalls are beginning to have an effect on tourism in some parts of our coastline. It is now fifty years since Kenneth Lindley (*op. cit.*) wrote "We cover our beaches with disgusting litter from the land and oil and tar from the sea, and still we sit on them". In more recent years surveys have shown that, at the time of the second Neptune Survey, water companies had spent more than £2 billion in improving bathing water quality over a ten-year period. This had been a response to the admission that some of the companies had been continuing to discharge untreated sewage off the coastline. At a conference in 2015, Robert Keirle, pollution programme manager for the Marine Conservation Society, warned that unless our bathing water quality was improved, tourists would begin to avoid the worst contaminated of our beaches. Significantly, the conference was held in Blackpool which was singled out as one of the worst offenders, but it came as something of a shock to find that the list also contained such well-known resorts as Bude and Penzance (Cornwall), Budleigh Salterton and Exmouth (Devon), and Criccieth and Llandudno (North Wales). The Government's Environment Agency was driven to introduce much stricter standards of inshore water quality in 2015, but forecasters stated that some 40 beaches (one in ten) in England and Wales would probably fail to reach those standards unless drastic action was undertaken. Some resorts have been self-conglaturatory by pointing to their inclusion in the list of 'Blue Flag' beaches but research has shown that even some of these highly listed beaches have, on occasion, failed to meet the standards during very wet summers. Most people will be unaware that sewage outflows – which operate at times of heavy rain – are supposed to function on average only three times during any one bathing season but some resorts have reported more than 100 sewage spills during very wet summers. Three major culprits have been noted: Coastal authorities who have failed to replace out-dated Victorian sewage systems; farmers who have increased intensive farming schemes that have allowed manure and other pollutants to leak onto our beaches; and a number of individual cases where raw sewage outlets have been irresponsibly connected to surface water drains.

Not all coastal litter comes from the land because the BBC's documentary series "Blue Planet II" has recently highlighted the previously unpublicised degree to which fishing gear is befouling our shores. We are told that dozens of lost fishing nets, hundreds of mislaid crab and lobster pots, miles of fishing line and tens of thousands of lead weights have been recovered from our inshore waters during the last decade. It has to be made clear that in the majority of cases these items had been lost by accident, because fishermen point out that they cannot afford to lose expensive articles that would have led to loss of income. In my own family County of Pembrokeshire, I was heartened to learn that a volunteer army of amateur divers, termed 'Neptune's Army of Rubbish Cleaners', have spent more than ten years retrieving tonnes of such litter from the seabed of this National Park coast, where it has had very deleterious effects on both marine and on birdlife. However, not all this lost gear had come from commercial fishing boats, for large amounts had been left behind by sea-anglers at such well-known resorts as Martins Haven and Stackpole Quay. John O'Connor, the Chairman of the Welsh Federation of Sea Anglers, was quick to respond to these types of pollution by launching a campaign to reduce this wastage by setting up recycling centres and introducing stricter instructions to its members. International bodies, such as World Animal Protection, have pointed out that the impact on wildlife is largely because fishing gear that was once made from natural materials, like hemp and wood, that would naturally degrade, has now been almost entirely replaced by manufactured plastic. The National Trust has long been aware of the pollution of its own beaches, ranging from the oil slicks in Cornwall (1967) and Pembrokeshire (1996) and in South Devon (2007) when 41,000 tonnes of cargo, ranging from motorcycles to nappies and perfume, were spilled from a wreck onto Branscombe's beach. The Trust rapidly responded to such threats by instituting a Marine Pollution Contingency Plan for all its coastal properties that not only provided instructions on how to carry out sensitive restoration but also drew up detailed maps for evey single accessible beach in its ownership. Alongside this innovation The National Trust in Wales launched a 3-year project to raise public awareness of its conservation schemes in order to publicise the opening of its 870-mile long coastal path, which made Wales the first country in the world to open its entire coastline to the public. Richard Neale, the Trust's Coastal Engagement Manager, told me how proud he was to have been engaged in such a project that was fully supported by the Welsh Government, in which habitat restoration and new visitor centres were being introduced as part of a programme of 'sustainable tourism'.

It was gratifying to learn that by 2012 the publicity about the threat to our coastal waters was beginning to bear fruit because, after a 15-year campaign, supported by evidence from more than one million people, the Government had been persuaded to designate no less than 31 marine Conservation Zones (MCZ's) around the shores of England and Wales. Although some of these are not strictly at the 'edge of the land', such as those off the Isles of Scilly, the Swallow Sands off the Northumbrian coast and the Celtic Deep in the Irish Sea, it was gratifying to read of such enlightened thinking. This was especially true of the latter designation because it was a welcome example of co-operation between the British and Irish governments. A British environmental poll had already established that 89% of the respondents believed that protecting our marine life was more important than commercial dredging and the exploitation of 'industrial fishing'. It has been pointed out by Sue Wells, the National Trust's Marine Project Manager, that whilst it was possible to delimit the Neptune acquisitions along our coasts, "...you can't put a fence around an area of sea" in order to protect it. It is important to remember that a healthy seabed is an indication of a healthy foreshore. Significantly, over 70% of the National Trust's coastline is exposed at low tide, revealing an area that not only provides endless pleasure to millions of people who use our beaches, but also contains vital habitats for the wellbeing of our marine life. Moreover, protection of our offshore fish-stocks has to be seen in terms of their value to the future breeding cycles of many of our coastal birds. A decline in the number of sand-eels, for example, has already caused a decrease in numbers of one of our most-loved seabirds, the puffin. In some places, such as in the vicinity of Porth Dinllaen, a National Trust property in North Wales, the Trust has installed environmentally friendly boat moorings in order to protect one of the nation's largest and densest seagrass beds. These are intended to protect such a fragile habitat from being damaged by anchors of seafarers. Such schemes may not be seen as of great significance until we all begin to recognise that negative environmental changes in our tidal zones can lead to even more severe shifts in the fundamental 'food chain'. Hence my heartfelt plea to treat both our shores and our marine life with respect and follow what I will call the 'Coastal Code' in line with our Countryside Code. Its guidelines have been clearly listed by the Marine Conservation Society.

When I first set out to consider the pressures that are continuing to threaten our coastline I believed that the most ominous was the growing amount of litter strewn along the foreshore. That which appears to cause the most dismay is the 'blizzard' of indestructible plastic, not only as a visual eyesore but also because of its damaging effect on wildlife. I had intended to write at length about this abomination but have come to realise that the media have given so much publicity to the spread of 'plastic pollution' in our seas and coastlines that it would be burdensome to replicate their views. It appears that the general public are very much aware of this blight and there are now many reports of volunteer parties scouring our beaches. Thus, it will suffice to include a modicum of facts and figures to illustrate what I have heard referred to as "The Age of

Plastic". Amusingly, one person has said that in future millenia geologists will discover a thin stratum of solid plastic among the sedimentary record of the world's rock layers.

One of the most striking statistics is that which demonstrates that 80% of plastic waste emanates from inland sources via rivers and sewage outfalls before being carried by waves and tidal currents along our shores. That which is dumped at sea may add to the shore pollution or, as in the Pacific, may be caught up in a gigantic ocean 'gyre' which swirls incessantly like a monstrous whirpool. In many worldwide instances, harbour authorities, such as San Francisco, have installed extensive booms or introduced a paddle boat with a 'trash wheel' to scoop up the floating plastic. Closer to home I found it disheartening to discover that 28% of the fish sampled in the Thames estuary had ingested plastic fibres, whilst the number in the Clyde estuary in Scotland was as high as 39%. Even more worrying are the recent hospital reports of the presence of plastic fragments in the gut of certain patients. These are the sort of figures that should give real cause for concern for they are clearly having severe effects on the food chain. On turning to a final example of plastic pollution on our beaches, I was saddened to hear that in Devon and Cornwall alone, no less than 14,000 bodyboards are abandoned every year on some of our finest beaches. The polystyrene boards cost about £6 and are so flimsy that they break into tiny pieces which endanger wildlife, especially seabirds. I ponder the question whether the same people who dump the boards are the same ones who leave hundreds of tents and great amounts of litter at many of the British pop festivals. If so then the nation needs to target the particular age groups in a 'name and shame' campaign, for this cannot be fair on other holidaymakers.

The public were made aware of the insidious effects of pesticides on wildlife at about the same time that the National Trust were formulating their policy on coastal management that culminated in Enterprise Neptune. It was in 1962, that I remember reading the seminal book "Silent Spring" by Rachel Carson, when writing my new lecture courses at Reading University, having just returned from my academic employment in Los Angeles. It is probably true to say that it was this volume, more than any other, that steered me into the fields of environmental impact studies and conservation planning. Since that time there have been many more publications that have highlighted how the use of pesticdes in regimes of intensive farming, often encouraged by successive governments, has led to harmful effects on the British countryside and its wildlife. It has to be said that farmers are not the only injudicious party to be involved, because many British garden-lovers have continued to pour all manner of chemicals onto their lawns and flower beds without thinking that the toxic run-off will finish on the ocean littoral. I do not propose to dwell for long upon a detailed diatribe because, as in the case of plastic pollution, the pesticide problem has already been well documented by such writers as Fiona Reynolds (*op. cit.*) and Mark Cocker, especially in his recent book "Our Place" whose sub-title poses the question "Can We Save Britain's Wildlife Before It Is Too Late?". Cocker records, for example, that the total pesticide usage in the UK doubled during the 1970's and that those used on cereals have doubled again in succeeding decades. Moreover, from a personal viewpoint, I was horrified to read in his book that lapwing losses in Britain are substantially above the European average, and that these beautiful birds have declined by 65% since the 1970's. These were the birds that adorned the coastal fields when I worked on the Llyn Peninsula in the

1950's and 1960's and are a prominent part of the Whittow family coat-of-arms in Pembrokeshire. Even more disheartening was to read that this is not the only bird species that will continue to decline if we do not mend our ways. But, we are reliably informed, change is inevitable, especially at the 'edge of the land'.

My old colleague, Phil Dyke, the Coast and Marine Adviser at the National Trust, has recently sent me a summary of a coastal project that is close to my heart: "Sand dunes, mobility and impacts on cultural heritage along the Atlantic coasts of Europe". It is not surprising that such a topic immediately reminded me not only of my childhood days among the dunes of Rhyl in North Wales but also of the seminar on the Danish coast which, in a way, led to my involvement in the launch of Enterprise Neptune, all those years ago. As an undergraduate I was made familiar with the most important text on sand dune morphology, "The Physics of Blown Sand and Desert Dunes" by R. A. Bagnold (1941), from which I learnt not only how they were formed but also their value in coastal preservation and protection. In the accompanying report, Phil Dyke spoke of how "They form an energy absorbing buffer between the sea and low-lying land, but they need to be able to move and many have become over-stabilised". He went on to explain how the conventional wisdom of "...fixing dunes with marram grass", as I had been taught on the Danish island of Rømø almost sixty years previously, has recently been questioned and replaced by a policy termed 'remoblisation'. Artificial dune-fixing is currently seen to go hand in hand with other 'hard' engineering solutions such as breakwaters, groynes, seawalls and rock revetments. Dyke continues: "The problems with such 'macho' defences is that, time has revealed, they merely deflect the sea's energy, causing unintended consequences elsewhere. They also always fail, eventually". Such is the conclusion of a recently published booklet by the National Trust entitled "Shifting Shores" which introduces the public to what is claimed to be a more sustainable approach to coastal management. At a time of rising sea levels and increased storminess, induced by climatic change, it is appropriate that I must now focus on a topic in which I have invested much of my research time, that of environmental hazards and in particular coastal erosion.

It was only when I began the research for my book "Disasters: The Anatomy of Environmental Hazards" (1980), that I became quite seriously aware that the World's climate was changing at an increasing rate, somewhat faster than had previously been thought. Since the millenium, scientists have discovered that Antarctica's ice sheet is melting five times faster than normal, due to global warming, and that the released water could add significantly to long-term rises in sea level. It had already been predicted that such melting, both in Antarctica and in Greenland, could result in a sea level rise of up to five feet by 2100. Moreover, experts have already demonstrated that between 2010 and 2016 almost 2,500 square miles of Antarcica's undersea ice had disappeared as a result of warming oceans leading, potentionally, to disastrous effects on coastal communities in the future.

In 1979 I had stood on the banks of the Thames at Woolwich and had gazed at the awesome array of metallic truncated domes that stretched across to the other side of the estuary. Sunlight glinted on their silvery humps and a blustery east wind caused waves to break against their giant portals and stir up the froth of plastic flotsam that bounced along their concrete embankments. This was the partly-completed Thames Barrier, the much vaunted 'technological fix' that was being constructed as a safeguard to prevent catastrophic flooding of London. It had been built as a direct response to the devastating East Coast floods of 1953 when a storm surge had been driven down the North Sea by hurricane-force winds. The barrier became operational in 1982, just in time to cope with a higher than normal tide only four months later. Since then the barrier has been closed far more frequently than had been predicted and had been forced into action some fifty times during the stormy winter of 2013–2014, compared with a total of 124 closures during the previous thirty years. In line with scientific predictions of the rate of rising sea-levels, it has been claimed that the barrier will remain effective until about 2070. We are told, however, that plans have been made for a new and larger barrier to be built near to the Dartford crossing of the Thames.

I had brought a party of Reading University undergraduates not only to see the barrier but also to visit the low-lying coast of Canvey Island in Essex. As we walked along its high sea-wall and looked down on the roofs of the bungalows, all of which stand below high-tide level, we realised why the monstrous waves in 1953 had breached the sea-defences and drowned no less than 58 unfortunate residents. I reminded these young students of the vulnerability of the low-lying coasts of East Anglia, whose shores were already sinking as a result of geophysical forces in the North Sea basin (almost one inch since 1900). I also told them of the crumbling unconsolidated rocks that formed these shores and how sea-defences might be unable to survive future storms. We discussed the ways in which artificial defences might prove to be futile and enormously expensive to maintain by the local authorities in future years. A few decades later the National Trust had been forced to face similar problems along some of its coastal properties and had responded in 2005 by publishing its first edition of "Shifting Shores: Living with a changing coastline" (Updated in 2014). Its findings were somewhat disconcerting for it was discovered that:

60% of National Trust land (at 169 sites) would suffer different degrees of loss by erosion.

1. 10% of the losses could push the coastline back by as much as 200 yards in some places.
2. 5% of the losses are likely to be in excess of 200 yards.
3. 126 sites are already at risk of tidal flooding.
4. 33 further sites are at risk of tidal and river flooding within the next 100 years.

Coast erosion is nothing new on our shores, it has been continuous ever since the Ice Age, as seawater has spread across the newly exposed land surface. The post-glacial eustaic rise had virtually tailed-off by the time it was discovered that the rising sea-level associated with global warming was setting up an increased rate of erosion on our coastlines. One of our most dramatic forecasts came from our famous Chesil Beach where scientists have predicted that its iconic 18-mile length will continue to push landwards, split into sections and eventually lead to the isolation of the Isle of Portland. More than ten years ago the National Trust published a list of their most 'fragile' coastal sites that are at risk of destruction or, at least, diminution in size. These sites included such well-known places as Orford Ness, Blakeney Point, Cornwall's Loe Pool and Dorset's Studland Bay. And rececently, the wild winter storms of 2017–2018 have taken a further toll on our coasts. Great cliff-falls have been recorded from the White Cliffs of Dover, several Cornish beaches have simply disappeared and the newly constructed infamous railway line at Dawlish has come under a renewed threat of destruction. Scientific measurements have shown that Dover's chalk cliffs are eroding about ten times faster now than in the preceding few thousand years and also that average winter wave heights around the Atlantic shores have been rising exponentially over the past 70 years. By the spring of 2018 reports came 'flooding' into the press, bewailing the serious losses of some of Britains's finest coastal golf links. The Royal North Devon and the historic course at Montrose in Angus were amongst the worst hit and it was suggested that the even more famous Scottish links, at St Andrews and Carnoustie, could be under future threat from storm surges. Of a much more serious matter were the reports from such different coastal sites as the Thames estuary and a location to the south of Dublin, where waves are eroding disused landfill dumps. Over the years similar sites had been used to raise land-levels or had been incorporated into coastal defences. The Environment Agency now reports that there are as many as 1,264 disused landfill sites along the shores of England and Wales and that some of these are eroding, leading to spills of toxic materials into the sea. Researchers from London University discovered that over one-third of England's coastal landfills lie close to environmentally designated sites and that half of them are located in close proximity to coasts where bathing waters are at risk of future contamination. Finally, in this 'doomwatch' scenario, the Government has been warned by coastal engineers of the dangers of continuing to build some of our next-generation nuclear power stations on coastlines of unconsolidated rocks or on unstable shingle ridges. Sizewell and Dungeness are singled out as being at particular risk and almost all the rest could be in danger of coastal flooding in the future. But one is forced to ask, rhetorically, where else are we expected to obtain sufficient cooling water? Moreover, one has to conclude that it still remains difficult, if not impossible, to predict coastal change with any sort of exactitude.

The National Trust booklet "Shifting Shores" concluded that "The scale and pace of the changes shown by [their] risk assessment has strengthened the Trust's awareness of both the immediate and long-term effects [of erosion] at its sites. We now need to take into account these forecasts of change in everything we do, from the acquiring of coastal land to the daily management of coastal sites". There was now a clearer understanding of future policy-making including the decision to abandon traditional coastal protection schemes that had involved major concrete and rock structures. Almost a century ago Professor A. S. Woodward, President of the Linnaen Society, had suggested that such 'hard' protective structures in one place could have disastrous effects on another part of the coast, as I have pointed out in chapter two. It was this realisation that made the Trust decide that hard defences should only be used as a last resort and that "...working with natural processes is the most sustainable approach. In some cases this will mean undoing past mistakes, taking out hard defences and letting the coast realign naturally". Before long the term 'managed retreat' had been replaced by that of 'managed realignment' in which the sea was to be allowed to advance beyond the coastline in certain critical places, thereby creating totally new vistas at the 'edge of the land'.

The whole new concept of working with natural processes is simply a recognition of the necessity of 'adaptation' that will benefit both wildlife and people and that managed realignment schemes will create new spaces for salt marshes and dunes to flourish. By 2014 Phil Dyke had warned us that "...the winter storms of 2013/14 put [the Trust] on fast-forward – decisions and changes that we thought had a decade or more to make now have to be made overnight". One of the first sites to be affected was the attractive coastline of Porlock Bay in Somerset where the protecting shingle beach was being slowly destroyed. There were many who demanded that new shingle should be brought to strengthen the beach but the National Trust decided to allow the sea to break through and create a new salt marsh that would act as an 'energy sponge' against future storm waves. A further example came from Wales in 2016, where the village of Fairbourne, on Cardigan Bay, was faced with future inundations after the local council had refused to find the finance to replace the crumbling 3-foot high sea wall. A report from the Environment Agency (Wales) had earlier reported that £135 million would have to be spent annually on flood and coastal defences by 2035 simply to maintain the status quo. Needless to say, all the coastal management bodies are being faced with a funding dilemma and it is likely that some may begin to follow the policies introduced by the National Trust. There have been numeous public outcries against the changing policies and such attitudes were epitomised at the AGM of the Trust in 2016 when a resolution to build sea defences to protect a shoreline café in Studland Bay, Dorset, was defeated by the members who supported the Trust's intention of moving it to a safer site rather than building revetments that would have a limited lifespan. Furthermore, Studland's iconic beach huts, that had already been relocated twice before, were to be 'future proofed' in a scheme which entailed re-designing them to make them more robust in the face of escalating oceanic storminess. One of the outcomes of the increasing awareness by the Trust, concerning the impractability of trying to hold back the encroaching sea on a rapidly eroding coast, was the decision to purchase parcels of land at some distance behind the shoreline itself. Calculations had shown that this innovative policy would be necessary to protect the coastal path if nothing else, whilst the public would be less than happy if their access to the coast became roped off as too dangerous.

As I write this chapter, an alarming report has been released by the Committee on Climate Change. Some may think that it is nothing but scare-mongering but their stark forecasts speak for themselves. They predict that, by 2100, sea levels could rise by at least a metre, thereby putting 82,000 homes and 1.2 million coastal dwellers at risk. They claim that "Shoreline management plans developed by the Environment Agency and local councils contained unrealistic assumptions about funding defences". Professor Jim Hall, a member of the Committee, believed that not only would sea defences be too costly in many places but also that they could lead to losses of beaches and other coastal habitats elsewhere – sentiments that I have outlined above. The Committee have produced a map of vulnerable sites which, unsurprisingly, highlight the coasts of Holderness and eastern Norfolk where relatively unconsolidated rocks and miles of easily eroded glacial drift make up the coastline. The map illustrates areas where, with no active intervention, our shores may have retreated by more than 25 yards during the period 2005 to 2025. Some people will be very concerned at this report, which also suggests that this rate of cliff-recession will also occur on such well-known holiday coasts as Sussex, Hampshire, the Isle of Wight and much of Lancashire. A Committee spokesperson concluded that in places, coastal dwellers should receive assistance to help them to move inland and that it was unacceptable to leave new coastal house-buyers under the misapprehension that their homes would be protected.

One of the most important recommendations of the National Trust's report entitled "Shifting Shores", had been the necessity to work with like-minded bodies in co-operative efforts to tackle the future coastal problems. Phil Dyke has now ensured that one of the most important of these bodies, the Marine Management Organisation (MMO), has been approached, in order to discuss co-operation over a wide range of environmental management. This organisation had been established in 2009 by the Coastal Access Act of 2009 "…with the remit to deliver the UK Government's vision for clean, healthy, safe, productive and biologically diverse oceans and seas". Its aim was to "…guide marine users and regulators across England, [by] balancing the sustainable development of marine industries like wind farms, fishing, oil and gas exploration, with the need to conserve and protect marine species and habitats". I have shown how offshore changes will influence both inshore and foreshore habitats and the MMO have recognised that offshore wind farms will, perforce, have impacts on the coastline due to the need for cable connections and maintenance of switching stations. Consequently, their marine management plans aim to work in harness with the terrestrial planning systems of such agencies as the National Trust and the planning officers of the National Parks and AONB's. In view of the rapid development of wind farms in the North Sea it came as no surprise to learn that the first of the MMO's 'Marine Plans' stretched from Flamborough Head in Yorkshire to the port of Felixstowe in Suffolk.

As I sat down to write this book I learnt that permission had been given to commission the world's largest offshore wind farm in the North Sea opposite Hornsea in Yorkshire. Not only will it generate considerably more electricity (2400 MW) than any other British offshore wind farm but it will produce it much more cheaply than the electricity due to be generated at the new nuclear power station currently being built at Hinkley Point in Somerset. Such a development does not mean that Britain intends to cut down its nuclear programme because everyone is aware that on many occasions the wind ceases to blow. Critics of wind power have long pointed to this fact and claimed that the costings for wind-generated electricity fails to include the expense of back-up facilities and the cost of their installation, possibly on our coasts.

It was shown in 2016 that 61% of the UK power sources came from Gas (41.7%) and Nuclear (19.3%) and, by comparison, windpower contributed a mere 11.1% (Onshore 6.2% and Offshore 4.9%). But in future years all this is set to change and it would be interesting to speculate on the type of changes that may occur on our coastal environments once the newer and larger wind farms come onstream. At present some 44 wind farms are operative off the British coasts: 14 off Scotland; 2 off North Wales; 1 off Sussex and the remainder in the North Sea – a total of British installations greater than those in the rest of the world when taken all together. But the British public remains sceptical of the validity of onshore windfarms because of the visual intrusion created by the massive turbines, some of which have been located in coastal zones. Indeed, a former energy minister has been quoted as saying that we have already suffered enough from the visual impact from coal, gas and nuclear power plants, with their accompanying mesh of pylons, so why add to these? Even members of the Friends of the Earth, a powerful 'green lobby', have recognised that the objections to more power lines (connecting to offshore wind farms) are here to stay. Therefore, one has to face the dilemma that Britain needs an increase in energy supplies from renewable sources, as fossil fuels are phased out, and what better replacement than that of utilising free offshore wind power? But most people understand that the undersea power cables have to come ashore somewhere and be linked into the National Grid. Questions have been raised about the degree of impact that this necessity might have on our coastal zone – first in the degree of visual intrusion and, secondly, the increased number of bird fatalities that will occur on the migratory routes which often follow coastlines. Whilst realising that electricity-generating companies have official 'way-leaves' for their transmission lines and that these will remain unassailable because of the high cost of 'undergrounding', the responsibility of determining the least sensitive routes, from a visual viewpoint, will remain with the terrestrial planning authorities. On turning to the second issue, that of increased bird 'strikes' there has been a remarkable response from the RSPB. Dr Ivan Scrase, one of their spokespersons, whilst recognising the problem, has been quoted as saying that such losses from wind-turbine blades are relatively small and pale into insignificance "...in comparison to the wider threats posed by climate change. Our starting point is climate change and we can't tackle that without low carbon energy". Bearing in mind the decline of bird populations from the wide variety of pollutants, as noted above, these are sentiments with which I must agree, although it is noteworthy that in Portugal experiments have shown a way of ameliorating the number of bird strikes caused by wind turbines, which Boris Johnson has, in his cavalier fashion, described as 'giant bird blenders'. On the birds' major migratory routes, the engineers have installed a system of radar instruments that warn of the approach of very large flocks and signal to the wind farms to temporarily switch-off the turbines. It would be good to know if the British authorities are following suit.

Strangely enough, it was the vision of offshore wind turbines that caught my eye during my last visit to the coast of North Wales a couple of years ago. I had been invited by the National Trust to visit their latest coastal acquisition, bought from Neptune funds, at Llandudno of all places. It comprised an 858-acre farm (including grazing rights) on the very top of the Great Orme. The National Trust saw as it as a unique opportunity to create a conservation regime of sheep-grazing whilst retaining the survival of rare plants and butterflies, together with allowing public access. Dan Jones, a Welsh shepherd from Anglesey, had been appointed as the custodian of Parc farm because he understood "…how to move sheep around in tune with the seasons and respond to what the landscape needs" said a Trust spokesperson. The Trust was eager to prove that in this windswept coastal environment, modern-day farming and conservation practices can work together successfully – in other words "working with nature". It was soon followed by a similar scheme at Rhossili on the Gower where six intensively farmed fields were returned to seventeen smaller traditional 'strip fields' where cereal crops were interspersed with natural grassland and wild flowers, to the immense benefit of the local plants and wildlife to say nothing of improving the experience of the large number of visitors to this scenic spot.

I had been asked if I would like to view the enterprising experiment on the Great Orme and to meet up again with Richard Neale, the Trust's Coastal Events Manager in Wales. What I didn't know that this was intended as a special event for, much to my surprise, the BBC Outside Broadcasting team suddenly appeared. On the 680-foot summit, buffeted by a gusting wind,

I was asked to make a broadcast for Radio 4, describing the changes that I had perceived since Diane and I had mapped this stretch of coast in the Neptune campaign fifty years previously. I was pleased to discover that I was being interviewed by Tom Heap, of 'Countryfile' renown, and I responded to his first question that there had been no wind-farms in Liverpool Bay in 1965 and that the Ministry of Defence were still occupying strategic Great Orme sea-cliff sites at that date. An even greater surprise lay in store, for Richard presented me with a framed replica of the Llandudno area map that we had completed for the Neptune campaign in 1965. This was a further recognition by the National Trust of my contributions over the succeeding fifty years and, when I listened to the broadcast some weeks later, my gasp of astonishment at the gift is quite audible. At the close of the interview Richard and I moved over to the western slopes of the Orme and watched the waves break against the base of the limestone cliffs. Before us stretched a panorama of my life – a veritable seascape of memories. This sweeping view, one of the best in Wales, encapsulated some of the coastlines that had defined both my life's work and, possibly, some of my personal characteristics. In a sense it was a microcosm of all the features that had engendered my enthusiasm for British coastal scenery. Near at hand were the sandy beaches of Llandudno's West Shore where I first played as a young child and where we introduced our baby daughter, Fiona, to the joys of the seaside. Not far beyond I could see the dominant crag supporting Deganwy Castle ruins that overlooked my parents' former home. Cloud shadows raced across the tawny slopes of Conwy Mountain where, seemingly a lifetime ago, a callow undergraduate had learnt the processes of Earth Science and how to value our natural environment. Across the bay a train pulled slowly away from the tiny station at Penmaenmawr, evoking memories of the sunlit rambles and the laughter of a group of teenagers, just after the war had finished and life appeared to be so carefree. The misty peaks of Snowdonia rose steeply up from the coast whose gleaming Lavan Sands were speckled with countless flocks of birds. The far-distant coastline of Anglesey served as a backdrop to the majestic scene and also as a reminder of those far-off days when Neptune occupied most of my thoughts. This was once my world – my very own and personal 'Edge of the Land'.

BIBLIOGRAPHY

Ashton N. Early Humans. 2017.

Aldersey-Williams H. Tide: The Science and Lore of the Greatest Force on Earth. 2017.

Appleton J. The Experience of Landscape. 1975.

Arnold M. Dover Beach.

Balchin W. G. V. Cornwall. 1954.

Barkham P. Coastlines. 2015.

Black's Picturesqe Guides: Wales. 1858.

Betjeman J. Cornwall: A Shell Guide. 1964

Betjeman J. Collected Poems. 1955.

Blythe R. (Ed.) Places: An Anthology of Britain.1961.

Blythe R. The Time by the Sea.

Borrow G. H. Wild Wales. 1862.

Burns R. Ceri Richards and Dylan Thomas: Keys to Transformation. 1981.

Cabot D. & Goodwillie R. The Burren. 2018.

Campbell S. & Bowen D. Q. Quaternary of Wales. 1989.

Chamberlain B. Tiderace. 1962.

Cocker M. Our Place: Can We Save Britain's Wildlife Before It's Too Late? 2018.

Collins W. Rambles Beyond Railways. 1851.

Condry W. M. The Natural History of Wales. 1981.

Connop-Price M. R. Pembrokeshire: The Forgotten Coalfield. 2004.

Cornish V. the Beauties of Scenery, 1943.

Crabbe G. The Poetical Works. 1947.

Crane N. Coast: Our Island Story. 2010.

Crane N. Great British Journeys. 2017.

Cross T. Painting the Warmth of the Sun. 1984.

Cross T. The Shining Sands. 1994.

Cross T. Helford: A River and Some Landscapes. 2005.

Davies H. Mapping Our Shores: 50 years of land use change at the coast. 2015.

Davies M. The Report of the Land Utilisation of Britain. 32: Pembrokeshire. 1939.

Defoe D. A Tour Through the Whole Island of Great Britain. 1746.

Du Maurier D. Vanishing Cornwall: The Spirit and History of Cornwall. 1967.

Fisher J. & Lockley R. M. Seabirds. 1954.

Fisher J. Rockall. 1956.

Flower R. The Western Island or The Great Blasket. 1954.

Floyd M. The Face of Ireland. 1937.

Folliot-Stokes A. G. The Cornish Coast and Moors. 1931.

Freeman T. W. Ireland. 1950.

Gillham M. E. Coastal Downs: Ogmore and Dunraven. 1993.

Gillham M. E. Memories of Welsh Islands. 2004.

Goodall B. & Whittow J. B. The Recreational Potential of Forestry Commission Holdings. 1973.

Gooding M. Ceri Richards. 1982.

Gray T. The Irish Answer: An Anatomy of Ireland. 1966.

Greenly E. The Geology of Anglesey. 1919.

Hardyment C. Writing Britain. 2012.

Harris A. Weatherland. 2015.

Hayward R. Connacht (Galway). 1952.

Henry P. An Irish Portrait. 1952.

Hockin J. R. A. Walking in Cornwall. 1936.
Howells R. The Sounds Between. 1968.
Hubbard T. A Year in Cornwall. 2000.
Hughes C. A. A Wanderer in North Wales. 1949.
Humphreys R. The British Landscape Through the Eyes of The Great Artists. 1989.
Hutchinson T. Calum's Road. 2006.
Jackman B. Wild About Britain. 2017.
James H. English Hours. 1883.
Jefferies R. L. The North Norfolk Coast: Nature in Norfolk. 1976.
Jennett S. Connacht. 1970.
Knight G. The Swordfish and The Star. 2016.
Larkin P. High Windows. 1974.
Lewis C. A. The Glaciation of Wales and Adjoining Areas. 1970.
Lewis S. Topographical Dictionary of Wales. 1842.
Lindley K. Coastline. 1967.
Lloyd T. et al. The Buildings of Wales: Pembrokeshire. 2004.
Lockley R. M. Pembrokeshire. 1957.
MacCulloch D. B. The Wondrous Isle of Staffa. 1927.
Macleod N. Raasay: The Island and its People. 2002.
Marshall E. M. Music in the Landscape. 2011.
Macfarlane R. The Wild Ways. 2007.
McInnes R. British Coastal Art (1770–1930). 2014.
Miller A. A. Land, Air and Ocean. 1951.
Miller H. the Cruise of the Betsey. 1861.
Mitchell F. The Way That I Followed: A Naturalist's Journey Around Ireland. 1990.
Mitton G. E. Cornwall. 1915.
Morris L. The Fishing Lass of Hakin.
Morton H. V. In Search of England 1927.

Munro N. The Clyde. 1907.

National Parks Commission. The Coasts of South West England. 1967.

National Parks Commission. The Coasts of North Wales. 1968.

National Parks Commission. The Coasts of East Anglia. 1968.

Newton. L. (Ed). Painting at the Edge: British Coastal Art Colonies (1880–1930). 2005.

North F. J., Cambell B. & Scott R. Snowdonia. 1949.

O'Crithin T. The Islandman. 1934.

O'Faolain S. The Story of Ireland. 1937.

O'Faolain S. & Henry P. An Irish Journey. 1941.

O'Siochain P. A. Aran: Islands of Legend. 1962.

O'Sullivan T. Twenty Years A-Growing.

Owen G. Description of Pembrokeshire. 1603.

Pavord A. Landskipping. 2016.

Payne C. Where the Land Meets the Sea: Artists on the Coast in 19th century Britain. 2007.

Pennant. T. Tours in Wales. 1791.

Piper J. & Ingrams R. Piper's Places. 1983.

Plath S. The Bell Jar. 1963.

Praeger R. L. Natural History of Ireland. 1950.

Praeger R. L. The Way That I Went. 1969.

Pye-Smith C. In Search of Neptune. 1990.

Ramsay A. C. The Old Glaciers of Switzerland and North Wales. 1860.

Rees S. A Guide to Ancient and Historic Wales: Dyfed. 1992.

Robb. I. Memories of the East Anglian Fishing Industry. 2010.

Robinson A. & Millward R. The Shell Book of the British Coast. 1983.

Robinson T. Setting Foot in Connemara and Other Stories. 1996.

Roscoe T. Wanderings and Excursions in North Wales. 1836.

Sayers P. Peig. 1936.

Scarfe N. Shell Guide to Suffolk. 1960.

Scott C. Poppyland. 1886.

Scott-Moncrieff G. The Scottish Islands. 1952.

Sherlock R. L. Man as a Geological Agent. 1922.

Sinclair I. Black Apples of Gower. 2015.

Soper T. A Natural History Guide to the Coast. 1984.

Soulsby I. The Towns of Medieval Wales. 1982.

Spender. S. Collected Poems. 1955.

Steers J. A. The Coastline of England and Wales 1947.

Steers J. A. The Sea Coast. 1953.

Steers J. A. Coastal Features of England and Wales. 1982.

Stephens C. St Ives Artists: Terry Frost. 2000.

Stephens N. & Glasscock R. E. Irish Geographical Studies. 1970.

Stoddart A. Shifting Sands: Blakeney Point and the Environmental Imagination. 2013.

Synge J. M. In Wicklow, West Kerry and Connemara. 1919.

Thomas E. The South Country. 1909.

Thomas J. G. Political Development. In Bowen E. (Ed.) Wales. 1957.

Timmins H. Nooks and Corners in Pembrokeshire. 1895.

Tolhurst P. East Anglia: A Literary Pilgrimage. 1996.

Toorians L. Wizo Flandrensis and the Flemish Settlement in Pembrokeshire. 1990.

Trevelyan G. M. Must England's Beauty Perish? 1929.

Tuke J. H. A Visit to Connaught in the Autumn of 1857.

Vale E. The Seas and Shores of England. 1936.

Wade S. Lost to the Sea: Britain's Vanished Coastal Communities: Norfolk & Suffolk). 2017.

Waterson M. The National Trust: The First Hundred Years. 1994.

Waterson M. A Noble Thing: The National Trust and its Benefactors. 2011.

Watkins V. Selected Poems (1930–1960). 1967.

Whittow J. B. Geology and Scenery in England and Wales (with Hardy J. R.) 1972.

Whittow J. B. Geology and Scenery in Ireland. 1974.

Whittow J. B. Geology and Scenery in Scotland. 1977.

Whittow J. B. Disasters: The Anatomy of Environmental Hazards. 1980.

Whittow J. B, Rocks and Pebbles. Penguin Nature Guide. 1980.

Whittow J. B. The Penguin Dictionary of Physical Geography. 1984.

Whittow J. B. Landscapes of Stone. 1986.

Whittow J. B. Geology and Scenery in Britain. 1992.

Whittow J. B. The Whittow Family of Pembrokeshire. 2016.

Whyte C. & Dymock E. Sorley Maclean: Collected Poems. 2011.

Wilcox S. (Ed.). Sun, Wind and Rain: The Art of David Cox. 2008.

Wooldridge S. W. & Linton D. L. Structure, Surface and Drainage in South East England. 1955.

Wormleighton A. Lamorna: A Place Apart. In Newton L. 2005 (*op. cit.*).

INDEX OF PLACES

D

INDEX OF NAMES

G

H